GOD IS

ENGINEERING CHEMISTRY

AF798356

Prof. Dr. Preeti Jain
M.Sc. (Organic, Inorganic Chemistry), Ph.D., FICCE
Head of the Chemistry Department,
Medi-Caps Institute of Technology & Management,
Indore

Variety Books Publishers Distributors, DELHI

SECOND PREFACE

We feel encouraged by the widespread response from teachers and students. We are presenting this third edition thoroughly revised and enlarged in all humbleness. All possible efforts to have been made enhance further the usefulness of the book. The feedback received from different sources has been incorporated.

In this edition a new topic on Biopolymers has been added in view of the fact that it is essential for engineering students.

The other highlights of this revised edition are:

(a) The subject contents have been developed, refined and restructured at several points.
(b) The several new problems have also been added at the end of various chapters for the benefits of students and
(c) Every pages of this book has been read very carefully so as to improve it's quality.

We are grateful to Dr. Anjali Soni, Mr. Jeetendra Bhawsar, Ms Pranita Mahadik and in preparing this revised edition. We firmly believe that there is always scope for improvement and accordingly. We shall look forward to receive suggestions for further enriching the quality of text.

-Authors
Dr. Preeti Jain
Dr. S.L. Garg

PREFACE

The present edition of the book has been prepared according to the latest syllabus of First Year classes of Engineering students of RGPV university, Bhopal and other Universities of India.

Our main aim is to give an up-to –date account of the relevant topics while trying to avoid unnecessary details. We have tried to make the text readable and accessible without technical jargon. At the same time, enough data and depth are presented to make this book suitable for BE I st year course and a valuable resource for students who will keep this book in their personal library.

The presentation of the text of the book is simple and completely organic. It has been presented in a lucid manner so that the students may develop interest in the subject. The subject matter has been further simplified with several illustrations and numerical examples, wherever desirable. The language of the book is simple so that it may be in the reach of even an ordinary English knowing student.

The book is complete in all respects and very useful to students and teachers. The authors believe that the book will largely meet the required demands of students of Engineering.

Timely completion of this book was made possible by cooperation and assistance of many people. We are obliged to all those who offered their advice, help and encouragement. Authors are grateful to staff members of journal "RESEARCH JOURNAL OF CHEMISTRY AND ENVIRONMENT" for sincere response. We are very much thankful to the Director Dr. Shamsher Singh, all the faculty members of Medi-Caps Institute of Technology and Management, Indore for constant support and valuable suggestions in the preparation of this text book. We also express our gratitude to friends and members of both the families for their moral support, patience, understanding and never ending encouragement. Although every care has been taken to check mistakes and misprints, yet it is difficult to claim perfection.

Lastly, the authors will be pleased to receive any comments, criticisms and suggestions made by teachers and students for improvement of second edition of this book. We are sure that this text book will serve its purpose and book will be beneficial to all the students of chemistry and chemical engineering for engineering colleges.

-Authors
Dr. Preeti Jain
Dr. S.L. Garg

VARIETY BOOKS PUBLISHER'S DISTRIBUTORS
(ISO 9001: 2015 Certified - IAF Certified)
Head Office
4759 1st Floor, 23 Ansari Road, Daryaganj, New Delhi-110002
Phone: 011-35780655,
Mobile: +91-8810311911
E-mail: varietybooks2009@gmail.com

First Edition: 2026

ISBN: 978-93-6391-903-7

RGPV SYLLABUS

COURSE CONTENTS

Category of Course	Course Title	Course Code	Credits-6C			Theory Papers (ES)
			L	T	P	
Basic Science BS-1	Engineering Chemistry	**BE101**	3	1	2	Max.Marks-100 Min.Marks-35 Duration-3hrs.

Branch: Common Semester

Course: BE101 Engineering Chemistry

Unit I

Water analysis & treatment: Sources, Impurities, Hardness & its units, Industrial water Requirement & characteristics, softening of water by various methods (L.S., Zeolite, ion exchange resin), Boiler trouble (carry over, scale and sludge, caustic embrittlement) Boiler corrosion causes, effect & remedies, internal treatments to boiler feed water. Characteristics of municipal water & its treatment: - water analysis (determination of alkalinity, temporary and permanent hardness by complexometry) Numerical problems based on water analysis and water softening processes.

Unit II

Fuels & combustion: Fossil fuels & classification, Calorific value, Determination of calorific value by Bomb calorimeter Proximate and Ultimate analysis of coal and their significance, calorific value Computation based on ultimate analysis data, Carbonization, Manufacturing of coke & recovery of by products. Cracking of higher Hydrocarbons & mechanism of cracking, Knocking, relationship between' knocking & structure of hydrocarbon, improvement of anti knocking characteristics of IC engine fuels, Diesel engine fuels, Cetane number, combustion and it related numerical problems.

Unit III

Lubricants: Introduction, Mechanism of lubrication, Classification of lubricants, Lubricating oils, grease & semisolid lubricants, solid lubricants, synthetic lubricants, Properties and Testing of lubricating oils, Viscosity & Viscosity index, flash and fire points, cloud and pour point, Anline value, Steam Emulsion Number, Neutralization No., Saponification Value, Iodine value, carbon residue); Numerical problems based on Viscosity Index

Unit IV

Polymerization: Introduction, types and classification of polymerization, Reaction Mechanism, Natural & Synthetic Rubber; Vulcanization of Rubber, Preparation, Properties & uses of the following- Polythene, PVC, PMA, PMMA, Teflon, Poly acrylonitrile, PVA, Nylon, Nylon 6;6, Terylene, Phenol Formaldehyde, Urea - Formaldehyde Resin, Glyptal, Silicone Resin, Polyurethanes; Butyl Rubber, Neoprene, Buna N, Buna S. Flow sheet manufacturing diagram of Nylon 6:6 & Decron.

Unit V

(A) **Instrumental Techniques in Chemical Analysis**
Basic concepts of spectroscopy: IR,UV, Visible, Applications of EPR,NMR
Chromatography- Gas Chromatography, Colorimetry, Lambert's and Beer's Law

(B) **Cement:** Portland Cement, Manufacturing, Setting & Hardening, Plaster of Paris (Preparation,properties & uses)
Refractory: Definition, Classification and important properties of Refractories.

Engineering Chemistry Practicals

Note: At least 10 of the following experiments should be performed during the session.

1. **Water Testing**
   - (i) Determination of Total hardness by Complexometric titration method.
   - (ii) Determination of mixed alkalinity (a) OH^- & $C0_3^{--}$ (b)$C0_3^{--}$ & HCO_3^-
   - (iii) Chloride ion estimation by Argentometric method.
2. **Fuels & Lubricant Testing:**
   - (i) Flash & fire point's determination by
     - a) Pensky Martin Apparatus, b) Abel's Apparatus,
     - c) Cleveland's open cup Apparatus. d) Calorific value by bomb calorimeter
   - (ii) Viscosity and Viscosity index determination by
     - a) Redwood viscometer No.1 b) Redwood viscometer No.2
   - (iii) Proximate analysis of coal
     - a) Moisture content b) Ash content
     - c) Volatile matter content d) Carbon residue
   - (iv) Steam emulsification No & Anline point determination
   - (v) Cloud and Pour point determination of lubricating oil
3. **Alloy Analysis**
   - (i) Determination of percentage of Fe in an iron alloy by redox titration using N-Phenyl anthranilic acid as internal indicator.
   - (ii) Determination of Cu and or Cr in alloys by Iodometric Titration.

CONTENTS

Unit-I

Water Analysis and Treatment

1.1 INTRODUCTION

Water is the most precious gift of nature and most vital for sustenance of life next to air. Water influences economical, agricultural and industrial growth of any country. It is most commonly and widely distributed resource of the earth. It is evident that the ancient civilization had mainly flourished along perennial surface water resources i.e. Rivers and Streams. This civilization wiped out due to improper management of water resources. Water is not eternally pure and inexhaustible gift of God. The importance of water can be ascertained by the fact that our body contains 70 percent of water and its absence would warm up or cool down much more rapidly than the normal cooling and warming of the body. An average man needs 1.4 kg food, 2.25 kg air and about 10 liters of water daily to survive. One tonne of food grain requires 10^5 liter of water to grow and one tonne of rice needs 2 x 10^6 liter. India has an annual precipitation of around 4000 billion cubic meters, out of this, 1869 billion cubic meter runoff is accessible but nearly 1179 billion cubic meters gets wasted on drains into the sea or ocean.

The planet earth is often called a 'watery planet' and the very existence of life on this planet is because of presence of water. There is no other planet in the galaxy, as far as we know, which has water in its environment. Of the total volume of 1,385 million km^3 of water in the planet earth, 96.5 percent is salt water (ocean), the fresh water is mostly ice (24 million km^3) and deeply seated ground water (23.4 million km^3). Fresh water available as annual stream flow is 46,768 km^3 which is 0.00034 percent of the total global water.

The fresh water, although renewable, is growing.short of usable water and it is going to be a major issue of the 21st century. The World Bank has predicted that the wars between countries will be fought over water and not for oil and land. We need to apprehend that we are heading towards catastrophe with no way of turning back.

The world water consumption in 1990 was estimated as 4123 km^3:
2680 km^3 for agriculture
973 km^3 for industry
300 km^3 for municipal supply
170 km^3 for reservoirs

Table 1.1: Water requirements for different uses (Quantity in km^3)

S.N.	**Uses**	**Year**	**Year 2010**			**Year 2025**			**Year 2050**		
		1997-98	**Low**	**High**	**%**	**Low**	**High**	**%**	**Low**	**High**	**%**
1	Irrigation	524	543	557	78	561	611	72	628	807	68
2	Domestic	30	42	43	6	55	62	7	90	111	9
3	Industries	30	37	37	5	67	67	8	81	81	7
4	Power	9	10	19	3	31	33	4	63	70	6
5	Inland Navigation	0	7	7	1	10	10	1	15	15	1
6	Flood Control	0	0	0	0	0	0	0	0	0	0
7	Environment	0	0	0	0	0	0	0	0	0	0

	1.Afforestation										
8	Environment 2. Ecology	0	5	5	1	10	10	1	20	20	2
9	Evaporation Losses	36	42	42	6	50	50	6	76	76	7
	TOTAL	629	694	710	100	784	843	100	973	1180	100

Source: Government of India, Report of the National Commission for Integrated Water Resources Development Plan, Vol. 1, 1999

Sources of water: The various sources of water available can be classified as follows:

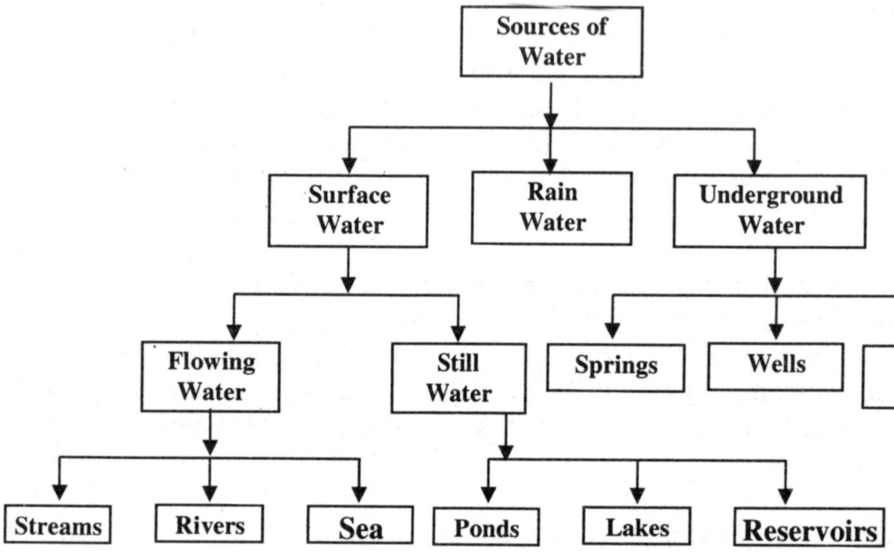

Fig.1.1: Water Sources

Surface water (River and Lake Water): It contains dissolved CO_2 and upon contact with basic materials, it dissolves them as bicarbonates. In similar manner, chlorides and sulphates present also get dissolved.

$$CaCO_3 + CO_2 + H_2O \rightarrow Ca(HCO_3)_2$$

(Insoluble) (Soluble)

$$MgCO_3 + CO_2 + H_2O \rightarrow Mg(HCO_3)_2$$

(Insoluble) (Soluble)

Deep ground water: The water emerging from some deep groundwaters must have fallen as rain many decades, hundreds, thousands or in some cases millions of years ago. Soil and rock layers naturally filter the ground water to a high degree of clarity before it is pumped to the treatment plant. Such water may emerge as springs, artesian springs or may be extracted from boreholes or wells. Deep ground water is generally of very high bacteriological quality (i.e. pathogenic bacteria such as Campylobacter or the pathogenic protozoa Cryptosporidium and Giardia are typically absent), but the water typically is rich in dissolved solids, especially carbonates and sulphates of calcium and magnesium. Depending on the strata through which the water has flowed, other ions may also be present including chloride and bicarbonate.

Shallow groundwater: Water emerging from shallow groundwater is usually abstracted from wells or boreholes. The bacteriological quality can be variable depending on the nature of the catchment. A variety of soluble materials may be present including (rarely) potentially toxic metals such as zinc and copper.

Arsenic contamination of groundwater is a serious problem in some areas, notably from shallow wells in Bangladesh and West Bengal in the Ganges Delta.

Although the total replenishable ground water resources in India is about 432 bcm (billion cubic meters), the present level of ground water development is only 3 percent. Notwithstanding this fact, the level of development in some states is very high leading to a situation of over exploitation in certain pockets of the country. Out of 5,711 number of blocks/modals/ taluks watersheds in the country, 310 are over exploited and 160 are dark where the level of exploitation is 85 percent to 100 percent of the replenishable quantum.

Table 1.2: Requirement of water as per population in India

Year	Population (in million)	Per Capita Water Availability
1951	361	5177
1955	395	4732
1991	846	2209
2001	1027	1820
2025	1394(projected)	1341
2050	1640(Projected)	1140

Upland lakes and reservoirs: Typically located in the headwaters of river systems, upland reservoirs are usually sited above any human habitation and may be surrounded by a protective zone to restrict the opportunities for contamination. Bacteria and pathogen levels are usually low, but some bacteria protozoa or algae will be present. Where uplands are forested or peaty, humic acids can colour the water. Many upland sources have low pH which require adjustment.

Low land reservoirs: Low land surface waters will have a significant bacterial load and may also contain algae, suspended solids and a variety of dissolved constituents.

Sea water: In the ocean, the major anionic constituents are chloride, carbonate, sulphate and silicate. Chloride is the major anionic constituent in the sea water. Calcium and sodium are the predominant cations in the sea water. Sea water contains about 2000 times more dissolved salts than that of fresh water. The average chemical composition (world over) of rivers and lake water is expressed as follows:

Table 1.3: Chemical compositions of rivers and lake water

Anions	Cations
CO_3^{2-} - 35.2%	Ca^{2+} - 20.4
SO_4^{2-} - 12.1 %	Mg^{2+}- 3.4
Cl^- -5.7 %	Na^+- 5.8
SiO_2^- - 11.7 %	K^+- 2.1
NO_3^- -0.9 %	$(Fe, Al)_2O_3$ – 2.7

Chemically speaking, sea water is a solution of 0.5 M NaCl and 0.05 M $MgSO_4$, containing traces of all conceivable matter in the universe. The oceans are the final sink for many substances involved in numerous geochemical processes, as well as the waste dumped as a result of human activities. The most abundant elements (except H and O), viz. Na, Cl, Mg constitute 90% of the matter in sea water, K, Ca and S (SO_4^{2-}) 3% and the other elements together 7%.

Table 1.4: The elemental composition of sea water

Element	Abundance mg/L (pop)	Principal species	Residence time (year)
Na	10.5×10^3	Na^+	6×10^3
Mg	1.35×10^3	Mg^{2+}, $MgSO_4$	4.5×10^7
Ca	400	Ca^{2+}, $CaSO_4$	8.0×10^4
K	380	K^+	1.1×10^7
Sr	8	Sr^{2+}, $SrSO_4$	1.1×10^7
Rb	0.12	Rb^+	2.7×10^5
Ba	0.03	Ba^{2+}, $BaSO_4$	8.4×10^4
Fe	0.01	$Fe(OH)_3$ (S)	1.4×10^2
Zn	0.01	Zn^{2+}, $ZnSO_4$	1.8×10^5
Al	0.01	$Al(OH)_3$	1.0×10^2
Mo	0.01	MoO_4^{2-}	5.0×10^5
U	0.003	$UO_2(CO_3)_3^{4-}$	5.0×10^5
Cu	0.002	Cu^{2+}, $CuSO_4$	5.0×10^5
Ni	0.002	Ni^{2+}, $NiSO_4$	1.8×10^4
Mn	0.002	Mn^{2+}, $MnSO_4$	1.4×10^2
V	0.002	$VO_2(OH)$	1.0×10^4
Ti	0.001	-	1.6×10^2
Co	5×10^4	Co^{2+}, $CoSO_4$	1.8×10^4
Cd	11×10^{-5}	Cd^{2+}, $CdSO_4$	5.8×10^5
Cr	5×10^{-5}	-	3.5×10^2
Ag	4×10^{-3}	$AgCl_2^-$, $AgCl_3^{2-}$	2.1×10^4
Hg	3×10^{-3}	$HgCl_3^{3-}$, $HgCl_3^{4-}$	4.2×10^4
Pb	3×10^{-5}	Pb^{2+}, $PbSO_4$	2.0×10^3
Cl	19×10^3	Cl^-	-
S	885	SO_4^{2-}	-
Br	65	Br^-	-
C	28	HCO_3^-, H_2CO_3, CO_3^{2-}OrganicComp.	-
B	4.6	$B(OH)_3^-$,$B(OH)_2O^-$	-
F	1.3	F^-	-
As	0.003	$HAsO_4^{2-}$, H_2AsO_4	-

Still water: Lakes and ponds water have organic impurities due to the decomposition of plants and animals. A barrier in the form of dams may be constructed across the river so as to form a pool of water. This pool or artificial lake is called storage reservoir. The quality of reservoir is just the same as that of river water.

Atmospheric water: Generation of atmospheric water is a new technology that can provide high quality drinking water by extracting water from the air by cooling the air and then condensing the water vapour.

Rainwater harvesting : Rainwater harvesting or fog collection which collects water from the atmosphere can be used especially in areas with significant dry seasons and in areas which experience fog even when there is little rain.

Fresh Water : Classification of fresh water according to Central Pollution Control Board (CPCB), India is as follows:

Class A - Drinking water source without conventional treatment but after disinfection.
Class B - Outdoor bathing.
Class C- Drinking water source with conventional treatment followed by disinfection.
Class D - Propagation of wildlife and fisheries.
Class E - Irrigation, industrial cooling and controlled water disposed.

Table 1.5: Classification of Fresh Water

Water Quality Criteria	Class of Fresh Water				
	A	**B**	**C**	**D**	**E**
Dissolved Oxygen	6 mg/lit. min.	5mg/lit. min.	4mg/lit. min.	4mg/lit min.	
Biological Oxygen	2mg/lit.max.	3mg/lit.max.	3mg/lit. max	-	
MPN of Coliform per 100 ml	50max.	500max.	5000 max.	-	-
pH	6.5-8.5	6.5-8.5	6.0-9.0	6.5-8.5	6.00-8.5
Free ammonia as N	-	-	-	1.2mg/lit. Max.	
Sodium Absorption Ratio (SAR)	-	-	-	-	

1.2 IMPURITIES IN WATER AND THEIR SOURCES

The unique ability of water to dissolve, to some extent, virtually every chemical compound and support practically every form of life means that water is essential ingredient inspite of the impurities present for every human being, plant and animal. The raw water supplies contain many contaminants. The major categories of impurities found in raw water include:

- Suspended particles, including colloids
- Dissolved inorganic salts
- Dissolved organic compounds
- Micro-organisms
- Pyrogens
- Dissolved gases

Suspended particles: Suspended matter in water includes silt, pipe work debris and colloids. Colloidal particles (which can be organic or inorganic) are not truly in solution or suspension and give rise to haze or turbidity in the water. The degree of colloidal contamination can be determined by fouling index test or by turbidimetry.

Dissolved inorganic salts: Inorganic substances in solution include hardness salts derived from rock strata. The bicarbonates of calcium and magnesium give rise to 'temporary hardness', while the sulfates and chlorides cause "permanent hardness". The other inorganic impurities present in water include:

- Carbon dioxide which dissolves in water to give weakly acidic carbonic acid
- Sodium salts
- Silicates leached from sandy river beds
- Ferrous and ferric iron compounds derived from minerals and rusty iron pipes
- Chlorides from saline intrusion
- Aluminium from dosing chemicals and minerals
- Phosphates from detergents
- Nitrates from fertilizers

Dissolved organic compounds: Organic impurities in water arise from the decay of vegetable matter-principally humic and fulvic acids - and from farming, paper making, domestic and industrial waste. These include detergents, fats, oils, solvents and residues from pesticides and herbicides. In addition, water-borne organics may include compounds leached from pipe work, tanks and purification media.

Micro-organisms: Surface water contains a wide variety of micro-organisms, including amoebae, bacteria, paramecia, rotifers, diatoms and algae. However, since most laboratory water comes from municipal water treatment plants and is extensively treated to remove micro-organisms, the chief micro-organisms of concern for water purification systems are bacteria

Dissolved gases: Oxygen and carbon dioxide are the two gases most commonly found in natural waters. Carbon dioxide behaves as a weak anion and is removed by strongly basic anion exchange resins. Dissolved oxygen can also be removed by degassing or by anions.

Effects of Impurities

Odour: Decaying aquatic organisms and certain chemicals impart odour to water.

Turbidity: Extremely fine suspended particles such as clay, silt, finely divided matters (Organic and inorganic), micro -organisms impart turbidity to water.

Taste: It is due to the presence of dissolved minerals:

- Bitter taste can be due to the presence of iron, aluminium, manganese, sulphates or excess of lime.
- Soapy taste can be due to the presence of large amount of sodium bicarbonate.
- Brackish taste is due to the presence of unusual amount of salts.
- Palatable taste is due to the presence of dissolved gases (CO_2) and minerals (like nitrates) in water.

Colour: Colour in water is caused by metallic substances like iron, manganese, humus material, tannins, peat etc.

- Yellowish tinge - Indicates the presence of chromium.
- Yellowish Red - Indicates the presence of iron.
- Red Brown - Indicates the presence of peaty matter.
- Excess quantity of metals and dissolved gases make it corrosive.

Bacteriological impurities: They are due to pathogenic bacteria which make water unfit for drinking or domestic purpose.

pH: pH of the fresh water is polluted by the waste release by the DDT, explosives and battery industries. Water will become highly acidic in nature; the use of such water causes health problems to human being and cattle.

Temperature: Because of the discharge of the effluents into the fresh water from industries, such effluents containing impurities will increase the temperature of water that will decrease the growth of algae which will reduce the dissolved oxygen.

Dissolved salts increase the hardness of water. Hence, the water from any source has to be treated before it is used for domestic as well as for industrial purpose.

1.3 HARD WATER

Water is of two types – Soft Water and Hard Water.

Soft Water: Soft water produces lather readily with soap solution. In soft water hardness is below 100mg/lit. Soft water contains little amount of Ca^{2+}, Mg^{2+}, Fe^{2+} and Al^{3+} ions.

Advantages of Soft Water

1. Absence of colour, iron and manganese as they are removed.
2. A non-corrosive water quality.
3. Conservation of soap in laundry works.
4. High quality filtered water.
5. Protection against scale formation in steam boilers.
6. Proper cooking and saving of fuel in cooking.

Hard water: It is that type of water, which does not produce lather (foam) with soap solution readily. The water having hardness of about 100 mg/lit is said to be hard water.

Hardness of Water: Hardness has been refered as the capacity of water to produce lather with soap. It is caused by the soap consuming properties of mainly calcium and magnesium ions. They are derived primarily from bicarbonates and sulphates of calcium, magnesium and other heavy metals dissolved in it. No lather is formed until all these ions are completely removed and thus a large amount of soap is wasted.

$$2C_{17}H_{35}COONa + CaCl_2 \rightarrow (C_{17}H_{35}COO)_2Ca \downarrow + 2NaCl$$

(Sodium Steareate) (Calcium Stearate Insoluble)

$$2C_{17}H_{35}COONa + MgSO_4 \rightarrow (C_{17}H_{35}COO)_2Mg \downarrow + 2Na_2SO_4$$

(Magnesium Stearate Insoluble)

Types of Hardness

1. Temporary, Alkaline or Carbonate Hardness: This is caused due to the bicarbonates of calcium and magnesium in water and can be removed even by boiling. The bicarbonates are decomposed on boiling, yielding insoluble carbonates or hydroxides, which are deposited as a crust at the bottom of vessel.

$$Ca(HCO_3)_2 \xrightarrow{\Delta} CaCO_3 \downarrow + H_2O + CO_2 \uparrow$$

Calcium Bicarbonate Calcium Carbonate (Insoluble)

$$Mg(HCO_3)_2 \xrightarrow{\Delta} Mg(OH)_2 \downarrow + 2CO_2 \uparrow$$

Magnesium Bicarbonate Magnesium hydroxide

The following is the equilibrium reaction when calcium carbonate ($CaCO_3$) is dissolved in water:

$$CaCO_3(S) + H_2O(l) + CO_2(g) \rightleftharpoons Ca^{2+}(aq) + 2HCO_3^-(aq)$$

2. Permanent, Non alkaline or non-carbonate hardness: This is because of the presence of sulphates and chlorides of calcium, magnesium, iron and other heavy metals. Hence the salts responsible for permanent hardness are- $CaCl_2$, $MgCl_2$, $CaSO_4$, $MgSO_4$, $FeSO_4$, $Al_2(SO_4)_3$ etc. Permanent hardness is not dcstroyed on boiling.

Degree of Hardness: The hardness of water is usually expressed in terms of equivalent amount of $CaCO_3$ but it is never present in the form of calcium carbonate because it is insoluble in water. Reasons for choosing $CaCO_3$ as a standard for reporting hardness are:

1. It is the most insoluble salt that can be precipitated in water treatment.
2. Its molecular weight being 100 (eq. wt = 50) renders calculations easy.

1.4 EQUIVALENTS OF CALCIUM CARBONATE

$$\text{Equivalents of } CaCO_3 = \frac{\begin{bmatrix}\text{Mass of hardness}\\ \text{producing substances}\\ \text{in mg/lit.}\end{bmatrix} \times \begin{bmatrix}\text{Chemical equivalent}\\ \text{of } CaCO_3\end{bmatrix} \times 2}{\begin{bmatrix}\text{Chemical equivalent of hardness producing}\\ \text{substances}\end{bmatrix} \times 2}$$

$$= \begin{bmatrix}\text{Mass of hardness}\\ \text{producing substances}\\ \text{in mg/lit.}\end{bmatrix} \times \left[\frac{100}{\begin{matrix}2 \times \text{Chemical equivalent of}\\ \text{hardness producing substances}\end{matrix}}\right]$$

$$= \begin{bmatrix}\text{Mass of hardness}\\ \text{producing substances}\\ \text{in mg/lit.}\end{bmatrix} \times (\text{multiplication factor}) \text{in} \frac{\text{mg}}{\text{lit.}} \text{ or ppm}$$

Table 1.6: Multiplication factors for different salts

Constituent salt/ion	Molar mass	n-factor	Chemical equivalent $\frac{\text{Molar mass}}{\text{n-factor}}$	Multiplication factor for converting equivalent of $CaCO_3$
$Ca(HCO_3)_2$	162	2	162/2=81	100/(2 x 81) = 100 /162
$Mg(HCO_3)_2$	146	2	146/2=73	100/(2 x 73) = 100 /146
$CaSO_4$	136	2	136/2=68	100/(2 x 68) = 100 /136
$MgSO_4$	120	2	120/2=60	100/(2 x 601) = 100 /120
$CaCl_2$	111	2	111/2=55.5	100/(2 x 55.5) = 100 /111

$MgCl_2$	95	2	95/2=47.5	100/(2 x 47.5) = 100 /95
$CaCO_3$	100	2	100/2=50	100/(2 x 50) = 100 / 100
$MgCO_3$	84	2	84/2=42	100/(2 x 42) = 100 /84
CO_2	44	2	44/2=22	100/(2 x 22) = 100 /44
$Mg(NO_3)_2$	148	2	148/2=74	100/(2 x 74) = 100 /148
HCO_3^-	61	1	61/1=61	100/(2 x 61) = 100 /122
OH^-	17	1	17/1=17	100/(2 x 17) = 100 /34
CO_3^{2-}	60	2	60/2=30	100/(2 x 30) = 100 /60
$NaAlO_2$	82	1	82/1=82	100/(2 x 82) = 100 /164
$Al_2(SO_4)_3$	342	6	342/6=57	100/(2 x 57) = 100 /114
$FeSO_4.7H_2O$	278	2	278/2 = 139	100/(2 x 139) = 100 /278
H^+	1	1	1/1=1	100/(2 x 1) = 100 / 2

Advantages of Hard Water

- The taste of hard water is usually better than soft water due to the presence of Ca^{2+} and Mg^{2+}ions.
- Dissolved calcium present in hard water helps to produce strong teeth and healthy bones in children.
- In old houses, lead piping is used for distribution of water. Hard water coats these pipes with a layer of insoluble $CaCO_3$. This prevents the lead dissolving in the drinking water.

1.5 DISADVANTAGES OF HARD WATER

Domestic

- The amount of minerals in water affects the amount of soap and detergent necessary for cleaning. Soap used in hard water combines with the minerals to form a sticky soap curd. Some synthetic detergents are less effective in hard water because the active ingredient is partially inactivated by hardness, even though it stays dissolved.
- Bathing with soap in hard water leaves a film of sticky soap curd on the skin. The film may prevent removal of soil and bacteria. Soap curd interferes with the return of skin to its normal slightly acidic condition and may lead to irritation.
- Soap curd on hair may make it dull, lifeless and difficult to manage. Scaling, which is the precipitation of minerals to form a deposit is called limescale.
- Scale can clog pipes and can decrease the life of toilet flushing units. It can coat the inside of tea and coffee pots and clog and ruin water heaters.
- The insoluble salts that get left behind from using regular shampoo in hard water tend to leave hair rougher and harder to detangle.
- When doing laundry in hard water, soap curds lodge in fabric during washing to make fabric stiff and rough. Incomplete soil removal from laundry causes graying of white fabric and the loss of brightness in colors. A sour odor can develop in clothes. Continuous laundering in hard water can shorten the life of clothes.
- In addition, soap curds can deposit on dishes, bathtubs and showers and all water fixtures.
- The boiling point of water is increased because of presence of salts. Hence more fuel and time are required for cooking.
- Hard water causes bad effects on our digestive system.

Industrial

- **Textile Industry**: Hard water causes wastage of soap. Precipitates of calcium and magnesium adhere to the fabrics and cause difficulty in dyeing. If iron and manganese are also present, then they cause brown or red spots on fabrics, thereby spoiling their beauty.

- **Sugar Industry**: Water containing sulphates, nitrates, carbonates etc. cause difficulties in crystallization of sugar.
- **Dyeing Industry**: The dissolved salts in hard water may react with costly dyes forming precipitates.
- **Paper Industry**: Calcium, magnesium, iron salts in hard water may affect the quality of paper.
- **Pharmaceutical Industry**: Hard water may cause some undesirable products during the manufacturing of pharmaceutical products.

Table 1.7: Key cations and associated anions causing hardness

Cations	Anions
Ca^{2+}	HCO_3^-
Mg^{2+}	SO_4^{2-}
Sr^{2+}	Cl^-
Fe^{2+}	NO_3^-
Mn^{2+}	SiO_3^{2-}

1.6 UNITS OF HARDNESS

Types of measurement: It is possible to measure the level of hard water by water testing kit. There are several different scales used to describe the hardness of water in different contexts.

m mol/L (millimoles per litre) - mg/L calcium carbonate equivalent

grains/gallon (gpg) - 1 gr/U.S. gal = 17.11 mg/L

parts per million - weight/volume (ppm *w/v* or ppm *m/v*)): It is the parts of $CaCO_3$ equivalent hardness per million parts of water.

1 ppm = 1 part of $CaCO_3$ in 10^6 parts of water

(One part per million is a unit weight of solute per million unit of solution)

Milligram per liter (mg/liter): It is the number of milligram of $CaCO_3$ equivalent hardness present per liter of water.

1 part of $CaCO_3$ equivalent per 10^6 parts of water.

Clark degrees (°Clark) / English degrees (°E): conversion to mg/L calcium: divide by 0.175.
One degree Clark corresponds to one grain of calcium carbonate in one imperial gallon of water which is equivalent to 14.28 parts calcium carbonate in 1,000,000 parts water.Or It is the number of grains (or 1/70,000) of $CaCO_3$equivalent per gallons (10 lbs) of water.

1 part of $CaCO_3$ equivalent = 70,000 parts of water.

German degrees (°dH): conversion to mg/L calcium: divide by 0.14.One degree German corresponds to one part calcium oxide in 100,000 parts of water.

French degrees (°Fr): (shares symbol with degree Fahrenheit, but in lower case) - conversion to mg/L calcium: divide by 0.25.One degree French corresponds to one part calcium carbonate in 100,000 parts of water.

1 part of $CaCO_3$ equivalent = 10^5 parts of water

Mili equivalent per million (e.p.m): It is the number of equivalents of substance present per million, hence known as equivalent per million.

Degree of general hardness (dGH): One degree of general hardness corresponds to 10 mg of calcium oxide or magnesium oxide per litre of water. The precise mixture of minerals dissolved in the water, together with the acidity or alkalinity (pH) and temperature will determine the behaviour of the hardness, so single number on a scale does not give a full description.

Table 1.8: Classification of Water Hardness

Classification	mg/l or ppm	Grains/gal
Soft	0 – 17.1	0 – 1
Slightly hard	17.1 - 60	1 - 3.5
Moderately hard	60 - 120	3.5 – 7.0
Hard	120 - 180	7.0 - 10.5

Langelier Saturation Index (LSI): The Langelier Saturation Index (LSI) (sometimes also called Langelier Stability Index) is a calculated number used to predict the calcium carbonate stability of water that is, whether water will precipitate, dissolve or be in equilibrium with calcium carbonate. Langelier developed a method for predicting the pH at which water is saturated in calcium carbonate (called pHs). The LSI is expressed as the difference between the actual system pH and the saturation pH.

$$LSI = pH - pHs$$

If the actual pH of the water is below the calculated saturation pH, the LSI is negative and the water has a very limited scaling potential. If the actual pH exceeds pHs, the LSI is positive and being supersaturated with $CaCO_3$, the water has a tendency to form scale. At increasing positive index values, the scaling potential increases.

Boiler Problems: Various problems in boilers are:

- Scale and Sludge formation.
- Boiler Corrosion.
- Priming and Foaming.
- Caustic Embitterment.
- Carry Over.

1.7 SCALE AND SLUDGE FORMATION IN BOILERS

Raw water contains varying amount of mineral salts such as calcium, magnesium, iron and silica. When these materials exceed their solubility point due to the rise in water temperature and increased cycles of

Fig. 1.2: (a) Sludge (b) Scale in boilers

concentration, the minerals precipitate out of water and produce scale forming salt. When these deposits adhere directly to heating surfaces, they form layers of insulation on the metal and substantially decrease the heat transfer efficiency. This hard insulated layer deposited on metal surface is known as scale. If the precipitates formed are loose and slimy, these are known as sludge.

Composition of Scale and Sludge

Scale: e.g. $CaCO_3$, $CaSO_4$, Mg $(OH)_2$ etc.

Sludge: e.g. $MgCO_3$, $MgCl_2$, $MgSO_4$, $CaCl_2$ etc.

Formation of Scales in the boiler

a. **Decomposition of bicarbonates:** When hard water is boiled in the boiler, the bicarbonates of Ca and Mg get decomposed and convert into insoluble Ca and Mg carbonate. These carbonates get deposited on the inner side of the boiler.

$$Ca(HCO_3)_2 \rightarrow \underset{\text{Scale}}{CaCO_3} + CO_2 + H_2O$$

$$Mg(HCO_3)_2 \rightarrow \underset{\text{Scale}}{MgCO_3} + CO_2 + H_2O$$

However, scale composed chiefly of calcium carbonate is soft and is the main cause of scale formation in low pressure boilers. But in high pressure boilers, $CaCO_3$ is soluble due to the formation of Ca $(OH)_2$.

$$CaCO_3 + H_2O \rightarrow \underset{\text{Soluble}}{Ca(OH)_2} + CO_2$$

b. **Decomposition of calcium sulphate:** Calcium sulphate is soluble in cold water but almost completely insoluble in super heated water. Consequently, $CaSO_4$ gets precipitated as hard scale on the hotter part of the boiler.

c. **Hydrolysis of magnesium salts:** Dissolved magnesium salts undergo hydrolysis at prevailing high temperature inside the boiler forming hydroxide precipitate, which forms a soft type of scale.

$$MgCl_2 + 2H_2O \rightarrow \underset{\text{Scale}}{Mg(OH)_2 \downarrow} + 2HCl$$

d. **Presence of silica:** Silica (SiO_2) if present in small quantity, may deposit as calcium ($CaSiO_3$) and/or magnesium silicate ($MgSiO_3$). This deposit sticks very firmly on the inner side of the boiler surface and is very difficult to remove.

Disadvantages of Scale Formation

- **Wastage of Fuel:** The scale formation causes decrease of heat transfer, as a result over heating is required which causes more consumption of fuel.

Table 1.9: Thickness of Scale and Wastage of Fuel

Thickness of Scale (mm)	0.325	0.625	1.25	2.5	12
Wastage of fuel	10%	15%	50%	80%	150%

- **Lowering of Boiler safety:** Due to scale formation, over heating of boiler is done which results in distortion of boiler tube and also makes the boiler unsafe to bear the pressure of the steam, especially in high pressure boiler.

- **Decrease in efficiency:** Due to the deposition of scale in the valve and condensers of the boiler, choking takes place. This results in decrease in efficiency of the boiler.
- **Danger of explosion:** The uneven expansion of the scale may lead to the cracking of the scale. The super heated steel plates come in contact with boiler water. This leads to the formation of a large amount of steam suddenly, creating high pressure inside the boiler. When the boiler material is not strong enough to withstand the pressure, it bursts.

Removal of Scales

- Soft scales are removed with the help of scrapper made of wire brush.
- Hard and brittle scales can be removed by giving thermal shocks i.e. heating the boiler and suddenly cooling with cold water.
- Certain chemicals are used to dissolve scales e.g. $CaCO_3$ scales can be dissolved by using 5-10% HCl. $CaSO_4$ scales dissolve in EDTA solution, EDTA forms soluble complex with Ca.

Prevention of Scale Formation

- External Treatment: In this type of treatment efficient softening of water is done.
- Internal Treatment: In this type of treatment, ions are prohibited to exhibit their original characteristics.

Sludge: Sludge is soft, loose and slimy precipitate formed within the boiler. It is formed at comparatively colder portion of the boiler and gets deposited at places where the flow rate is slow.

Removal of Sludge

- Sludge can easily be removed by scrapping off with a wire brush.
- Sludge can also be removed by polymeric and organic sludge dispersants.

Prevention of Sludge Formation

- Sludge formation can be prevented by using soft water.
- By frequently "blow down operation" i.e. removal of a portion of concentrated water through a tap and replacing it by fresh water.

Table.1.10: Differences between Sludge and Scale

S. N.	Sludge	Scale
1	Sludge is soft, slimy and loose precipitate.	Scales are hard deposits.
2	They are suspended particles and can easily remove.	They adhere very firmly to inner surface of boiler and are difficult to remove.
3	Composed of substances like $MgCl_2$, $MgCO_3$, $MgSO_4$, $CaCl_2$ etc.	Composed of substances like $CaSO_4$, $CaCO_3$; $Mg(OH)_2$ etc.
4	Formed at comparatively colder portions of the boiler.	Formed generally at the heated portion of the boiler.
5	They are poor conductor of heat and also decrease the efficiency of boiler but they are less dangerous.	They are also poor conductor of heat and decrease the efficiency of boiler and chances of explosion are also there.
6	They can be removed by blow down operation.	They can be removed by using HCl or EDTA solution.

1.8 BOILER CORROSION

Corrosion is the reversion of a metal to its ore form. Iron, for example, reverts to iron oxide as the result of corrosion. The process of corrosion however is a complex electro chemical reaction and it takes many forms. Corrosion may produce general attack over a large metal surface or it may result in pinpoint penetration of metal. Corrosion is a relevant problem caused by water in boilers. Corrosion can be of widely varying origin and nature due to the action of dissolved oxygen, to corrosion currents set up as a result of heterogeneities on metal surfaces, or to the iron being directly attacked by the water. While basic corrosion in boilers may be primarily due to reaction of the metal with oxygen, other factors such as stresses, acid conditions and specific chemical corrodents may have important influence and produce different forms of attack. It is necessary to consider the quantity of the various harmful substances that can be allowed in the boiler water without risk of damage to the boiler.

Corrosion occurs, if Fe of the boiler material gets converted to Fe^{2+} ions and combines with the water molecule to produce ferrous hydroxide which reacts with oxygen to form Fe $(OH)_3$ or rust.

$$2Fe + 2H_2O + O_2 \rightarrow 2Fe(OH)_2 \downarrow$$
$$4Fe(OH)_2 + O_2 \rightarrow 2[Fe_2O_3 \cdot 2H_2O]$$

Ferrous Hydroxide Rust

Disadvantages of Boiler Corrosion

- Reduces boiler life.
- Leakages of the joints, rivets and bend portions.
- Increase the repair and maintenance cost.

Main Factors for Boiler Corrosion

- Dissolved Oxygen
- Dissolved Carbon dioxide
- Mineral acids

Dissolved Oxygen: It is one of the main causes of corrosion. At room temperature about 8 ml of dissolved oxygen is present in water. In boilers, oxygen enters through raw water supply. When water is heated in the boiler, the dissolved oxygen is set free and attacks the boiler material to form rust.

$$2Fe + 2H_2O + O_2 \rightarrow 2Fe(OH)_2 \downarrow$$
$$4Fe(OH)_2 + O_2 \rightarrow 2[Fe_2O_3 \cdot 2H_2O]$$

Ferrous Hydroxide Rust

Removal of Dissolved Oxygen: There are two methods by which oxygen can be removed.

i) Mechanical De-aeration and

ii) Chemical Methods.

i) Mechanical De-aeration: In this method, water is passed in a perforated plates-fitted tower, which is heated from sides and connected to vacuum pump. Large exposed surface, high temperature and low pressure decrease the solubility of the gas and the water free from DO is collected at the bottom.

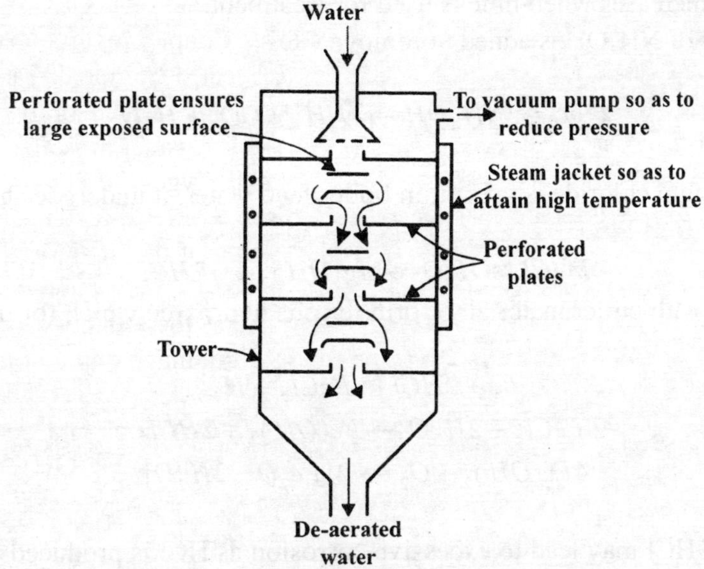

Fig. 1.3: Mechanical deaeration of water

ii) Chemical Method: By adding calculated amount of chemicals like Na_2S, Na_2SO_3 and N_2H_4, oxygen can be removed from the boiler feed water.

$$Na_2S + 2O_2 \rightarrow Na_2SO_4$$
Sodium Sulphide

$$2Na_2SO_3 + O_2 \rightarrow 2Na_2SO_4$$
Sodium sulphite

$$N_2H_4 + O_2 \rightarrow N_2 + 2H_2O$$
Hydrazine

Sodium sulphide and sodium sulphite react with oxygen to form sodium sulphate. Hydrazine reacts with oxygen to form nitrogen gas which does not form harmful products. Pure hydrazine is an explosive inflammable liquid, but 40% aqueous solution is safe to use. Hydrazine should be added in calculated amount, because excess of it decomposes to give NH_3 which may cause corrosion of alloys like copper etc. used in condenser tubes.

$$3N_2H_4 \rightarrow 4NH_3 + N_2$$

Carbon dioxide: Under high temperature, dissolved bicarbonates present in raw water decompose and form carbon dioxide.

$$Mg(HCO_3)_2 \rightarrow MgCO_3 + CO_2 + H_2O$$

Carbon dioxide reacts with water to form carbonic acid which has slow corrosive effect on boiler material.

$$H_2O + CO_2 \rightarrow H_2CO_3$$
Carbonic acid

Removal of CO_2

CO_2 can be removed by mechanical de-aeration along with O_2.

- By passing water through lime-stone.

$$Ca(OH)_2 + CO_2 \rightarrow CaCO_3 + H_2O$$

- Hardness of water increases when lime is used for treatment.
- Calculated quantity of NH_4OH is added to remove CO_2

$$CO_2 + 2NH_4OH \rightarrow (NH_4)_2CO_3 + H_2O$$

Mineral acid: If magnesium chloride is present in boiler feed water, it undergoes hydrolysis and produces hydrochloric acid.

$$MgCl_2 + H_2O \rightarrow Mg(OH)_2 \downarrow + 2HCl$$

The liberated acid reacts with boiler material to form ferrous hydroxide which forms rust as follows:

$$Fe + 2HCl \rightarrow FeCl_2 + H_2$$
$$FeCl_2 + 2H_2O \rightarrow Fe(OH)_2 + 2HCl$$
$$4Fe(OH)_2 + O_2 \rightarrow 2[Fe_2O_3 \cdot 2H_2O]$$

Thus, a small quantity of HCl may lead to excessive corrosion as HCl is produced in a chain like manner. Consequently, presence of even a small amount of $MgCl_2$ leads to large extent of corrosion of boiler material. Formation of HCl is prohibited by adding calculated quantity of alkali from outside to neutralize the acid for preventing this corrosion.

1.9 CAUSTIC EMBRITTLEMENT

Caustic Embrittlement is a type of boiler corrosion. It takes place due to the use of highly alkaline water in the high pressure boiler. During this phenomenon the boiler material becomes brittle due to the accumulation of caustic substances. When the water is softened by lime-soda process, a slight excess of Na_2CO_3 is used for the complete removal of calcium and magnesium salts. Treatment with Na_2CO_3 does not cause any harm in low pressure boiler, but in high pressure boilers, the free Na_2CO_3 decomposes to give sodium hydroxide and CO_2.

$$Na_2CO_3 + H_2O \rightarrow 2NaOH + CO_2$$

NaOH produced along with the natural alkalinity of the water makes the boiler water "Caustic". The NaOH flows to the minute hair cracks rivets, bends and joints by capillary action. Due to continuous evaporation of water, the concentration of NaOH at these point increases with time due to poor circulation of water. This NaOH attacks the surrounding area thereby dissolving iron of boiler as sodium ferrate. This causes embrittlement of the boiler parts, mostly the stressed parts.

Favorable conditions for Embrittlement

- High Concentration of NaOH
- Stress at bend, rivet and joints
- Presence of sodium silicate
- Setting up of a concentration cell

The cause of caustic embrittlement is setting up of a concentration cell. The iron surrounded by dilute NaOH becomes cathodic end while the iron surrounded by concentrated NaOH becomes anodic site. The regeneration of NaOH dissolves the iron as sodium ferrate.

$$3Na_2FeO_2 + 4H_2O \rightarrow 6NaOH + Fe_3O_4 + H_2$$

Table 1.11: Setting up of a Concentration Cell

Iron at + ve Rivets Joints etc	Concentrated NaOH Solution	Dilute NaOH Solution	Iron at – ve Plane Surface

Prevention of Caustic Embrittlement

- In external treatment of boiler water, sodium phosphate can be used instead of sodium carbonate.
- Lignin and tannin should be added to block the hair cracks to prevent the infiltration of sodium hydroxide.
- Capillaries can be blocked by adding sodium sulphate or sodium phosphate. It is preferable to use Na_3PO_4 instead of Na_2SO_4 as it leads to the formation of scales due to $CaSO_4$.

1.10 PRIMING AND FOAMING

Priming: This is the ejection of boiler water into the steam take off or when the steam is formed rapidly in boilers, some droplets of the liquid are carried away along with the steam. This phenomenon of formation of wet-steam is called priming.

Causes: Priming is caused by

- High steam velocity.
- Presence of dissolved and suspended solids.
- High water level in the boiler.
- Operating the boiler below its design pressure - this increases the volume and the velocity of the steam will reduce from the water surface.
- Sudden boiling.

Priming can be avoided by

- Maintaining rapid change in steaming velocities.
- Lowering the water level.
- Proper boiler design fitted with mechanical steam purifiers.
- Ensuring sufficient softening.
- By removing sludge or scale from boiler time to time.

Foaming: This is the formation of foam in the space between the water surface and the steam take off or it is the formation of small persistent bubbles at the surface of water in boiler, which do not break easily. The following are the consequences of foaming:

- Water will trickle down from the steam connection of the gauge glass; this makes it difficult to determine the water level accurately.
- Alarms may be sounded and the burners may even lockout. This will require manual resetting of the boiler control panel before supply can be re-established.

Causes

- Presence of oil and alkali in boiler feed water.
- Foams formed due to the difference in concentration of solute between the surface film and the bulk of the liquid.
- Foaming tendency increases due to lowering of surface tension of the water (Oils and alkalis react to form soaps which generally lower the surface tension of water).

- The substances which increase the viscosity of the surface film also increase foam forming tendency.

Prevention of Foaming

- By adding antifoaming chemicals like polyamide antifoam, castor oil etc.
- Removal of oil from water by adding sodium aluminates and aluminium sulphate which get hydrolyzed to form aluminium hydroxide flocks which entrap oil drops.

Disadvantages of Priming and Foaming: These are highly objectionable as they carry some suspended and dissolved impurities along with the steam to the super heaters or turbine blades where they get deposited as the water evaporates. These deposits lower their efficiency by hindering the steam flow.

Carry Over

Carrying of suspended and dissolved impurities by steam along with water is called "Carry Over". This is due to priming and foaming. They are objectionable because –

- Suspended Solids and Dissolved Solids get deposited on super heater's turbine blades and thus reduce the efficiency of boiler.
- They enter the machine parts and interfere with its working and reduce their life.
- Increase the maintenance cost of the boiler.
- It is difficult to judge the actual height of water column for maintaining the boiler pressure.

Prevention of Plumbo Solvency: Water transported through lead pipes attacks metal in many ways. For example, lead hydroxide is formed in the presence of dissolved oxygen. This is known as Plumbo-Solvency.

$$2Pb + 2H_2O + O_2 \rightarrow 2Pb(OH)_2$$

The acids derived from the hydrolysis of dissolved calcium and magnesium salt in water may react with lead to form lead sulphate and lead chloride etc.

$$MgSO_4 + 2H_2O \rightleftharpoons Mg(OH)_2 + H_2SO_4$$
$$MgCl_2 + 2H_2O \rightleftharpoons Mg(OH)_2 + 2HCl$$
$$Pb + 2H_2SO_4 \rightleftharpoons PbSO_4 + H_2$$
$$Pb + 2HCl \rightleftharpoons PbCl_2 + H_2$$

Lead carbonate may also be formed as a result of reaction of dissolved CO_2 on $Pb(OH)_2$.

$$Pb(OH)_2 + CO_2 \rightleftharpoons PbCO_3 + H_2O$$

The lead compounds $PbCl_2$, $PbSO_4$, $PbCO_3$, and $Pb(OH)_2$ are more soluble in water, solubility order is $PbCl_2 > PbSO_4 > PbCO_3 > Pb(OH)_2$ so if lead compounds are present beyond the permissible limit, may cause lead poisoning.

Lead contamination may be removed by

- Treating water with alkali silicate and phosphate mixture followed by filtration.
- Passing water through a Zeolite bed which exchanges Na^+ with Pb^{2+} ions. The Pb^{2+} ions are thus retained by cation exchanger.

- Passing water through an activated charcoal bed whose calcium phosphate content reacts with soluble lead compound of water to form almost insoluble $Pb_3(PO_4)_2$.

1.11 WATER SOFTENING

The removal of hardness causing ions like Ca^{2+} and Mg^{2+} is termed as 'softening' of water. Softening is required, as hard water is unsuitable for domestic as well as industrial purposes.

Following methods are used for softening water:

I External treatment

II Internal treatment

I. External treatment: In external treatment method, water is externally treated before it is fed into the boiler. It can be done by following methods:

i.) Lime-Soda process.

ii.) Zeolite or permutit process.

iii.) Ion exchange or demineralization process.

i.) Lime-Soda Process: In this method soluble hardness causing impurities are converted into insoluble precipitates which can be removed by settling and filtration. First, soluble bicarbonate ion (HCO_3^-) is converted into insoluble carbonate (CO_3^{2-}) by raising pH to near 10.3 with the help of quick lime (CaO) or hydrated lime [$Ca(OH)_2$].

$$Ca(HCO_3)_2 + Ca(OH)_2 \rightarrow 2CaCO_3 \downarrow + 2H_2O$$

$$Mg(HCO_3)_2 + 2Ca(OH)_2 \rightarrow 2CaCO_3 \downarrow + Mg(OH)_2 + 2H_2O$$

If non-carbonate hardness is present, soda ash Na_2CO_3 would be added.

$$MgSO_4 + Ca(OH)_2 + Na_2CO_3 \rightarrow Mg(OH)_2 \downarrow + CaCO_3 + Na_2SO_4$$

Small quantities of coagulants like Alum [$K_2SO_4 \cdot Al_2(SO_4)_3 \cdot 24H_2O$], Aluminium sulphate [$Al_2(SO_4)_3$] or Sodium meta aluminate [$NaAlO_2$] are added to entrap the fine precipitates of $CaCO_3$ and Mg $(OH)_2$.

Types of lime-soda process are:

- Cold lime-soda process
- Hot lime-soda process

Cold lime-soda process: The hard water is first analyzed and is fed into the vertical circular chamber fitted with a stirrer. To this tank, calculated quantity of lime and soda ash are added. Small quantity of coagulant like $Al_2(SO_4)_3$ is added to entrap the precipitate of $CaCO_3$, $Mg(OH)_2$, Silica and oil if present in water. Constant stirring and mixing cause softening of water. The sludge settles down in the outer chamber and softened water comes up.

$$Al_2(SO_4)_3 + 3Ca(HCO_3)_2 \rightarrow 2Al(OH)_3 \downarrow + 3CaSO_4 + 6CO_2 \uparrow$$

The softened water is then passed through filtration unit and finally filtered soft water flows out through the outlet at the top. Cold lime soda process provides water containing residual hardness of 50-60 ppm.

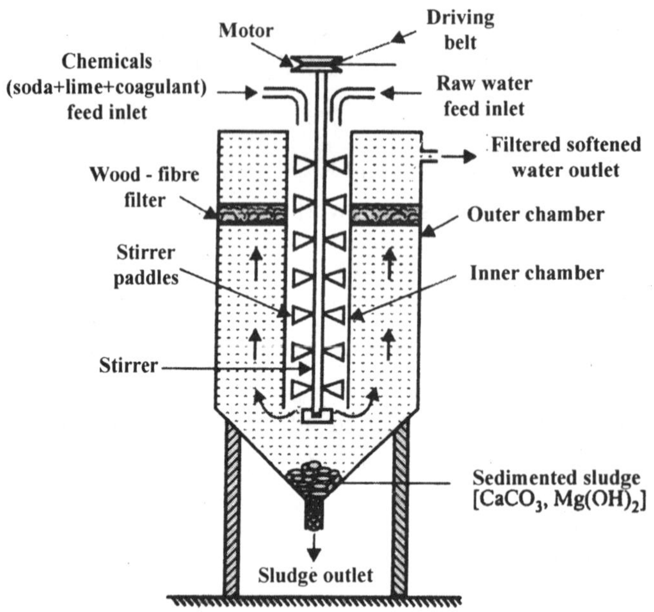

Fig. 1.4: Continuous cold lime-Soda softener

Limitation: In cold lime soda process, the reaction occurs at room temperature due to which partial softening of water takes place.

Hot lime-soda process: In hot-lime-soda process, water is treated with chemicals at a temperature of 94-100^{0}C. The reactions are much faster and the precipitation is almost complete. The precipitates form quickly and also settle down rapidly. So no coagulants are needed. Dissolved gases like O_2, CO_2 are also removed. A soft water with 15-30 ppm of residual hardness is obtained by this process.

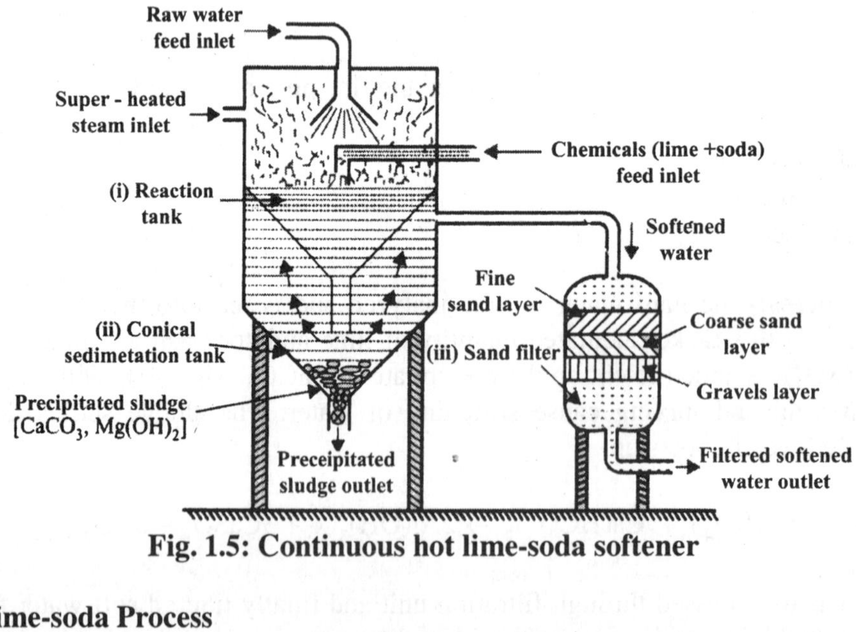

Fig. 1.5: Continuous hot lime-soda softener

Advantages of Lime-soda Process

- The process is very economical.
- Hydrated lime raises the pH to nearly 10.3; hence it has less corrosive tendencies.
- Along with the removal of hardness causing salts, it also reduces the total mineral content of water.
- To some extent, it helps in removing iron and manganese.

- Due to alkaline nature of treated water, pathogenic bacteria in water will also decrease.

Disadvantages of Lime-soda Process

- It requires skilled person and careful operation for efficient and economic softening.
- Disposal of sludge is a big problem. Theoretically each mg/l of $CaCO_3$ removed will produce 1 mg/l of sludge.
- This process does not produce water having zero hardness.
- Water softened by this process contains appreciable quantity of soluble salts such as sodium sulphate and can not be used in high pressure boilers.

Differences between cold and hot lime soda process are as follows:

Table 1.12: Difference between the Hot and Cold lime-soda process

S.No.	Cold lime soda process	Hot lime soda process
1	Reaction can take place at room temperature	Reaction takes place at 94-100^{0}C
2	Coagulants are required to settle down the precipitate.	Coagulants are not required.
3	It is a slow process.	It is a rapid process.
4	No fuel consumption	Steam is used.
5	Temporary hardness is removed by mixing lime.	Temporary hardness is removed by boiling. Hence no lime is consumed.
6	Treated water has residual hardness around 60 ppm.	Treated water has residual hardness of 15-30 ppm.
7	Dissolved gases are not removed.	Dissolved gases such as O_2, CO_2 etc. are removed to some extent.
8	Low softening capacity.	High softening capacity.

Various constituents present in water causing hardness can have following reactions:

Table 1.13: Reactions of constituents causing hardness

S.No.	Constituents	Reactions	Need
1	$Ca(HCO_3)_2$ (Temp.Ca)	$Ca(HCO_3)_2 + Ca(OH)_2 \rightarrow 2CaCO_3 \downarrow + 2H_2O$	L
2	$Mg(HCO_3)_2$ (Temp. Mg)	$Mg(HCO_3)_2 + Ca(OH)_2 \rightarrow Mg(OH)_2 + Ca(HCO_3)_2$ $Ca(HCO_3)_2 + Ca(OH)_2 \rightarrow 2CaCO_3 \downarrow + 2H_2O$	2L
3	Mg^{2+} (Perm.Mg from $MgCl_2$ or $MgSO_4$)	$Mg^{2+} + Ca(OH)_2 \rightarrow Mg(OH)_2 + Ca^{2+}$ $Ca^{2+} + Na_2CO_3 \rightarrow CaCO_3 \downarrow + 2Na^+$	L+S
4	HCO_3^- (e.g. $NaHCO_3$)	$2HCO_3^- + Ca(OH)_2 \rightarrow CaCO_3 + CO_3^{2-} + 2H_2O$ $CO_3^{2-} + 2Na^+ \rightarrow Na_2CO_3$	L – S
5	Ca^{2+}(Perm.Ca from $CaCl_2$ or $CaSO_4$)	$Ca^{2+} + Na_2CO_3 \rightarrow CaCO_3 \downarrow + 2Na^+$	S

6	CO_2	$CO_2 + Ca(OH)_2 \rightarrow CaCO_3 \downarrow + H_2O$	L
7	H^+ (free acids like H_2SO_4, HCl)	$2H^+ + Ca(OH)_2 \rightarrow Ca^{2+} + 2H_2O$ $Ca^{2+} + Na_2CO_3 \rightarrow CaCO_3 \downarrow + 2Na^+$	L + S
8	$FeSO_4$	$FeSO_4 + Ca(OH)_2 \rightarrow Fe(OH)_2 \downarrow + CaSO_4$ $2Fe(OH)_2 + 2H_2O + O_2 \rightarrow 2Fe(OH)_3 \downarrow + H_2O$ $CaSO_4 + Na_2CO_3 \rightarrow CaCO_3 \downarrow + Na_2SO_4$	L + S
9	$Al_2(SO_4)_3$	$Al_2(SO_4)_3 + 3Ca(OH)_2 \rightarrow 2Al(OH)_3 \downarrow + 3CaSO_4$ $3CaSO_4 + 3Na_2CO_3 \rightarrow 3CaCO_3 + 3Na_2SO_4$	L + S
10	$NaAlO_2$	$NaAlO_2 + 2H_2O \rightarrow Al(OH)_3 + NaOH$ NaOH is equivalent to $Ca(OH)_2$	- L

Note:

1. Equivalent weight of $NaAlO_2$ is equal to its molar mass. For this multiplication factor is required.
2. $Ca(HCO_3)_2$ and $Mg(HCO_3)_2$ are considered as ions ($Ca^{2+} + 2HCO_3^-$) and ($Mg^{2+} + 2HCO_3^-$) respectively , so results of calculation will be same.
3. If excess of Ca $(OH)_2$ and Na_2CO_3 is present , then treated water contains OH^- and CO_3^{2-} ions. So this excess amount should be added to the calculation.
4. If the impurities are in the form of $CaCO_3$ or $MgCO_3$, then it should be due to bicarbonates of calcium or magnesium respectively.
5. Substance like NaCl, KCl, Na_2SO_4, Fe_2O_3, SiO_2 etc. do not cause any hardness and therefore they do not consume any lime and soda. These should not be taken during lime and soda calculation.

Formula for lime and soda calculation

100 parts by mass of $CaCO_3$ are equivalent to

1. 74 parts of $Ca(OH)_2$ or
2. 106 parts of Na_2CO_3

∴ Lime requirement for softening

$$= \frac{74}{100}\left[\begin{array}{l} Temp.Ca^{2+} + 2\times Temp.Mg^{2+} + perm.\left(Mg^{2} + Fe^{2+} + Al^{3+}\right) \\ + CO_2 + H^+\left(HCl\, or\, H_2SO_4\right) + HCO_3^- - NaAlO_2 \\ all\, in\, terms\, of\, CaCO_3\, equivalent \end{array}\right]$$

∴ Soda requirement for softening

$$= \frac{106}{100}\left[\begin{array}{l} Perm.Ca^{2+} + Mg^{2} + Fe^{2+} + Al^{3+} + H^+\left(HCl\, or\, H_2SO_4\right) - HCO_3^- \\ all\, in\, terms\, of\, CaCO_3\, equivalent \end{array}\right]$$

ii) Zeolite or Permutit process: Zeolites (Greek, *zein*, "to boil"; *lithos*, "a stone") are minerals that have a micro-porous structure. The term was originally coined in the 18th century by a Swedish mineralogist named Axel Fredrik Cronstedt who observed upon rapidly heating a natural mineral that the stones began to dance about as the water evaporated. Using the Greek words which mean "stone that boils," he called this material zeolite.

More than 1500 zeolite types have been synthesized and 48 naturally occurring zeolites are known. They are basically hydrated alumino-silicate minerals with an "open" structure that can accommodate a wide variety of cations, such as Na^+, K^+, Ca^{2+}, Mg^{2+} and others. These positive ions are rather loosely held and can readily be exchanged for others in a contact solution. Zeolites are the aluminosilicate members of the family of microporous solids known as "molecular sieves". The term molecular sieve refers to a particular property of these materials, i.e. the ability to selectively sort molecules based primarily on a size exclusion process. Some of the more common mineral zeolites are: analcite, chabazite, heulandite, natrolite, phillipsite and stilbite.

Natrolite is a tectosilicate mineral species belonging to the zeolite group. It is a hydrated sodium and aluminium silicate with the formula $Na_2Al_2Si_3O_{10} \cdot 2H_2O$.

Natural zeolites form where volcanic rocks and ash layers react with alkaline groundwater. Zeolites also crystallized in post-depositional environments over periods ranging from thousands to millions of years in shallow marine basins. Naturally occurring zeolites are rarely pure and are contaminated to varying degrees by other minerals, metals, quartz or other zeolites. For this reason, naturally occurring zeolites are excluded from many important commercial applications where uniformity and purity are essential.

Principle of Water Softening: The illustration depicts a zeolite to which sodium ions are attached. Calcium or magnesium ions in the water displace sodium ions which are released into the water. As the zeolite gets converted to their Ca^{2+} forms, they gradually lose their effectiveness and must be regenerated. This is accomplished by passing a concentrated brine solution through them, causing the following reaction to be reversed.

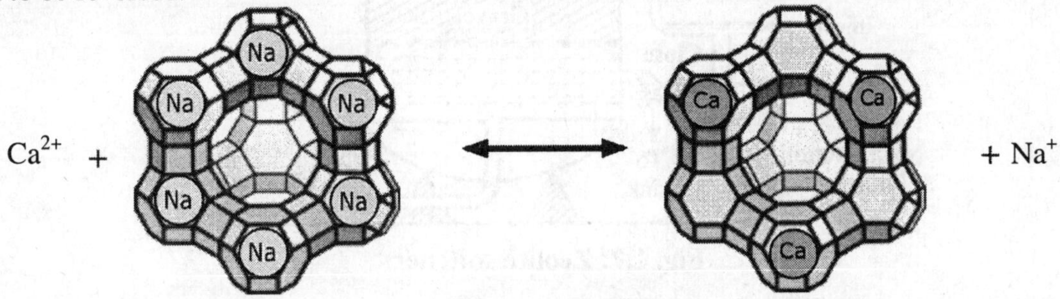

Fig. 1.6 : Zeolite

Reactions of Cation Removal

$$Ca(HCO_3)_2 + Na_2Ze \rightarrow CaZe + 2NaHCO_3$$

$$Mg(HCO_3)_2 + Na_2Ze \rightarrow MgZe + 2NaHCO_3$$

$$CaSO_4 + Na_2Ze \rightarrow CaZe + Na_2SO_4$$

$$MgSO_4 + Na_2Ze \rightarrow MgZe + Na_2SO_4$$

$$CaCl_2 + Na_2Ze \rightarrow CaZe + 2NaCl$$

$$MgCl_2 + Na_2Ze \rightarrow MgZe + 2NaCl$$

Regeneration of Zeolite : After some time, the zeolite is converted into calcium and magnesium zeolite and it loses its sodium exchange capacity i.e. it gets exhausted. To regenerate the exhausted zeolite, supply of hard water is stopped and it is reclaimed by treating the bed with a concentrated sodium chloride (10% brine) solution.

$$CaZe + 2NaCl \rightarrow Na_2Ze + CaCl_2$$

$$MgZe + 2NaCl \rightarrow Na_2Ze + MgCl_2 \text{(Washing)}$$

Exhausted Zeolite   Regenerated Zeolite

The washings containing $CaCl_2$ and $MgCl_2$ are led to the drain and the regenerated zeolite bed obtained is used again for softening purpose.

Process: A zeolite softener consists of a steel tank packed with a thick layer of permutit. The hard water is percolated at a specific rate through zeolite bed. Ca^{2+} and Mg^{2+} ions are retained by zeolite (CaZe and MgZe) respectively. The outgoing water contains sodium salts.

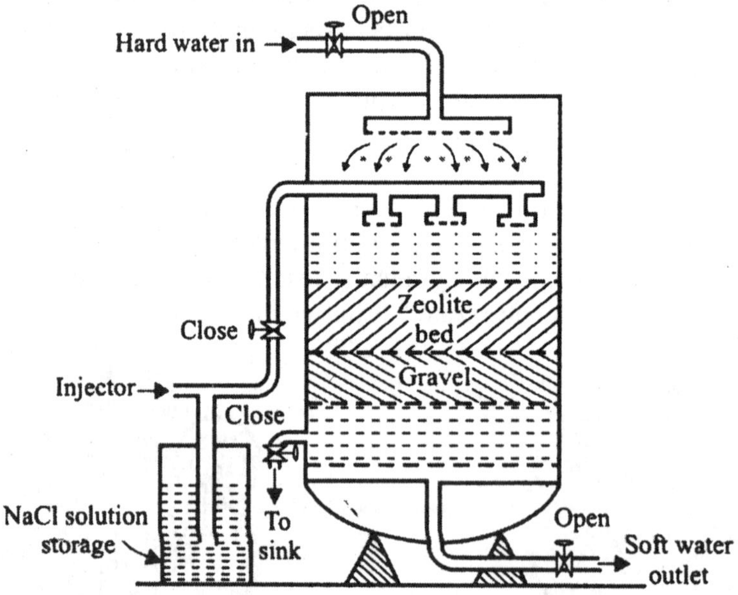

Fig. 1.7: Zeolite softener

Advantages of Zeolite Process

- Water of about 10 ppm hardness is produced.
- The equipment is compact and occupies less space.
- In this process, the hardness causing ions are simply exchanged with sodium ions. As the process does not involve any precipitation, there is no problem of sludge formation.
- The running, maintenance and operation costs are quite less.
- Less skilled person can also operate and maintain the plant.
- The process adjusts automatically according to the hardness of incoming water.

Disadvantages of Zeolite Process

- The drawback of this process is that most of the salt employed in the regeneration process gets flushed out of the system and is usually released into the soil or drainage system- something that can have damaging consequences to the environment, especially in arid regions. For this reason, many jurisdictions prohibit such release and require users to dispose off the spent brine at an approved site or to use a commercial service company.

- This process is not suitable for treating turbid water as it clogs the pores of zeolite bed and thus makes it inactive.
- Mn^{2+} and Fe^{2+} should be removed before water is fed in zeolite softener because these ions produce manganese and iron zeolites which are difficult to regenerate.
- In zeolite softener, water should be free from acid, as it destroys the zeolite bed.
- Hot water should not be used as it tends to dissolve zeolite bed.
- The treated water contains more sodium salts than lime-soda process.
- Only cations are removed by this process. Anions like HCO_3^- combine with Na^+ ions and form $NaHCO_3$ which decompose in high pressure boiler.

$$NaHCO_3 \rightarrow NaOH + CO_2$$

- These are undesirable compounds; CO_2 forms H_2CO_3 and makes the water acidic, which causes corrosion of boiler material. NaOH leads to caustic embrittlement.

Uses of Zeolites

- Zeolites are widely used as ion-exchange beds in domestic and commercial water purification and softening.
- Zeolites have the potential of providing precise and specific separation of gases including the removal of H_2O, CO_2 and SO_2 from low-grade natural gas streams.
- Synthetic zeolites are widely used as catalysts in the petrochemical industry, for instance in fluid catalytic cracking and hydro-cracking.
- Zeolites have uses in advanced reprocessing methods, where their micro-porous ability to capture some ions while allowing others to pass freely, allows many fission products to be efficiently removed from nuclear waste and permanently trapped.
- In agriculture, clinoptilolite (a naturally occurring zeolite) is used as a soil treatment. It provides a source of slowly released potassium.
- Zeolite-based oxygen generation systems are widely used to produce medical grade oxygen. The zeolite is used as a molecular sieve to create purified oxygen from air in a process involving the absorption of undesired gases and other atmospheric components, leaving highly purified oxygen and up to 5% argon.
- Zeolites can be used as solar thermal collectors and for adsorption refrigeration.
- Synthetic zeolite is used as an additive in the production process of warm mix asphalt concrete.

iii) **Ion exchange, Deionization or Demineralization process:** In an ion-exchange process, a reversible exchange of ions takes place between the stationery ion exchange phase and the external liquid mobile phase. An ion exchange resin consists of an insoluble polymer matrix that is permeable. Ion exchange resins consist of cross linked, long chain organic polymers with a micro porous structure. The functional groups attached to the polymer are responsible for ion exchange.

Most typical ion exchange resins are based on crosslinked polystyrene. The required active groups can be introduced after polymerization, or substituted monomers can be used. For example, crosslinking is often achieved by adding 0.5-25% of divinyl benzene to styrene at the polymerisation process.

a) Cation Exchange Resins (RH^+): These are usually styrene divinyl benzene copolymers which on

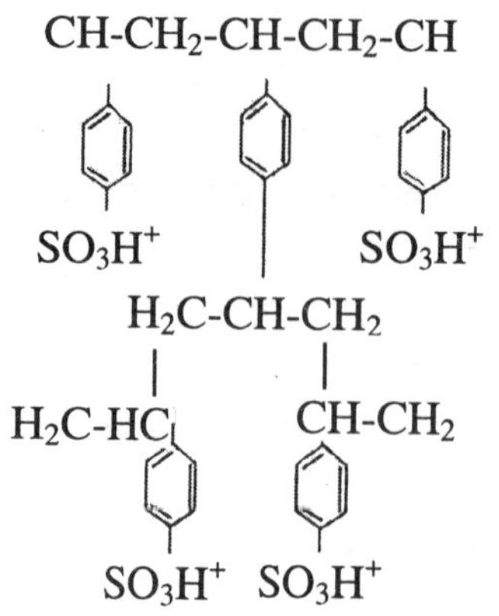

Fig. 1.8: Sulphonate form of cation exchanger

carboxylation or sulphonation become capable of exchanging their H^+ ions with the cations of the solution.

b) Anion Exchange Resins (ROH): These are styrene divinyl benzene or amine formaldehyde copolymers which on treatment with dilute NaOH solution become capable to exchange their OH^- anions with anions in water.

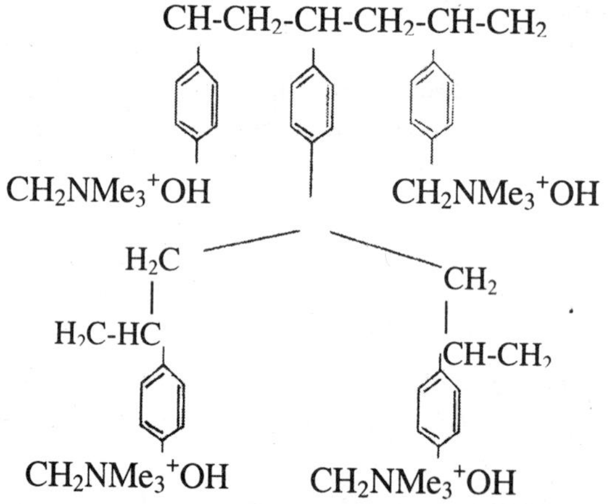

Fig. 1.9: Hydroxy form of anion exchanger

- Amberlite IR-120 and Dowex-50 are examples of commercially available cation exchange resins.
- Amberlite-400 and Dowex-3 are examples of commercially available anion exchange resins.

National Chemical Laboratory, Pune, has developed polystyrene based cation exchangers and melamine based anion exchangers which are available in the market with different trade names.

Process: It is a two stage process, the water first passes through the column containing hydrogen exchanger [Cation exchanger] and then through second column containing hydroxyl exchanger [Anion exchanger]. H^+ and OH^- ions released from cation exchanger and anion exchanger columns get combined to produce water molecule.

Cation Removal

$$2RH^{+} + Ca^{2+} \rightarrow R_2Ca^{2+} + 2H^{+}$$

$$2RH^{+} + Mg^{2+} \rightarrow R_2Mg^{2+} + 2H^{+}$$

Anion Removal

$$R'OH^{-} + Cl^{-} \rightarrow R'Cl^{-} + OH^{-}$$

$$2R'OH^{-} + SO_4^{2-} \rightarrow R_2SO_4^{2-} + 2OH^{-}$$

$$2R'OH^{-} + CO_3^{2-} \rightarrow R_2CO_3^{2-} + 2OH^{-}$$

Deionizer Water

$$H^{+} + OH^{-} \rightarrow H_2O$$

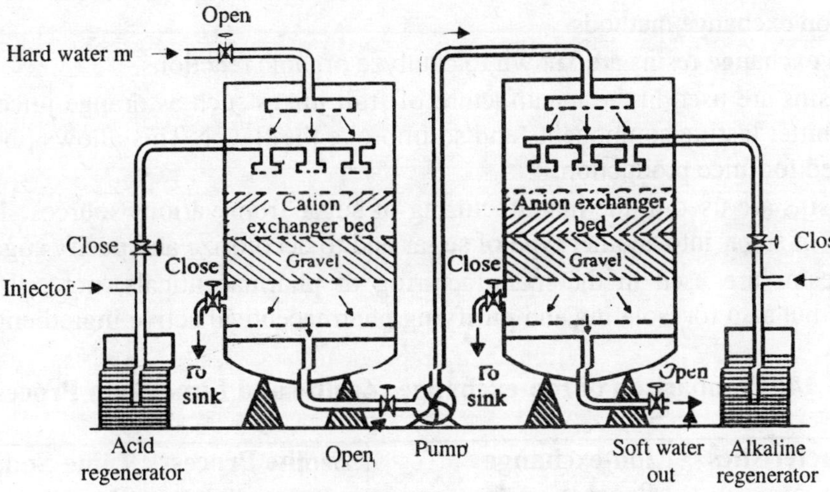

Fig. 1.10 Demineralization of water

Regeneration: After some time the cation and anion exchanging resins lose the capacity to remove H^+ and OH^- ions respectively, they are then said to be exhausted.

An exhausted cation exchange resin is regenerated by passing a solution of dilute HCl or H_2SO_4.

$$R_2Ca^{2+} + 2H^{+} \rightarrow 2RH^{+} + Ca^{2+} \text{ (Washing)}$$

The exhausted anion exchange resin is regenerated by passing a solution of dilute NaOH.

$$R_2'SO_4^{2-} + 2OH^{-} \rightarrow 2R'OH^{-} + SO_4^{2-}$$

The columns are washed with deionized water and washings (which contain Ca^{2+}, Mg^{2+}, SO_4^{2-}, Na^+ ions) are passed to sink or drain. The regenerated resins are again used.

Advantages

- It produces the water of 2 ppm hardness which is very good and can be used in high pressure boilers.
- Highly acidic or alkaline water can be softened by this process.
- Both anions and cations are removed by this process.

Disadvantages

- The equipment is costly and costly chemicals are needed for regeneration.
- Turbid water can not be used as it decreases the efficiency of resins.

Uses of Resins

- In this application, ion-exchange resins are used to replace the magnesium and calcium ions found in hard water with sodium ions.
- This is the method of operation used in dishwashers that requires the use of 'dishwasher salt'. The salt is used to recharge an ion exchange resin which itself is used to soften the water so that limescale deposits are not left on the cooking and eating utensils being washed.
- In this application, ion exchange resins are used to remove poisonous (e.g. copper) and heavy metal (e.g. lead) ions from solution, replacing them with more innocuous ions such as sodium and potassium.
- Water of highest purity is required for electronics for production of superconductor and nuclear industry among others. Such water is produced using ion exchange processes or combinations of membrane and ion exchange methods.
- In chemistry ion exchange resins are known to catalyze organic reactions.
- Ion exchange resins are used in the manufacture of fruit juices such as orange juice where they are used to remove bitter tasting components and so improve the flavor. This allows poorer tasting fruit sources to be used for juice production.
- Ion exchange resins are used in the manufacturing of sugar from various sources. They are used to convert one type of sugar into another type of sugar and to decolorize and purify sugar syrups.
- Ion exchange resins are used in the manufacturing of pharmaceuticals, not only for catalyzing certain reactions but also for isolating and purifying pharmaceutical active ingredients.

Table 1.14: Comparison of Ion-exchange, Zeolite and Lime-Soda Process

S.No.	Characteristics	Ion-exchange Process	Zeolite Process	Lime-Soda Process
1	Capital Cost	Very high	High	Low
2	Operating expenses	High	Low	High
3	Size of plant	Large	Compact	Bulky and large
4	Requirements	Cation and anion exchange resins	Zeolite salt	Lime, Soda and coagulants
5	Exchange of ions	Both cation and anions are exchanged.	Exchange only cations.	No exchange.
6	Man Power	No skilled person required.	No skilled person required.	Skilled person required to operate plant.
7	Raw Water	Should not be turbid. Both acidic and alkaline water can be treated.	Should not be turbid. Should not be acidic.	Any type of water can be treated.
8	Sludge problem	No sludge formation. Prior knowledge of hardness not required.	No sludge formation. Prior of knowledge or hardness not required.	Sludge formed. Prior knowledge of hardness is essential.
9	Automation	Possible	Possible	Not Possible
10	Residual hardness	Least (0-2 ppm)	Low (0-15 ppm)	High (15-60 ppm)

II. Internal Treatment: In the internal treatment process, water is treated inside the boiler. In this process (also called sequestration) an ion is prohibited to exhibit its original character by complexing or converting it into more soluble salt by adding appropriate reagent. In this process certain chemicals are added, which either convert the scale forming impurities in the form of sludge, which can be removed by blow down operation or by converting it in the form of dissolved salts which do not cause any harm. To remove the accumulated sludge, following internal treatment methods are used:

i). **Colloidal Conditioning:** Scale formation can be avoided by introducing colloidal substances like kerosene, tannin, glue, agar-agar etc. to the boiler water. These substances get adsorbed over the scale forming impurities, thereby forming non-sticky and loose deposits which can be removed by blow down operation. This process is suitable for low pressure boiler.

ii). **Carbonate Conditioning:** In the low pressure boilers, scale formation can be avoided by adding sodium carbonate to boiler water, when salts like $CaSO_4$ etc. are converted into calcium carbonate in equilibrium.

$$CaSO_4 + Na_2CO_3 \longrightarrow CaCO_3 + Na_2SO_4$$

By this process deposition of $CaSO_4$ scale is prevented and $CaCO_3$ formed can be removed by blow down operation.

iii). **Phosphate Conditioning:** In high pressure boiler, scale formation is avoided by mixing sodium phosphate which reacts with hardness causing salt to form non adherent and easily removable sludge which can be removed by blow down operation.

$$3CaCl_2 + 2Na_3PO_4 \rightarrow Ca_3(PO_4)_2 + 6NaCl$$

The selection of phosphate salts depends upon the alkalinity of the boiler feed water.

- Tri sodium phosphate $Na_3PO_4 \Rightarrow$ for low alkaline water.
- Di sodium hydrogen phosphate $Na_2HPO_4 \Rightarrow$ for sufficient alkaline water.
- Sodium dihydrogen phosphate $NaH_2PO_4 \Rightarrow$ for highly alkaline water.

iv). **Calgon Conditioning:** Sodium hexa meta phosphate $Na_6(PO_3)_6$ is also known as Calgon. It is a co-ordinate compound. It prevents the scale and sludge formation by forming soluble complex compound with $CaSO_4$. In high pressure boilers, calgon reacts with scale forming impurities and forms non-adherent and easily removable sludge which can be removed by blow down operation.

$$\underset{\text{Calgon}}{Na_2[Na_4(PO_3)_6]} \rightleftharpoons [Na_4P_6O_{18}]^{2-} + 2Na^+$$

$$2CaSO_4 + [Na_4P_6O_{18}]^{2-} \rightarrow \underset{\text{Soluble Complex}}{[Ca_2P_6O_{18}]^{2-}} + 2Na_2SO_4$$

v). **Treatment with sodium meta aluminate ($NaAlO_2$):** Sodium meta aluminate is a coagulant which hydrolyses in water and forms NaOH and colloidal or gelatinous white precipitate of aluminium hydroxide.

$$NaAlO_2 + 2H_2O \rightarrow NaOH + Al(OH)_3 \downarrow \text{Gelatinous ppt}$$

The sodium hydroxide produced reacts with magnesium chloride and forms Mg $(OH)_2$

$$MgCl_2 + 2NaOH \rightarrow Mg(OH)_2 + 2NaCl$$

Suspended and colloidal impurities are entrapped by $Mg(OH)_2$ and $Al(OH)_3$ which form sludge. The sludge formed can be removed by blow-down operation.

vi). Complexometric Method: This is the best internal treatment method. In this method 1.5% alkaline (pH 8.5) solution of EDTA is added to the boiler feed water. The EDTA combines with the scale forming cations and forms stable and soluble complex.

Advantages

- No Scale and sludge formation in boiler.
- Prevents the deposition of iron oxide in the boiler.
- Prevents the carry over of dissolved salts with steam.
- Protects the boiler parts from corrosion by wet steam.

1.12 TREATMENT OF WATER FOR DOMESTIC USE

Water is perhaps the most important nutrient in our diet. In fact, a human adult needs to drink approximately 2 liters (8 glasses) of water every day to replenish the water that is lost from the body through the skin, respiratory tract and urine. But some water sources cannot safely be used to meet our requirement for drinking water. In response to this need for reliable supplies of clean and usable freshwater, Governments all over the world have formed organizations and passed legislations to monitor, treat and protect our water supplies. The Clean Water Act, passed in 1972 and revised in 1978, established the policy of contracting water-treatment facilities and implemented enforcement procedures to ensure that our water supplies would be kept clean for human use.

Water from a water supply scheme may contain physical, chemical and biological impurities. Physical impurities impart colour, taste, odour and turbidity to the water. Chemical impurities cause hardness and water pollution. Excess quantities of metal and dissolved gases cause corrosion of pipes and fittings. Bacteriological impurities are due to pathogenic bacteria which spread diseases such as cholera, typhoid, diarrhea and dysentery. Hence the objectives of treatment of water are:

1. To remove colour, objectionable odour and taste.
2. To remove dissolved gases, dissolved and suspended impurities.
3. To remove suspended as well as dissolved organic impurities.
4. To remove pathogenic bacteria.
5. To make water safe for drinking and domestic purpose.

The water which is safe and fit for human consumption is known as potable or drinking water. The characteristics of clean and drinkable water are:

1. It should be clear, odourless and colourless.
2. It should be pleasant in taste.
3. It should not be hot.
4. Its turbidity should be less than 10 ppm.
5. It should be reasonably soft.
6. Its pH should be in the range of 7.0-8.5.

7. It should be free from objectionable dissolved gases like H_2S.
8. It should contain 8 ppm of dissolved oxygen.
9. Total dissolved solids should be less than 500 ppm.
10. Chloride contents should be less than 250 ppm.
11. Fluoride contents should be less than 2 ppm.
12. It should be free from pathogens (i.e. disease producing micro organisms.)

Table 1.15: Indian Standard drinking water specifications (BIS 1050011991)

S.No.	Substance Essential Characteristics	Requirement (Desirable Limit)	Permissible limit in the absence of alternate source.
1	Colour (Hazen units Max)	5	25
2	Odour	Unobjectionable	Unobjectionable
3	Taste	Agreeable	Agreeable
4	Turbidity (NTU,Max)	5	10
5	pH value	6.5 to 8.5	No Relaxation
6	Total Hardness (as $CaCO_3$)mg/l	300	600
7	Chlorides (as Cl) mg/l Max	250	1000
8	Iron (as Fe) mg/l Max	0.3	1.0
9	Residual free chlorine mg/lit min	0.2	-
10	Dissolved Solids mg/l max	500	200
11	Calcium (as Ca) mg/l max	75	200
12	Copper (as Cu) mg/l max	0.05	1.5
13	Sulphate (as SO_4) mg/l max	200	400
14	Nitrate (as NO_3) mg/l max	45	100
15	Fluoride (as F) mg/l max	1.9	1.5
16	Mercury (as Hg) mg/l max	0.001	No relaxation
17	Arsenic (as As) mg/l max	0.01	No relaxation
18	Lead (as Pb) mg/l max	0.05	No relaxation
19	Alkalinity mg/l max	200	600
20	Chromium (as Cr) mg/l max	0.05	No relaxation

Municipalities have to supply potable water. Water from rivers, ponds canals and lakes etc. does not meet all the specification of potable water. There are four major steps in the treatment of water: screening, sedimentation followed by coagulation, filtration and disinfection. Hence to remove different impurities, following treatment processes are employed:

(1) Screening: This process is used to remove the impurities like stones, logs, leaves etc. The raw water is passed through screen having holes, which retain the larger impurities of bigger size than the screen size.

Fig. 1.11: Screening

This drawing shows some of the large objects in surface water that are removed as the water passes through a screen into water treatment facility. The larger black arrows show the direction of water flow through the screen.

(2) Sedimentation: Other suspended (insoluble) particles, such as sand and dirt, are small enough to pass easily through the screens. These particles must be removed from the water by another process known as sedimentation. When water is allowed to settle, heavy suspended particles (e.g. sand) will settle to the bottom over time because they are denser than water. By this process suspended impurities are removed. Water is allowed to stand undisturbed in big tanks for 2-8 hrs, where most of the suspended particles settle down at the bottom due to gravitational force. With the help of pumps, clear water is drawn from tank through sedimentation force. Sedimentation is always followed by coagulation to remove the fine clay particles and colloidal matter.

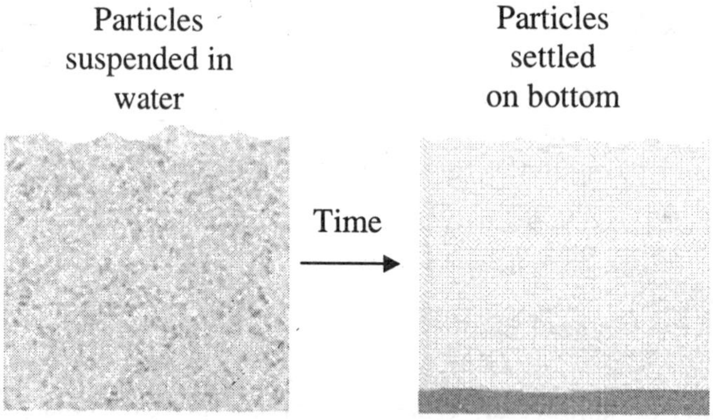

Fig. 1.12: Sedimentation

Sometimes the insoluble particles are too small to settle out quickly enough to use sedimentation alone. Then, two processes, known as flocculation and coagulation, are used to create larger particles that will settle quickly to the bottom. In flocculation, small particles with non-rigid surfaces are made to agglomerate by mixing the water (and thus bringing the particles into contact with one another so that the surfaces can become stuck together). When the agglomeration of the particles gets large enough, the aggregate can settle in still water by sedimentation. Other suspended particles do not agglomerate well by flocculation. To remove these particles from the water, coagulation must be used.

(3) Coagulation: It is the process of gathering particles into a cluster or clot, often achieved by the addition of special chemicals known as coagulants. The most common coagulant used in water-treatment facilities is aluminium sulfate [$Al_2(SO_4)_3$]. Other Al and Fe salts, including poly-aluminium chloride, ferric chloride and alum ferric sulfate may be used as well. These salts react with ions naturally found in the water to produce a solid precipitate. As this precipitate forms, other particles are caught in the solid forming a mass that will settle to the bottom via sedimentation. These are the commonly used coagulants.

Alum [$K_2SO_4.Al_2(SO_4)_3.24H_2O$]

$$\underset{\text{Coagulants}}{Al_2(SO_4)_3} + \underset{\text{Calcium bicarbonate}}{3Ca(HCO_3)_2} \rightarrow \underset{\text{Aluminium Hydroxide}}{2Al(OH)_3\downarrow} + 3CaSO_4 + 6CO_2$$

Sodium Meta Aluminate ($NaAlO_2$)

$$NaAlO_2 + 2H_2O \rightarrow \underset{\text{Gelatinous floc}}{Al(OH)_3} + NaOH$$

Gelatinous precipitate, so formed arrests the fine impurities and forms bigger molecules which settle down easily.

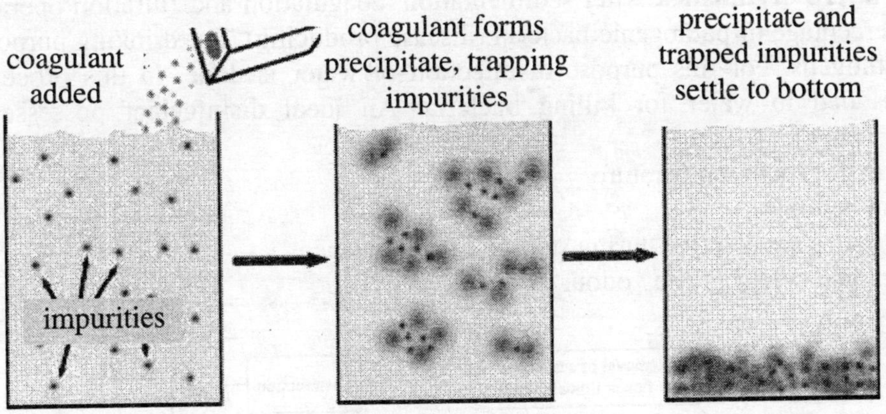

Fig. 1.13: Coagulation

Particles that are insoluble in water may be suspended in the water, particularly if the water is turbulent (stirred up). If the particles are heavy enough, they will settle to the bottom when the water is allowed to sit still over time.

(4) Filteration: Filtreration is the process of removing colloidal and bacterial impurities from water by passing it through beds of fine sand, coarse sand and other granular material. There are number of sand filters like gravity filter, slow sand filter and pressure filter.

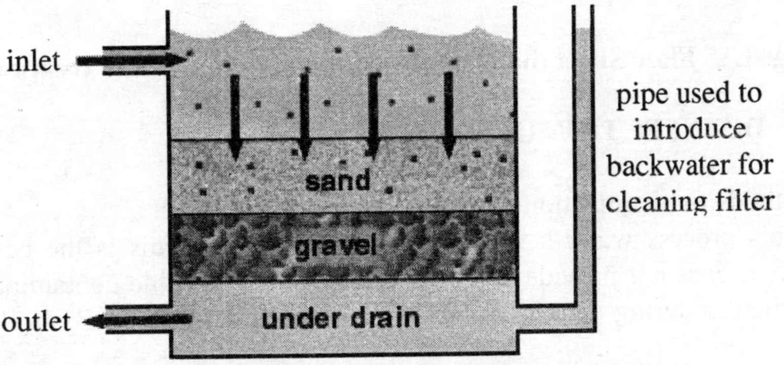

Fig. 1.14: Filteration

Water containing solid impurities enters the filter through an inlet at the top and is forced by gravity through layers of sand and gravel. The solids get trapped between the sand and gravel pieces. The water that emerges into the under drain at the bottom of the filter is cleaned off these solids and exits the filter through an outlet at the bottom.

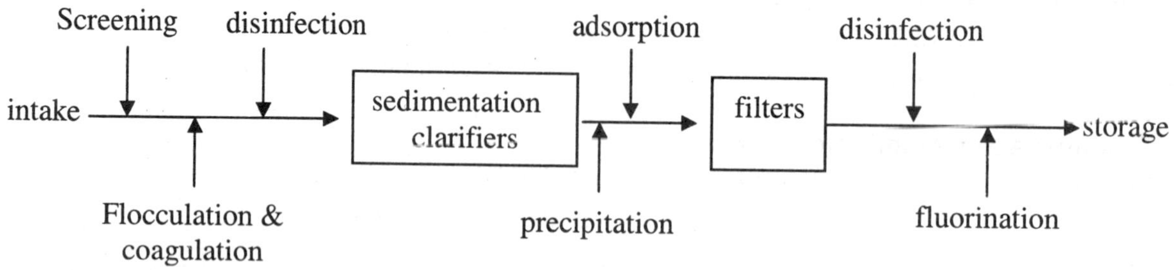

(5) Removal of micro-organisms: After sedimentation, coagulation and filtration operations, water still contains small percentage of pathogenic bacteria (disease producing). For drinking purpose, water should be free from pathogens. For this purpose disinfection of water is done. In this process, chemicals or substances are added to water for killing bacteria. An ideal disinfectant possesses the following properties:

1. It should work at room temperature.
2. It should not be toxic.
3. It should work as a protective during storage or conveyance.
4. It should not add colour / taste / odour to water.

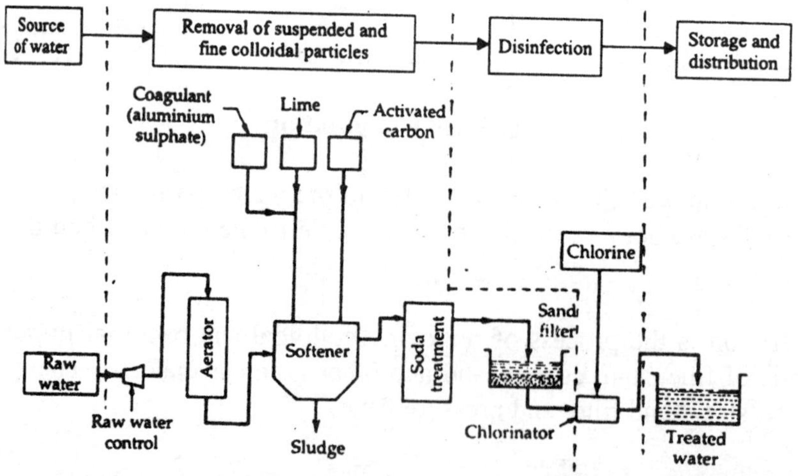

Fig. 1.15 Flow Sheet diagram showing municipal water treatment

1.13 METHODS OF DISINFECTION OF WATER

There are various methods for disinfection of water:

(1) By Boiling: In this process water is boiled for 10-15 minutes. This is the best method to kill the bacteria but this method does not provide any protection against possible contamination in future that is why it is used in particular during epidemics break up in the town or city. By boiling, taste of water is lost.

(2) By adding bleaching powder: Bleaching powder gives following reaction:

$$CaOCl_2 + H_2O \rightarrow Ca(OH)_2 + Cl_2$$
$$Cl_2 + H_2O \rightarrow HCl + HOCl \text{ (Hypochlorous acid)}$$
$$HOCl \rightarrow HCl + [O]$$
$$\text{Germs} + [O] \rightarrow \text{Killing}$$

Previously it was believed that the nascent oxygen destroys the pathogens by oxidation. But research has proved that hypochlorous acid deactivates the enzyme metabolism of micro organism, which is essential for the metabolic process and thus results in the death of micro-organism.

Drawbacks of using bleaching powder

- It increases the hardness of water by liberating $Ca(OH)_2$.
- It imparts bad taste and smell to treated water.
- It is not stable so it deteriorates due to its continuous decomposition during storage.

(3) By Chlorination: Chlorine can be employed to the water in liquid or gaseous form. It involves hypochlorous acid, which is a powerful germicide. The liquid chlorine is kept in steel cylinder called chlorinator. From its top, raw water and chlorine solution are introduced which get mixed during their passage through the tower. For filtered water about 0.3 to 0.5 ppm of Cl_2 is sufficient. The excess of chlorine is removed by sulphites known as antichlor.

$$SO_2 + Cl_2 + 2H_2O \rightarrow H_2SO_4 + 2HCl$$
$$Na_2SO_3 + Cl_2 + H_2O \rightarrow Na_2SO_4 + 2HCl$$

Factors affecting efficiency of Chlorine

(i) Time of contact: It is experimentally shown that death rate of micro-organism by chlorine is proportional to the number of micro-organisms remaining alive. Initially death rate is high and it goes on decreasing with time.

(ii) pH of water: At lower pH (5-6.5), a small contact period is required to kill the same number of pathogens.

(iii) Temperature of water: Death rate is directly proportional to increase in temperature.

Advantages of Chlorine

- It is economical and more effective than bleaching powder.
- Less space is required for storage and it does not deteriorate on keeping.
- It can be used at high as well as low temperature.
- It does not introduce any salt impurities in the treated water.
- It is most ideal disinfectant.

Disadvantages of Chlorine

- Excess of chlorine imparts unpleasant taste, odour and irritation of mucous membrane.
- Treated water should not contain more than 0.1-0.2 ppm of free chlorine.
- It is less effective at higher pH values.
- Chlorine disinfection results in wide variety of bye-products. One class of chlorination bye products, known as trihalomethanes (THM's) are suspected carcinogens. Because of concern about these products in the water supply, chlorine is now kept to minimum levels and other methods of disinfection are being used.

Break Point Chlorination/Free-residual Chlorination: Chlorine is added to such an extent that living organisms as well as other organic impurities in water are destroyed. Chlorine is added in dosages whose results can be seen graphically in figure. The graph shown in figure can be divided into four stages –

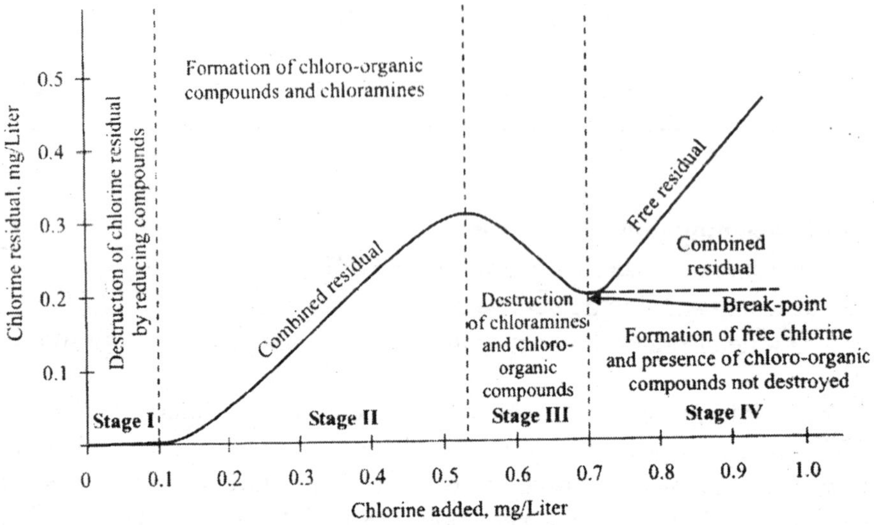

Fig. 1.16: Break-point chlorination curve

1. When small quantity of chlorine is added, all the chlorine gets consumed and there is no residual chlorine. This chlorine reacts with inorganic impurities present in water forming chlorides which do not have any residual oxidizing power.
2. In the second stage, residual chlorine increases and forms chloramines i.e. chlorine is consumed by NH_3. Chloramines remain in water body for longer periods, which help to kill the micro-organisms even in a distribution system. Simultaneously this stage also corresponds to the formation of chloro organic compounds without oxidizing them. These are responsible for bad odour and unpleasant taste in water.
3. When chlorine is further added, it oxidizes chloramine and chloro-organic compounds due to which free residual chlorine decreases a bit when the oxidation is complete. This point is known as break point. At this point complete oxidation of organic compounds takes place which gives bad taste and odour to water.
4. After break point, the added chlorine is not used in any reaction, thus residual chlorine keeps increasing in direct proportion to added chlorine. The residual chlorine helps in the post disinfection of water.

Addition of chlorine in such dosages is known as break point or free residual chlorine.

Advantages of break-point chlorination

- It destroys organic compounds which impart bad odour, colour and unpleasant taste to water.
- It destroys all the disease causing bacteria.
- It prevents the growth of weeds and algae in water.

(4) By using Chloramines ($ClNH_2$): When chlorine and ammonia are mixed, compound chloramine is formed.

$$Cl_2 + NH_3 \rightarrow ClNH_2 + HCl$$

$$ClNH_2 + H_2O \rightarrow HOCl + NH_3$$
$$HOCl \rightarrow HCl + [O]$$
$$\text{Germs} + [O] \rightarrow \text{Killing}$$

Advantages of using Chloramines

- It does not impart chlorinous taste to water.
- Chloramines form more stable disinfectants and pose less risk of harmful bye products.

(5) Ozonization: Ozone is an excellent disinfectant. This is produced by passing silent electric discharge through oxygen.

$$3O_2 \rightarrow 2O_3$$

Ozone is unstable and liberates nascent oxygen.

$$O_3 \rightarrow O_2 + \underset{\text{Nascent oxygen}}{[O]}$$
$$\text{Germs} + [O] \rightarrow \text{Killing}$$

The nascent oxygen is very powerful oxidizing agent and kills all the bacteria. The ozone and water are allowed to pass through separate inlets in a sterilizing tank. Ozone improves the taste of water. The only disadvantage is high cost involved in this process.

(6) Potassium Permanganate Method: The water is sterilized by adding calculated amount of $KMnO_4$. This method is not very popular as it is costly. It is mostly used in rural area for sterilizing well water.

(7) By using Ultra-violet rays: Water is exposed to UV rays from electric mercury vapour lamp immersed in water. This method is especially used for disinfection of swimming pool water as it is quite safe for human skin.

Desalination or Brackish Water : When water contains high concentration of dissolved solids or salts, it is known as brackish water, e.g. sea water contains near about 3.6% of salts which make it unfit for drinking purpose. Brackish water contains dissolved solids between 1000 ppm and 3500 ppm. The process of removing dissolved solids (NaCl) from water is known as desalination. Commonly used methods for the desalination of brackish water are –

(1) Electrodialysis (2) Reverse Osmosis

(1) Electrodialysis: In this method, the ions of the salt present are pulled out of the salt water by passing direct current, using electrode and thin rigid plastic membrane (natural or synthetic) .The brackish water is filled inside and outside the cell. Electrodes are placed in the water outside the cell and when current is applied, the ions within the cell flow through the semi permeable membrane and are concentrated in the outside water. The cations are attracted towards the cathode and anions towards the anode. In this way water gets demineralised within the cells. This process is known as electrodialysis.

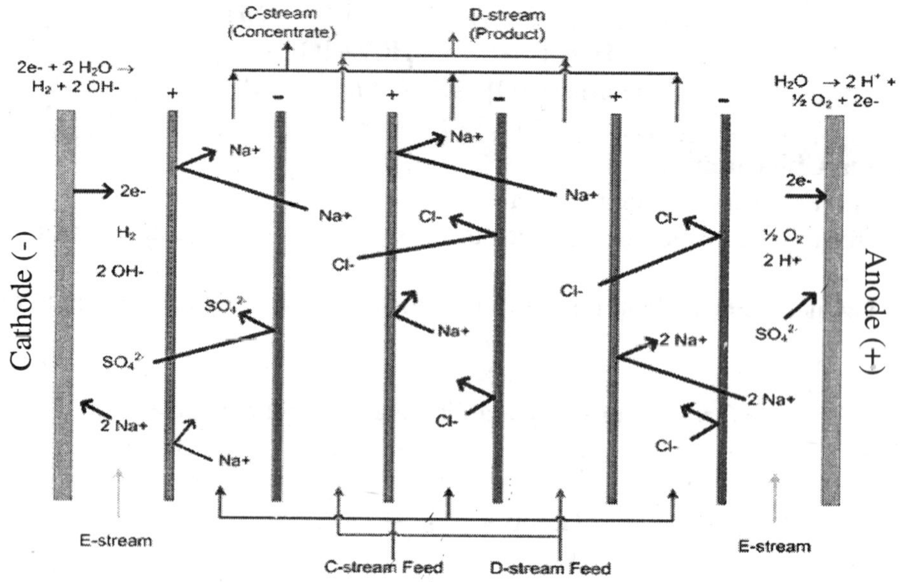

Fig. 1.17: Electrodialysis Process

Applications

- Electrodialysis is usually applied for deionization of aqueous solutions. However, desalting of sparingly conductive aqueous organic and inorganic solutions is also possible.
- Large scale brackish and seawater desalination and salt production.
- Small and medium scale drinking water production (e.g. towns and villages, construction and military camps, nitrate reduction, hotels and hospitals)
- Water reuse (e.g. industrial laundry wastewater, water produced from oil/gas production, cooling tower makeup and blowdown, metals industry fluids, wash-rack water)
- Pre-demineralization (e.g. boiler makeup and pretreatment, ultrapure water pretreatment, process water desalination, power generation, semiconductor, chemical manufacturing, food and beverage) .

(2) Reverse osmosis: It is a separation process that uses pressure to force a solvent through a membrane that retains the solute on one side and allows the pure solvent to pass to the other side. More formally, it is the process of forcing a solvent from a region of high solute concentration through a membrane to a region of low solute concentration by applying a pressure in excess of the osmotic pressure. This is the reverse of the normal osmosis process, which is the natural movement of solvent from an area of low solute concentration, through a membrane, to an area of high solute concentration when no external pressure is applied. The membrane here is semipermeable, which allows the passage of solvent but not the solute.

The membranes used for reverse osmosis have a dense barrier layer in the polymer matrix where most of the separation occurs. In most cases, the membrane is designed to allow only water to pass through this dense layer while preventing the passage of solutes (such as salt ions). This process requires that a high pressure be exerted on the high concentration side of the membrane, usually 2–17 bar (30–250 psi) for fresh and brackish water and 40–70 bar (600–1000 psi) for seawater, which has around 24 bar (350 psi) natural osmotic pressure which must be overcome. This process is best known for its use in desalination (removing the salt from sea water to get fresh water) and for naturally occurring freshwater for medical, industrial process and rinsing applications.

Applications

1. Household drinking water purification systems, including a reverse osmosis step, are commonly used for improving water for drinking and cooking.
2. Reverse osmosis is extensively used in the dairy industry for the production of whey protein powders and for the concentration of milk to reduce shipping costs.
3. In recent years, RO has been used increasingly in making processed water for dialysis in hospitals and certain cosmetics and drugs by pharmaceutical manufacturers. The energy requirements are 30% lower than that of distillation process. The maintenance cost includes mainly the replacement of semi permeable membrane, the life of which is quite high, extending to about 2 years.
4. Reverse osmosis product can be used for the production of deionized water.
5. Treatment of waste water.

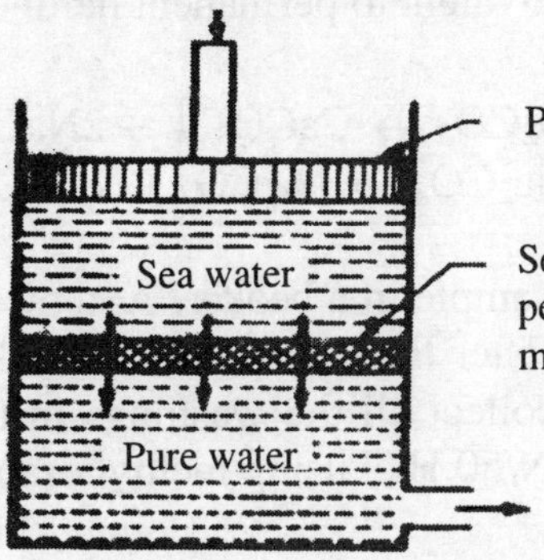

Fig. 1.18: Reverse Osmosis cell

1.14 CHEMICAL ANALYSIS OF WATER

Determination of Hardness: Hardness of water can be determined by following methods:-

i) 'O' Hehner's Method
ii) Soap titration Method
iii) EDTA Method

i) O' Hehner's Method: By this method, first temporary hardness is determined by finding the alkalinity of water before and after boiling. On boiling temporary hardness is removed.

$$Ca(HCO_3)_2 \xrightarrow{Boiling} CaCO_3\downarrow + H_2O + CO_2\uparrow$$

$$Mg(HCO_3)_2 \xrightarrow{Boiling} Mg(OH)_2\downarrow + 2CO_2\uparrow$$

Procedure: Pipette out 50 ml of water sample in a conical flask. To this water sample, add 2-3 drops of methyl orange indicator, then titrate the sample with N/50 HCl. Note the volume of acid used (say V_A ml). Now take 100 ml of water sample in a Pyrex beaker and evaporate it to dryness. Dilute the solution and wash the residue with distilled water. Add distilled water to make up the 100 ml solution. Take out 50 ml of this filtrate in conical flask and again titrate with N/50 HCl using methyl orange as indicator. Let the volume of acid used is V_B ml.

∴ Volume of N/50 HCl used by temporary hardness present in 50 ml of water

$$= (V_A - V_B) \text{ ml}$$

∴ Alkalinity due to temporary hardness in 50 ml of water sample

$$= (V_A - V_B) \text{ ml of N/50 HCl}$$

∴ Alkalinity due to temporary hardness in terms of $CaCO_3$ equivalent

$$= \frac{(V_A - V_B) \times 1 \times 50}{50 \times 50} \text{ g/l}$$

$= (V_A-V_B)/50$ g of $CaCO_3$ equivalent L^{-1}

$$= \frac{(V_A - V_B)10^6}{50 \times 10^3} \text{ ppm}$$

$$= 20\,(V_A-V_B) \text{ ppm}$$

Determination of Permanent Hardness: It is determined by adding excess of standard sodium carbonate solution. The chloride and sulphates of calcium and magnesium are titrated against a standard acid. The reduction in the amount of soda added is equivalent to permanent hardness.

$$CaCl_2 + Na_2CO_3 \rightarrow CaCO_3 \downarrow + 2NaCl$$
$$MgSO_4 + Na_2CO_3 \rightarrow MgCO_3 + Na_2SO_4$$

Procedure: Take 50 ml of the given water sample in a beaker. Add 50 ml of N/50 Na_2CO_3 solution to it. Boil for 15 minutes and cool the solution. Filter the precipitate and collect the filtrate in a conical flask. Wash the precipitate with distilled water, collect all the washings in the conical flask. Then titrate the unused Na_2CO_3 present in the flask against N/50 HCl using methyl orange as indicator. Let the titre value be V_1 ml.

Volume of N/50 Na_2CO_3 used for removing permanent hardness in 50 ml = $(50-V_1)$ ml

$\therefore$ Strength of permanent hardness in terms of $CaCO_3$ equivalent

$$= \frac{(50 - V_1) \times 50}{50 \times 50} \text{ g of } CaCO_3 \text{ equivalent}$$

$$= \left(\frac{50 - V_1}{50}\right) \text{g of } CaCO_3 \text{ equivalent}$$

$$\therefore \text{ Permanent hardness} = \frac{(50 - V_1) \times 10^6}{50 \times 10^3} \text{ ppm}$$

$$= 20(50-V_1) \text{ ppm}$$

ii) Soap Titration method: If the soap solution is added to hard water, it does not produce lather until a sufficient quantity has been added to precipitate all the hardness causing metal ions. When all hardness producing ions have been consumed, further mixing of soap gives lather.

$$2C_{17}H_{35}COONa + Ca(HCO_3)_2 \rightarrow (C_{17}H_{35}COO)_2Ca \downarrow + 2NaHCO_3$$

Sodium stearate — Insoluble Calcium stearate

$$2C_{17}H_{35}COONa + MgCl_2 \rightarrow (C_{17}H_{35}COO)_2Mg \downarrow + 2NaCl$$

Insoluble Magnesium stearate

$$2C_{17}H_{35}COONa + CaSO_4 \rightarrow (C_{17}H_{35}COO)_2Ca \downarrow + Na_2SO_4$$

Insoluble Calcium stearate

Procedure

(1) Preparation of standard hard water: Dissolve 1.0 g of dry $CaCO_3$ in small quantity of dilute HCl. Boil to dryness to remove excess of acid and CO_2. Dissolve the residue in distilled water and prepare 1 liter solution. This is 1N or standard solution.

(2) Preparation of Soap solution: Dissolve 100 gm of pure dry crystal soap in 800 ml of alcohol and 200 ml of distilled water.

(3) Standardization of soap solution: Take 50 ml of standard hard water in a 250 ml conical flask with glass stopper for sometime. Note the time for which lather (if any) persists. Continue titration till lather formed lasts for 2 minutes. Let the volume of soap solution used is V_A ml.

(4) Lather Factor of distilled water: Titrate 50 ml distilled water against soap solution till lather formed lasts for 2 minutes. Let the volume used be V ml. The volume is to be subtracted for all litre values.

(5) Total Hardness: Repeat the same titration by taking 50 ml of water sample. Let the volume of soap solution be V_B ml.

(6) Permanent Hardness: Take 250 ml of the water sample in 500 ml beaker. Boil it to reduce the volume up to 50 ml when all bicarbonates are decomposed into insoluble $CaCO_3$ and $Mg(OH)_2$. Filter and wash the residue with distilled water. Collect the titrate and wash in 250 ml conical flask. Finally make up the volume up to 250 ml by adding distilled water. Take out 50 ml sample to the conical flask and titrate against soap solution.
Let the titre volume of solution be V_3 ml

Calculation

50 ml of standard hard water $= (V_1 - V)$ ml of soap solution

50 x 1 mg of $CaCO_3$ $= (V_1 - V)$ ml of soap solution

$\therefore$ 1 ml of soap solution $= \dfrac{50}{(V_1 - V)}$ mg of $CaCO_3$ eq

$= (V_2 - V)$ ml of soap solution.

$= \dfrac{(V_2 - V)}{(V_1 - V)}$ mg of $CaCO_3$ eq

$\therefore$ 1 L (1000ml) of hard water $= \dfrac{(V_2 - V)}{(V_1 - V)} \times 1000$ mg of $CaCO_3$ eq

$\therefore$ Total Hardness of water $= \dfrac{(V_2 - V)}{(V_1 - V)}$ mg /l

$$= \frac{1000(V_2 - V)}{(V_1 - V)} \text{ ppm}$$

Also 50 ml of boiled water $= (V_3 - V)$ ml of soap solution

$$= \frac{(V_3 - V)}{(V_1 - V)} \times 50 \text{ mg of } CaCO_3 \text{ eq}$$

Permanent hardness $= \dfrac{(V_3 - V)}{(V_1 - V)} \times 1000$ ppm

$$= \frac{1000(V_3 - V)}{(V_1 - V)} \text{ ppm}$$

Hence Temporary hardness = [Total - Permanent] hardness

$$= \left[\frac{1000(V_2 - V)}{(V_1 - V)} - \frac{(V_3 - V)}{(V_1 - V)}\right] \text{ ppm}$$

or Temporary hardness $= \frac{1000(V_2 - V_3)}{(V_1 - V)}$ ppm

iii) EDTA Method: EDTA is a versatile chelating agent. A chelating agent is a substance whose molecules can form several bonds to a single metal ion. Chelating agents are multi-dentate ligands. A ligand is a substance that binds with a metal ion to form a complex ion. Multidentate ligands are many clawed, holding onto the metal ion to form a very stable complex. EDTA method is more accurate and is used mostly for the estimation of hardness in water. This is a complexometric method in which complex salt like sodium salt of ethylene diamine tetra acetic acid is used as titrant. EDTA can form four or six bonds with a metal ion.

$^{-}OOCH_2C$ CH_2COO^{-}
\ /
$N - CH_2\text{-}CH_2\text{-}N$
/ \
$^{-}OOCH_2C$ CH_2COO^{-}

Structure of the dianion of EDTA

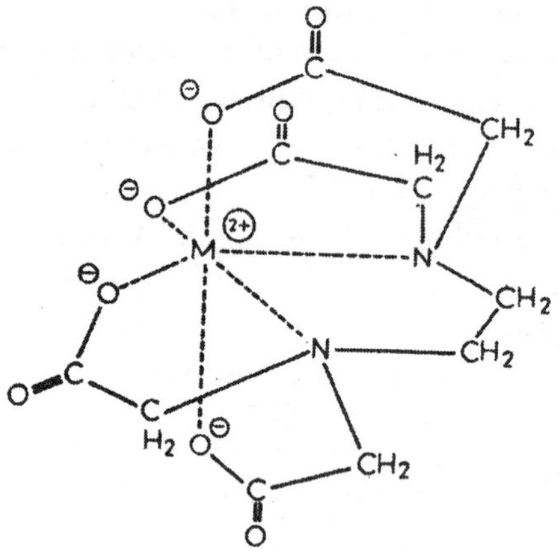

EDTA Complex with metal ions (M=Ca^{2+}, Mg^{2})

Fig. 1.19: Chelating Structure

It is frequently used in soaps and detergents because it forms complexes with calcium and magnesium ions. These ions which are in hard water are bound to EDTA and cannot interfere with the cleaning action of the soap or detergent. In this form sodium salt yields the anion which forms complex ions with Ca^{2+} and Mg^{2+}

It is used as disodium salt which is quite soluble in water. It is hexadentate ligand and can form 4 or 6 dative bonds with Ca^{2+} and Mg^{2+}. EDTA combines with Ca^{2+} and Mg^{2+} ions and form chelates.

Erio Chrome Black T Indicator: It is an azo dye, which forms soluble complexes with Ca^{2+} and Mg^{2+} ions. It contains a sulphonic acid group, which is completely ionized in water and two phenolic groups are partially ionized. Its chemical name is Sodium 1(1- hydroxyl,2-naphthylazo)6-nitro,2-naphthol,4-sulphonate. When it is chelated or acidified, it produces a pink red solution. When it is not chelated, then under basic conditions it is blue.

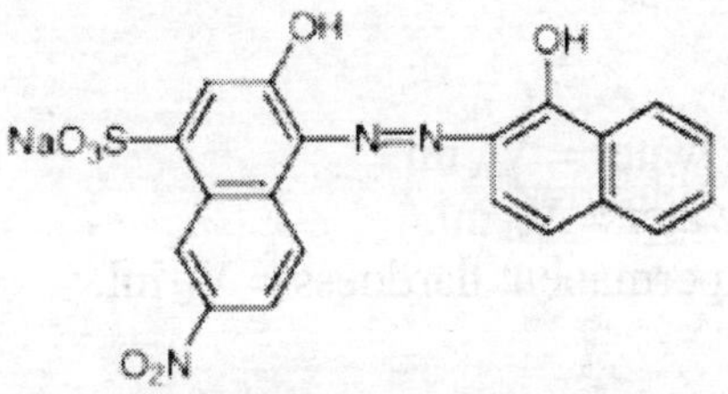

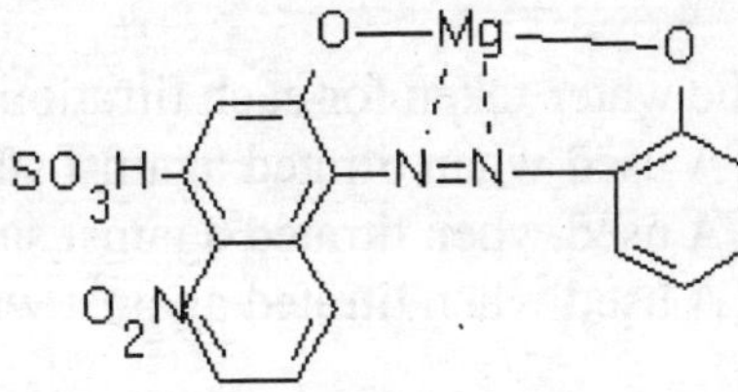

Fig. 1.20: (A) Structure of Erio Chrome Black – T **(B) Structure of Erio Chrome Black – T with Metal ion**

M^{2+} + EBT → [M- EBT] complex
(Ca^{2+} or Mg^{2+}) wine - red

[M- EBT] complex + EDTA → [M- EDTA] + EBT
Colourless complex Blue

Limitation of Erio chrome black-T: It decomposes slowly when kept for more time. In place of EBT, calamite can be used as it does not suffer from this disadvantage.

Principles of Complexometric titration

(1) EBT forms an unstable complex with Ca^{2+} and Mg^{2+} in water at a pH of 10. The complex is wine red in colour. In the course of the titration of water sample against EDTA, EDTA first combines with free Ca^{2+} or Mg^{2+} ions to give very stable and colorless metal EDTA complex. At the equivalence point, there is change is colour from wine red (Due to metal – EBT) to blue (due to free EBT)

Ca^{2+}/Mg^{2+} + EBT → $[Mg/Ca – EDTA]^{2+}$ + EBT
Stable complex Blue
(Colourless)

Thus, the amount of EDTA used corresponds to the hardness of water. The temporary hardness is removed by boiling and after the removal of precipitate by filtration the permanent hardness in the filtrate is determined by titration with EDTA. Difference of total hardness and permanent hardness will give the temporary hardness.

Procedure

1. Preparation of Standard Solution: Dissolve 1.0 g of dry $CaCO_3$ in small amount of HCl as it is insoluble in water and then evaporate to dryness. The residue left is dissolved in distilled water to make one litre solution. Each ml of this solution contains 1 mg of $CaCO_3$ equivalent hardness.
2. Preparation of EDTA Solution: Dissolve 3.7 g of disodium salt of EDTA in 1 litre distilled water.
3. Preparation of Indicator: It is prepared by dissolving 0.5 g of Erichrome Black- T in 100 ml of ethanol.
4. Preparation of Buffer solution: A buffer solution is prepared by dissolving 70 g of NH_4Cl in 570 ml of concentrated NH_3 and solution is diluted to 1 litre with distilled water.
5. Standardization of EDTA Solution: To find out the exact strength of EDTA solution, it is titrated against hard water using EBT and 10-12 ml of buffer solution. The end point changes from red to blue. EDTA is taken in the burette and water sample is taken in the titration flask.
6. Determination of total hardness: As per the procedure given above, the standard hard water is titrated against EDTA solution using Eri chrome black-T as indicator, in the presence of buffer solution.
7. Determination of permanent hardness: In 500 ml beaker takes 250 ml of water sample and boils it till the volume is reduced to 50 ml. If temporary hardness is present, filtrate is made to 250 ml by adding distilled water. This is now titrated against EDTA as in step 5 and 6.

Observations

Let volume of the water taken for each titration = 50 ml.
Volume of EDTA used when titrated against standard hard water = V_A ml.
Volume of EDTA used when titrated against sample hard water = V_B ml.
Volume of EDTA used when titrated against water having permanent hardness = V_C ml.

Calculation

a) Standardization of EDTA

1 ml of Standard Hard water (SHW) contains = 1 mg of $CaCO_3$
50 ml of SHW contains = 50 mg of $CaCO_3$
Volume of EDTA for 50 ml of SHW = V_A ml
$\therefore$ V_A ml of EDTA consumed for 50 ml of SHW = V_A ml

1 ml of EDTA is used for $= \frac{50}{V_A}$ mg of $CaCO_3$

Or strength of EDTA is used for $= \frac{50}{V_A}$ mg/ml of EDTA

(b) Total Hardness

Volume of EDTA used for 50 ml of sample hard water = V_B ml

Since 1 ml EDTA consumes $= \frac{50}{V_A} \times V_B$ mg of $CaCO_3$

Hence, 50 ml of sample water $= \frac{50 \times V_B}{V_A} \times \frac{1000}{50}$ mg of $CaCO_3$

$= \frac{V_B \times 1000}{V}$ mg

$\therefore$ Total Hardness $= \frac{V_B \times 1000}{V_A}$ ppm

(C) Permanent Hardness

Volume of EDTA used for 50 ml of water containing permanent hardness = V_C ml

V_C ml of EDTA will consume $= \frac{50}{V_A} \times V_C$ mg of $CaCO_3$

Hence, 50 ml of water contains permanent hardness $= \frac{50}{V_A} \times V_C$ mg of $CaCO_3$

1000 ml of water contains permanent hardness $= \frac{50}{V_A} \times \frac{V_C}{50} \times 1000$ mg of $CaCO_3$

Permanent hardness $= \frac{V_C}{V_A} \times 1000$ ppm.

Applications: EDTA is also used in foods. Certain enzymes are responsible for food spoilage. EDTA is used to remove metal ions from these enzymes. It is used to promote colour retention in dried bananas, beans, chick peas, canned clams, pecan pie filling, frozen potatoes and canned shrimp. It is used to improve flavour retention in canned carbonated beverages, beer, salad dressings, mayonnaise, margarine and sauces. It inhibits rancidity in salad dressings, mayonnaise, sauces and salad spreads.

Limitations: To determine the total permanent hardness, EDTA grabs all the metal ions in the water, not just the Ca^{2+} ions. This gives us a value which is not truly the concentration of Ca^{2+} ions. This causes an experimental error of about 1% which is acceptable due to the "fuzzy" end points in this type of titration.

ALKALINITY

This is another important characteristic of water. It is due to the presence of bicarbonate, carbonate and hydroxides of sodium, calcium, magnesium and potassium. Calcium and magnesium also cause hardness. Other bases such as borates, silicates, phosphates can also contribute to the total alkalinity to a small extent.

On the basis of anions present, the alkalinity can be classified as

1. Caustic alkalinity (due to OH^-, CO_3^{2-} ions)
2. Bicarbonate alkalinity (due to HCO_3^-)

Alkalinity in water is due to the presence of above mentioned ions alone or in combinations.

1. Hydroxide Only (OH^-)
2. Carbonate Only (CO_3^{2-}) ions
3. Bicarbonate Only (HCO_3^-)
4. Hydroxide and carbonate ($OH^- + CO_3^{2-}$)
5. Carbonate and bicarbonate ($CO_3^{2-} + HCO_3^-$)

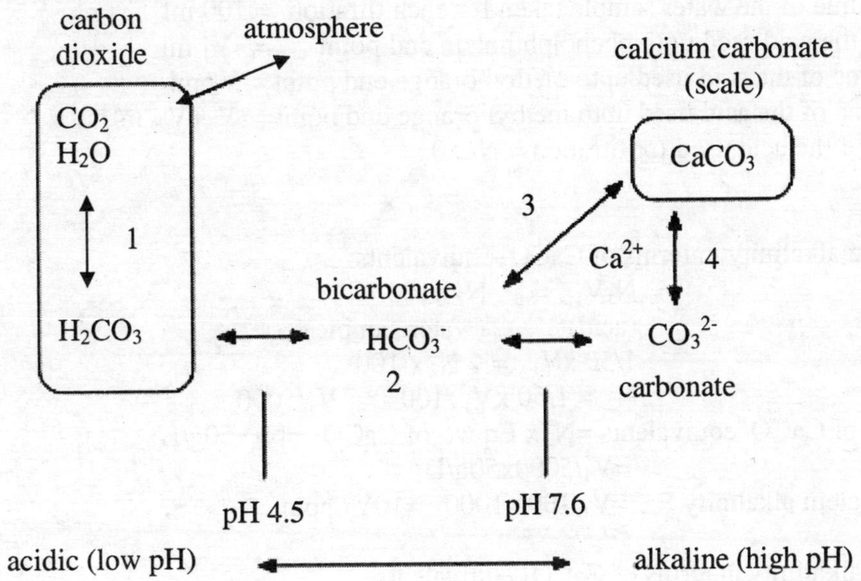

Fig. 1.21

Hydroxide and bicarbonate do not exist together because they combine together and form CO_3^{2-} ions. And hence the possibility of all the three ions existing together is also ruled out.

$$OH^- + HCO_3^- \rightarrow H_2O + CO_3^{2-}$$

Determination of Alkalinity

Principle: This is an acid base titration. Alkalinity producing ions are titrated against standard acid making use of indicators. The indicators used are phenolphthalein and methyl orange. Following reactions take place.

$$\left.\begin{array}{l} \left.\begin{array}{l} a)\ H^+ + OH^- \rightarrow H_2O \\ b)\ H^+ + CO_3^{2-} \rightarrow HCO_3^- \end{array}\right] P \\ c)\ H^+ + HCO_3^- \rightarrow H_2O + CO_2 \end{array}\right] M$$

- The volume of the acid used upto phenolphthalein end point corresponds to the reaction (a) and (b) i.e. complete neutralization of OH^- ions and neutralization of CO_3^{2-} ions upto HCO_3^- stage (half neutralization of CO_3^{2-} ions).
- The volume of the acid used upto methyl orange end point corresponds to the reaction (a), (b) and (c) i.e. complete neutralization of OH^-, CO_3^{2-} and HCO_3^- ions. Thus from the volume of the acid used , the respective strength of various ions can be determined as follows :

Procedure: A known volume of the sample water is titrated against a standard acid using phenolphthalein as indicator. The end point is disappearance of pink colour. To the same solution methyl orange is added as indicator. The solution is then titrated with the standard acid solution till end point from yellow to pink is reached.

Observations

Let the volume of the water sample taken for each titration = 100 ml
Volume of the acid used upto phenolphthalein end point = V_1 ml
Extra volume of the acid used upto methyl orange end point = V_2 ml
Total volume of the acid used upto methyl orange end point= (V_1+V_2) ml
Normality of the acid used for titration = N/ 50

Calculation

(1) Phenolphthalein alkalinity in terms of $CaCO_3$ equivalents

$$\underset{\text{(acid)}}{N_1V_1} = \underset{\text{(water sample)}}{N_2 \times 100}$$

$$1/50 \times V_1 = N_2 \times 100$$

$$N_2 = 1/50 \times V_1 / 100 = V_1/5000$$

Strength in terms of $CaCO_3$ equivalents $= N_2 \times$ Eq.wt. of $CaCO_3 = N_2 \times 50$ g/L

$$= V_1/5000 \times 50 \text{ g/L}$$

Phenolphthalein alkalinity P $= V_1/100 \times 1000 = 10V_1$ ppm

(2) Methyl orange alkalinity in terms of $CaCO_3$ equivalents

$$\underset{\text{(acid)}}{N_1(V_1+V_2)} = \underset{\text{(water sample)}}{N_2 \times 100}$$

$$1/50 \times (V_1+V_2) = N_2 \times 100$$

$$N_2 = 1/50 \times (V_1+V_2)/100$$

Strength in terms of $CaCO_3$ equivalent $= N_2 \times$ Eq. wt. of $CaCO_3$

$$= V_1+V_2/5000 \times 50 \text{ g/L}$$

Methyl orange alkalinity M $= 10(V_1+V_2)$ mg/L $= 10(V_1+V_2)$ ppm

Table 1.16: Calculation of Alkalinity of water

S.N.	Alkalinity	Hydroxide OH^-	Carbonate CO_3^{2-}	Bicarbonate HCO_3^-
1	P = O	Nil	Nil	M
2	P = M	P or M	Nil	Nil
3	$P=\frac{1}{2}M$	Nil	2 P	Nil
4	$P>\frac{1}{2}M$	(2P-M)	2(M-P)	Nil
5	$P<\frac{1}{2}M$	Nil	2P	M-2P

1. When P= 0, this implies that volume of the acid used till phenolphthalein end point is zero, this can only happen if CO_3^{2-} and OH^- both are absent. Whatever alkalinity is present, it is due to HCO_3^- ions and can be detected using methyl orange as indicator.
2. When $P = \frac{1}{2}M$, this implies that only CO_3^{2-} ions are present. Neutralization using phenolphthalein as indicator reaches upto HCO_3^- stage. Same amount of acid will be further used when methyl orange is used as indicator to neutralize HCO_3^- to H_2O and CO_2 as represented in equations (c). The strength of CO_3^{2-} will be given as M or 2P.
3. When $P<\frac{1}{2}M$, it means besides CO_3^{2-} ions, HCO_3^- ions are also present. The acid used upto phenolphthalein end point corresponds to half neutralization of CO_3^{2-} ions. Further titration using methyl orange as indicator corresponds to neutralization of HCO_3^- ions obtained from CO_3^{2-} ions and HCO_3^- originally present in the reaction mixture as shown in equation (b).
   Alkalinity due to CO_3^{2-} = 2P
   Alkalinity due to HCO_3^- = (M-2P)
4. When $P >\frac{1}{2}M$, this implies that besides CO_3^{2-} ions, OH^- ions are also present. OH^- will be completely neutralized by the acid where as CO_3^{2-} will be neutralized at the HCO_3^- stage, using phenolphthalein as indicator. On further titration with the acid using methyl orange as indicator, the neutralization of HCO_3^- takes place as shown below :

$$HCO_3^- + H^+ \rightarrow CO_2 + H_2O$$

   So alkalinity due to complete neutralization of CO_3^{2-} is 2(M - P) and alkalinity due to OH^- ions is M – 2 (M – P) = (2P – M)

5. When P = M, it means only OH^- ions are present. Alkalinity due to OH^- ions is P = M.

Dissolved Chlorides

Chlorides are present in natural water in the form of NaCl, $CaCl_2$ or $MgCl_2$. They get mixed with natural water due to the presence of marine, sedimentary deposits, discharge of effluents from the industries, irrigation etc.

Determination: This is known as argentometric titration. The silver nitrate is used as titrant using potassium chromate as indicator.

Principle: This method is based on precipitation titration. To the water sample, silver nitrate is added in the presence of K_2CrO_4. The chlorides present in it are precipitated as AgCl. As soon as all the chlorides are precipitated out, the last drop of $AgNO_3$ reacts with K_2CrO_4 and gives red precipitate of silver chromate. This indicates the end point.

$$AgNO_3 + NaCl \rightarrow AgCl \downarrow + NaNO_3$$
$$AgNO_3 + K_2CrO_4 \rightarrow \underset{\text{Brick red or Brown ppt}}{Ag_2CrO_4} + 2KNO_3$$

Procedure: Known volume of water sample is taken in conical flask. To this add 2-3 drops of K_2CrO_4. Then titrate the solution against N/50 $AgNO_3$ solution till the appearance of brick red colour.

Calculation

Let Volume of $AgNO_3$ used is = V_2 ml

Water Sample = $AgNO_3$ Solution

$N_1V_1 = N_2V_2$

$$\text{N chloride x V volume of sample} = \frac{1}{50} \times V_2$$

$$\text{N chloride} = \frac{1}{50} \times \frac{V_2}{V} = \frac{V_2}{50V}$$

$$\text{Strength of Cl}^- \text{ ions} = \frac{V_2}{50V} \times 35.5 \times 1000\, mg/l$$

Total Dissolved Solids

Solids: The term solids refer to the matter either filterable or infilterable that remains as residue upon evaporation and subsequent drying at a definite temperature.

Total Solids: Take 100 ml of the sample into the beaker which is kept in oven at 105-110^{0}C. Now residue is cooled in the desiccator. After cooling, weight is taken.

Calculation

W = Wt. of beaker

W_1= Wt. of beaker with total solids

$$\text{Total solids mg/l} = \frac{W_1 - W}{\text{ml. of sample}} \times 1000$$

Dissolved Solids: Filter 100 ml of sample through Whatmann filter paper No.42. W_2 Weight of beaker is taken after heating and cooling the beaker in the oven and desiccator respectively for the constant weight. Pour the filtrate into the beaker and keep it in the oven at 105-110° C for complete drying. After the complete dryness the beaker is kept for cooling in the desiccator. Take the weight of the beaker after cooling (W_3).

Calculation

$$\text{Dissolved solids mg/l} = \frac{(W_3 - W_2)\times 1000}{\text{ml of sample taken}}$$

Suspended Solids: Total solids and dissolved solids are analyzed as above and the difference of the two will give the suspended solids in the sample.

Total suspended solids = Total solids – Dissolved solids.

1.15 DISSOLVED OXYGEN

It is the oxygen dissolved in water per litre and is very important parameter of water quality and is an index of physical and biological processes going on in water. There are two main sources of Dissolved oxygen in water.

(i) Diffusion from air: Diffusion of oxygen from air to water is a physical phenomenon and depends upon the solubility of oxygen which in turn is influenced by factors like temperature, water movement and salinity etc.

(ii) Photosynthetic Activity within air: Photosynthetic Activity is a biological phenomenon carried out by autotrops (mainly phytoplankton in water) and depends upon the autotrops population, life conditions and available gases in water.

Near about 8 ppm of dissolved oxygen is required for potable water but its amount depends on physical, chemical and biological activities taking place in water. It is usually determined by Winkler's method or Iodometric titration. The Winkler test is used to determine the level of dissolved oxygen in fresh water samples. The test was first developed by Lajos Winkler in year 1888. The amount of dissolved oxygen is an indicator of the cleanliness of water. A high level of dissolved oxygen in a water sample shows that the water is clean and unpolluted.

Principle: The determination is based on the fact that Dissolved Oxygen in the water oxidizes Potassium Iodide and an equivalent amount of I_2 is liberated which is titrated against standard hypo solution using starch as indicator. Dissolved oxygen present in water is in molecular state and is not capable of reacting with KI, therefore manganese hydroxide is used as oxygen carrier. It is prepared by the reaction of $MnSO_4$ with KOH.

$$MnSO_4 + 2KOH \rightarrow Mn(OH)_2 + K_2SO_4$$

$$2Mn(OH)_2 + O_2 \rightarrow \underset{\text{Basic oxide}}{2MnO(OH)_2}$$

$$MnO(OH)_2 + H_2SO_4 \rightarrow MnSO_4 + 2H_2O + [O]$$

$$2KI + H_2SO_4 + [O] \rightarrow K_2SO_4 + H_2O + I_2$$

The liberated iodine is titrated against hypo solution.

$$2Na_2S_2O_3 + I_2 \rightarrow Na_2S_4O_6 + 2NaI$$

Some sources of water also contain nitrate and sulphates, which oxidize potassium iodide and increase the amount of I_2 (i.e. I^- to I_2 known as positive error). Generally, Sodium azide is used to decompose the nitrates or sulphates.

$$2NaN_3 + H_2SO_4 \rightarrow Na_2SO_4 + 2HN_3$$

$$HNO_2 + HN_3 \rightarrow N_2O + N_2 + H_2O$$

This is known as Alsterberg's modification. The reducing agents like Fe^{2+}, SO_3^{2-} reduce I_2 to I^- and produce negative effect. Generally, $KMnO_4$ is used to decompose these ions. This is known as Rideat-Stewart modification.

Procedure: A known amount of water sample is taken in a stopper bottle avoiding contact with air. 2ml of $MnSO_4$ and KOH solution are added to it. The bottle is stoppered and shaken thoroughly. 100ml of this solution is pipetted and titrated against N/100 hypo solution using starch as indicator. Disappearance of blue colour denotes the end point.

Calculation

$$\begin{array}{lcl} \text{Hypo} & & O_2 \text{ in water} \\ N_1V_1 & = & N_2V_2 \\ \frac{1}{100} \times V_1 & = & N_2 \times 100 \\ N_2 & = & \frac{V_1}{10000} \end{array}$$

Strength of dissolved oxygen = N_2 x equivalent of oxygen.

$$\frac{V_1}{10000} \times 8 \times 1000 \text{ mg/l} = 0.8V_1 \text{ ppm}$$

$$1 \text{ mole of } O_2 \rightarrow 4 \text{ moles of } Mn(OH)_2 \rightarrow 2 \text{ moles of } I_2$$

Therefore, after determining the number of moles of iodine produced, we can work out the number of moles of oxygen molecules present in the original water sample. The oxygen content is usually presented as mg/lit or ppm. In the above method, each milliliter of thiosulfate titer is equivalent to 0.1 mg of oxygen in the 10 ml subsample. Thus 1 ml of thiosulfate is equivalent to 1 mg oxygen per 100 ml fresh water.

Limitations: Success of the method is critically dependent upon the manner in which the sample is manipulated. At all stages, every method must be made to assure that oxygen is neither introduced nor lost from the sample. Furthermore, the sample must be free of any solutes that will oxidize iodide or reduce iodine. Instrumental methods for measurement of Dissolved Oxygen have widely supplanted the routine use of the Winkler test, although it is still used to check instrument calibration.

1.16 BIOLOGICAL OXYGEN DEMAND (BOD)

Biochemical oxygen demand is a measure of the quantity of oxygen used by micro-organisms aerobically in the oxidation of organic matter. Microorganisms such as bacteria are responsible for decomposing organic waste. When organic matter such as dead plants, leaves, manure and sewage are present in a water supply, the bacteria will begin the process of breaking down this waste. When this happens, much of the available dissolved oxygen is consumed by aerobic bacteria.

If there is a large quantity of organic waste in the water supply, there will also be a lot of bacteria present, working to decompose this waste. In this process the demand for oxygen will be high, so the BOD level will be high. As the waste is consumed or dispersed through the water, BOD level will begin to decline.

The temperature of the water can also contribute to high BOD levels. For example, warmer water usually will have a higher BOD level than colder water. As water temperature increases, the rate of photosynthesis by algae and other plant life in the water also increases. When this happens, plants grow faster and also die faster. When the plants die, they fall to the bottom where they are decomposed by bacteria. The bacteria require oxygen for this process so BOD is high at this location therefore increased water temperatures will speed up bacterial decomposition and result in higher BOD levels.

When BOD levels are high, dissolved oxygen (DO) levels decrease because the oxygen that is available in the water is being consumed by the bacteria. Since less dissolved oxygen is available into water, therefore fish and other aquatic organisms may not survive.

Procedure: To determine Biological Oxygen Demand (BOD), several dilutions of a sample are analyzed for dissolved oxygen before and after a five-day incubation at 20°C (68° F) in the dark. In some cases the sample must be provided a source of oxygen-using bacteria, called "seed", in order to obtain results. The difference in DO and the dilution factor is used to calculate BOD. The resulting number (usually reported in parts per million or milligrams per Liter) is useful in determining the relative organic strength of sewage or other polluted waters. The BOD test is an example of analysis that determines classes of materials in a sample.

Biochemical (or Biological) Oxygen Demand (BOD) is a chemical procedure for determining how fast biological organisms use up oxygen in a body of water. It is used in water quality management and assessment, ecology and environmental science. BOD is not an accurate quantitative test, although it could be considered as an indication of the quality of a water source.

BOD Values: Most pristine rivers will have BOD of less than 1 mg/l. Moderately polluted rivers may have a BOD value in the range of 2 to 8 mg/l. Municipal sewage that is efficiently treated by a three stage process would have a value of about 20 mg/l. as low as 200 mg/l . Slurry from dairy farms is around 8000 mg/l and silage liquor around 60000 mg/l.

Table 1.17: BOD Level of Water

BOD Level (in ppm)	Water Quality
1-2	Very Good-not much organic waste present
3-5	Moderately clean
6-9	Some what polluted
10+	Very polluted

Calculations

BOD can be calculated by:

Undiluted: Initial DO – Final DO = BOD

Diluted: [(Initial DO – Final DO) × Dilution Factor

Significance of BOD: The BOD values are very useful in process design and calculation of waste load. It gives qualitative index of the organic substances which are quickly degraded. It also helps in determining the purifying capacity of streams. It serves as a guide line for Regulatory Authorities to check the quality of effluent discharges into water bodies.

Limitation of BOD: It does not give correct value of organic matter of effluents of rayon, paper and pulp industries. In such cases BOD values should not be used as equivalent to organic load because of cellulose and other non degradable organic matter.

1.17 CHEMICAL OXYGEN DEMAND (COD)

COD is commonly used indirectly to measure the amount of organic compounds in water. Most applications of COD determine the amount of organic pollutants found in surface water (e.g. lakes and rivers), making COD a useful measure of water quality. It is expressed in milligrams per liter (mg/L) which indicates the mass of oxygen consumed per liter of solution. It is also expressed as parts per million (ppm).

Chemical oxygen demand is a measure of oxygen required in oxidizing the organic compound and oxidizable inorganic matter present in water, by means of chemical reaction involving oxidizing substances such as $K_2Cr_2O_7$ and $KMnO_4$. $K_2Cr_2O_7$ is most suitable oxidant, but for the water having more chlorides, $KMnO_4$ is used.

Chemicals used for COD Determination: $K_2Cr_2O_7$ Solution (0.25 N), Silver Sulphate (Dry powder), Mercuric Sulphate (Dry powder), Sulpuric Acid (Concentrated), Ferroin indicator.

Procedure: 20 ml of sample is taken in a flask of the reflux unit along with 10 ml of $K_2Cr_2O_7$, pinch of Ag_2SO_4 and $HgSO_4$ and 30 ml of conc. H_2SO_4. The flask is attached to the condenser and heated on a hot water bath for about 2-3 hrs to reflux the contents. Now this flask is cooled and the contents are diluted to about 100 ml by adding distilled water. A few drops of ferroin indicator solution are added and then the contents are titrated against ferrous ammonium sulphate solution. At the end point, the colour of the content changes to reddish blue.

Blanks: Because COD measures the oxygen demand of organic compounds in a sample of water, it is important that no outside organic material be accidentally added to the sample to be measured. To control this, a so-called blank sample is required in the determination of COD (and BOD for that matter). A blank sample is created by adding all reagents (e.g. acid and oxidizing agent) to a volume of distilled water. COD is measured for both the water and blank samples and the two are compared. The oxygen demand in the blank sample is subtracted from the COD for the original sample to ensure a true measurement of organic matter.

Measurement of excess potassium dichromate: For all organic matter to be completely oxidized, an excess amount of potassium dichromate (or any oxidizing agent) must be present. Once oxidation is complete, the amount of excess potassium dichromate must be measured to ensure that the amount of Cr^{3+} can be determined with accuracy. To do so, the excess potassium dichromate is titrated with ferrous ammonium sulfate (FAS) until all of the excess oxidizing agent has been reduced to Cr^{3+}. Typically, the oxidation-reduction indicator Ferroin is added during this titration step as well. Once all the excess dichromate has been reduced, the Ferroin indicator changes from blue-green to reddish-brown. The amount of ferrous ammonium sulfate added is equivalent to the amount of excess potassium dichromate added to the original sample.

Calculations

The following formula is used to calculate COD

$$\text{COD} = \frac{8000\,(b - s)n}{\text{sample volume}}$$

where b is the volume of FAS used in the blank sample, s is the volume of FAS in the original sample and n is the normality of FAS. If milliliters are used consistently for volume measurements, the result of the COD calculation is given in mg/L.

Inorganic interference: Some samples of water contain high levels of oxidizable inorganic materials which may interfere with the determination of COD. Because of its high concentration in most wastewater, chloride is often the most serious source of interference. Its reaction with potassium dichromate follows the equation:

$$6Cl^{-} + Cr_2O_7^{2-} + 14H^{+} \rightarrow 3Cl_2 + 2Cr^{3+} + 7H_2O$$

Prior to the addition of other reagents, mercuric sulfate can be added to the sample to eliminate chloride interference.

Importance of COD: COD is another index of pollution which measures the effect of pollutants on dissolved oxygen . COD value is not affected by the presence of toxins and other unfavourable conditions for the growth of microrganisms. Due to its rapid determination, COD is very important parameter in management and design of the treatment plants. COD values are taken as basis for calculation of efficiency of treatment plant. COD is important in proposing standards for discharging domestic and industrial effulents in various kinds of water.

Limitations of COD: COD value is a poor measure of strength of organic matter as oxygen also gets consumed in the oxidation of inorganic matter such as nitrates, sulphates, reduced metal ion etc. Although cellulose can be oxidised by this method but some organic materials like benzene, pyridine and few other cyclic organic compounds do not get oxidised by this test. COD test does not differentiate between bio-inert and biodegradable materials. It also does not indicate the rate at which the biologically oxidisable material stabilizes. .

OBJECTIVE QUESTIONS

1. Disadvantages of Hard water in paper industry are due to:
   (a) Ca and Mg Salts (b) Silica (c) Oxygen
   (d) Soaps (e) a and b both
2. Chemical equivalent of $CaCO_3$ is:
   (a) 50 (b) 100 (c) 0
   (d) 1 (e) 0.1
3. 1° Fr is equal to how many ppm:
   (a) 0.1 ppm (b) 10 ppm (c) 0.7 ppm
   (d) 0.01 ppm (e) 2 ppm
4. Solubility of $CaSO_4$ in water decreases with
   (a) Decrease in temperature (b) Rise in temperature
   (c) Independent to temperature (d) Pressure variation
5. Colloidal conditioning can be done by:
   (a) Kerosene (b) Tannin
   (c) Agar agar (d) All the above
6. Sodium Aluminate is
   (a) Sealant (b) Coagulant
   (c) Rust (d) Anti-foaming agent
7. Foaming in boilers can be avoided by:
   (a) Palm oil (b) Castor Oil
   (c) Lubrication (d) Softening of water
8. Permutit process is known as:
   (a) Ion exchange process (b) Deionization of water
   (c) Lime soda process (d) Zeolite process
9. Zeolite process removes hardness till
   (a) 20 ppm (b) 2 ppm
   (c) 0.45 ppm (d) 10 ppm
10. Objectionable problems in boiler are:
    (a) Priming (b) Foaming
    (c) Carry over (d) Boiler corrosion
    (e) All the above
11. Chloramines are used in drinking water for:
    (a) Disinfection (b) Filtration
    (c) Sedimentation (d) None of these
12. EDTA method of determination of hardness of water is used for:
    (a) Temporary hardness (b) All types of hardness
    (c) Permanent hardness (d) Alkaline hardness only
13. Pure water can be obtained by
    (a) Permutit process (b) Demineralization
    (c) L-S Process (d) None of these
14. Permanent hardness can be removed by:
    (a) Adding Soda (b) Distillation
    (c) Boiling (d) Adding Lime-Soda
15. Which of the following methods separates both ionic and non-ionic impurities from water?
    (a) Electrodialysis (b) Reverse osmosis
    (c) Deionization (d) All the above

16. The process of removing extra common salt from water is called:
(a) Deionization (b) Reverse osmosis
(c) Desalination (d) Disinfection
17. Coagulants help in setting of:
(a) Suspended impurities (b) Fine suspended matter only
(c) Colloidal Particles (d) Both b and c
18. Most popular and ideal disinfectant in waterworks is:
(a) Bleaching powder (b) Ozone
(c) Chlorine (d) Lime
19. The exhausting permutit is regenerated by percolating it through a solution of:
(a) Calcium chloride (b) Zinc chloride
(c) Magnesium chloride (d) Sodium chloride
20. Which one of the following dissolved salts in water does not cause hardness?
(a) $CaSO_4$ (b) Na_2SO_4
(c) $MgSiO_3$ (d) $MgCl_2$
21. Internal treatment of boiler feed water means:
(a) Treating water during evaporation
(b) Treating water before boiler feeding
(c) Treating chemically the steam formed
(d) Treating after some internal change in boiler design.
22. Scale formation in boiler causes:
(a) No loss of heat (b) Wastage of heat
(c) Increase in Efficiency (d) None of these
23. Disinfection of water removes:
(a) Hardness (b) Turbidity
(c) Bacteria (d) Odour
24. The presence of Nitrate in amount more than 50 ppm leads to disease called:
(a) Typhoid (b) Gaestroenteritis
(c) Mathenoglobenemia (d) None
25. Sodium Hexa Meta Phosphate is used as:
(a) Water softener (b) Ion-exchange resin
(c) Sulphate (d) Bicarbonate
26. Swimming for long time in soft water makes the skin of finger tips wrinkles. Which one is responsible for that
(a) Coagulation (b) Dialysis
(c) Osmosis (d) Electrodalysis
27. Red Brownish colour of water is due to presence of dissolved impurities of:
(a) Arsenic (b) Iron and Manganese
(c) Sulphate (d) Bicarbonates
28. The presence of Manganese in water causes the growth of:
(a) Mosquitoes (b) Flies
(c) Algae (d) Microorganisms.
29. Fe and Mn are removed by:
(a) Filtration (b) Chlorination
(c) Aeration (d) Lime-Soda treatment
30. Some fluorides are essential or desirable in potable water to prevent:
(a) Scale formation (b) Corrosion
(c) Dental cavities (d) Water borne diseases

31. Which ion is not there in naturally occurring zeolite?
(a) Na^+ (b) Al^{3+}
(c) Si^{4+} (d) Ca^{2+}
32. Which is not a cation exchanger?
(a) Amberlite (b) Dowex (c) Duolite
(d) Zeokarb (e) None
33. Alkalinity in water cannot be due to
(a) OH^- ion only (b) OH^- and CO_3^{--}
(c) OH^- and HCO_3^- (d) CO_3^{--} and HCO_3^-
34. Calgon is
(a) Na_3PO_4 (b) NaCl
(c) $(NaPO_3)_6$ (d) NaH_2PO_4
35. Potable water treatment does not involve:
(a) Demineralization (b) Disinfection
(c) Coagulation (d) Sedimentation
36. Which one of the following is a complexometric titration?
(a) FAS vs $K_2Cr_2O_7$ (b) $FeSO_4$ vs $KMnO_4$
(c) Hard Water vs EDTA (d) Acid vs Base
37. Chlorine is used in purification of drinking water:
(a) Sterilization (b) Coagulation
(c) Sedimentation (d) Filtration
38. A sample of water contains sodium chloride. It is-
(a) Soft water (d) Hard water
(c) Moderate (b) None
39. Desalination is the process of removing
(a) Oil (b) Common salt
(c) Mineral (d) Hardness from water
40. The Coefficient of thermal expansion of boiler scale is
(a) Same as that of boiler plate (b) Less than that of boiler plate
(c) Higher than that of boiler plate (d) None of these
41. Brackish water mostly contains:
(a) $CaCl_2$ (b) $BaSO_4$
(c) NaCl (d) HCl
42. Internal treatment of boiler feed water involves:
(a) To precipitate the scale forming substance in the form of sludge
(b) To convert them into soluble substance
(c) Both a and b
(d) None of a and b
43. Ultra violet rays are used in water treatment for:
(a) Sterilization (b) Coagulation
(c) Sedimentation (d) Filtration
44. Which of the following dissolved salts in water would cause the least hardness in water sample?
(a) 10 ppm of $CaSO_4$ (b) 10 ppm of $MgCl_2$
(c) 10 ppm of $CaSO_3$ (d) 25.5 ppm of $Mg(OH)_2$
45. Plumbo Solvency is a hazard in the transportation of:
(a) Soft water only (b) Hard water only
(c) Both a and b (d) None of these

46. The flow of water through the membrane from saline water in the fresh water takes place when the applied pressure on saline water is:
(a) Higher than Osmotic Pressure (b) Lower than Osmotic Pressure
(c) Equal to Osmotic pressure (d) Zero Osmotic pressure
47. Hardness in water is expressed in terms of equivalent of:
(a) $CaCl_2$ (b) $MgCl_2$
(c) $CaCO_3$ (d) $MgCO_3$
48. 13.6 mg./litre of $CaSO_4$ is equivalent to how many mg./litre of $CaCO_3$?
(a) 10 mg./lit. (b) 5 mg./lit
(c) 20 mg./lit. (d) 2 mg./lit
49. Calgon is the trade name of:
(a) Sodium silicate (b) Calcium phosphate
(c) Sodium zeolite (d) Sodium hexa meta phosphate
50. For the removal of $Ca(HCO_3)_2$ temporary hardness by Lime-Soda process, which is required ?
(a) Lime (b) Soda
(c) Lime and Soda (d) None of the above
51. Sterilization of water can be done by using:
(a) Ozone (b) Oxygen
(c) Hydrogen peroxide (d) Caustic potash

Answer Key

(1) e (2) a (3) b (4) b (5) d (6) b (7) b (8) d (9) d (10) e (11) a (12) b (13) b (14) d
(15) b (16) c (17) d (18) c (19) d (20) b (21) a (22) b (23) c (24) c (25) a (26) c (27) b (28) d
(29) d (30) c (31) c (32) d (33) c (34) c (35) a (36) c (37) a (38) a (39) b (40) b (41) c (42) c
(43) a (44) a (45) a (46) a (47) c (48) a (49) d (50) a (51) a

SOLVED NUMERICAL PROBLEMS

Problem 1

1.0 gm of $CaCO_3$ was dissolved in HCl and diluted to 1000 ml. 25 ml of this solution required 25 ml of EDTA solution for titration. In another titration 50 ml of hard water sample required 45 ml of EDTA solution. 50 ml of same hard water sample on boiling, cooling and filtering etc. required 20 ml of EDTA solution using Erichrome Black-T as indicator. Calculate Total hardness, Temporary hardness and Permanent hardness of water sample in different units.

Solution

(i) Standardization of EDTA solution -

1 L of standard hard water $= 1.0$ g of $CaCO_3$

1 ml of SHW $=$ 1mg of $CaCO_3$

25 ml of EDTA $=$ 25ml of SHW

$\therefore$ 1ml of EDTA $= \frac{25}{25} =$ 1mg $CaCO_3$

1ml EDTA solution $= 1$ mg $CaCO_3$

(ii) Determination of Total Hardness

50 ml of unknown hard water required 45 ml of EDTA

$\therefore$ 50 ml HW $= 45$ ml EDTA

$= 45 \times 1$ mg $CaCO_3$

$\therefore$ 1000 ml (1L) of unknown hard water sample $= \frac{45}{50} \times 1000 = 900$ mg of $CaCO_3$

Total Hardness = **900 ppm = 90°F=63°Cl Ans**

(iii) Determination of Permanent hardness

50 ml of boiled water = 20 ml EDTA

1000 ml of boiled water $= \frac{20}{50} \times 1000 = 400$ mg

Permanent hardness **= 400 ppm = 40° Fr=28°Cl Ans.**

(iv) Temporary hardness = [Total hardness-permanent hardness]

= 900 – 400 = **500 ppm Ans.**

Problem 2

50 ml of standard hard water containing 1.5 mg of pure $CaCO_3$ per ml consumed 44 ml of EDTA. 40 ml of water sample consumed 20 ml of same EDTA solution using EBT indicator. Calculate total hardness of water sample in ppm, °Cl and °Fr. **[RGPV 05]**

Solution

44 ml of EDTA = 50ml of 1.5 mg/ml of $CaCO_3$ equivalent

1 ml of EDTA $= 50 \times \frac{1.5}{44}$ =75/44 mg $CaCO_3$ equivalent

40 ml of HW = 20 ml of EDTA solution = 20 × 75/44 mg $CaCO_3$ equivalent

$\therefore$ 1 L of HW $= \frac{20 \times 75 \times 1{,}000}{44 \times 40}$ mg of $CaCO_3$ equivalent

= 852.27 mg of $CaCO_3$ equivalent

Total Hardness of water = **852.27 ppm °Fr = 85.22° Fr °Cl = 59.65° Cl Ans.**

Problem 3

100 ml of a raw water sample on titration with N/50 H_2SO_4 required 12.4 ml of the acid to phenolphthalein end point and 15.2 ml of the acid to methyl orange end point. Determine the types and extent of alkalinity present in water sample. **[RGPV 01]**

Solution

100 ml of water sample upto phenolphthalein end point

$= 12.4$ ml of $\frac{N}{50}$ H_2SO_4

$$N_pV_1 = N_2V_2$$

$$N_p \times 100 \text{ ml} = \frac{N}{50} \times 12.4 \text{ ml}$$

or $$N_p = \frac{1}{50} \times \frac{12.4 \text{ ml}}{100 \text{ ml}}$$

Strength of alkalinity upto phenolphthalein end-point in terms of $CaCO_3$ equivalent $= N_1 \times 50 \times 1000$ ppm

$$P = \frac{12.4}{100} \times \frac{1}{50} \times 50 \times 1000$$

P=124 ppm

100 ml of water upto methyl orange end point 15.2 ml of $\frac{N}{50}$ H_2SO_4

$$N_M V_1 = N_2V_2$$

$$N_M \times 100 = \frac{N}{50} \times 15.2 \text{ ml}$$

$$N_M = \frac{15.2}{100} \times \frac{1}{50}$$

So, strength (in terms of $CaCO_3$ equivalent) $M = N_M \times 50 \times 1000$ ppm

$$M = \frac{15.2}{100} \times \frac{1}{50} \times 50 \times 1000 \quad M = 152 \text{ ppm}$$

Since P>1/2 M, OH^- and CO_3^{2-} are present.

Alkalinity due to OH^- = 2P-M = 2 × 124 – 152 = 96 ppm

Alkalinity due to CO_3^{2-} = 2 (M-P) = 2(152-124) = 56 ppm

Hence water sample contains

OH^- Alkalinity = 96 ppm, CO_3^{2-} Alkalinity = 50 ppm,

Total Alkalinity = [96+56] ppm = 152 ppm Ans.

Problem 4

Calculate the hardness in terms of $CaCO_3$ equivalent, if water sample contains 410 mg of $CaSO_4$ per litre. **[RGPV 01, 07]**

Solution

$$\text{Hardness} = \text{Mass of } CaSO_4 \times \text{multiplication factor}$$

$$= 410 \times \left[\frac{\text{Chemical eq. of } CaCO_3}{\text{Chemical eq. of } CaCO_4}\right]$$

$$= 410 \times \frac{50}{68}$$

$$\text{Hardness} = \mathbf{301.47 \text{ ppm}} \quad \textbf{Ans.}$$

Problem 5

A water sample on analysis gave the following results –
Ca^{2+} = 30mg/l, Mg^{2+} = 18mg/I, K^+ = 19.5 mg/l, CO_2 = 11mg/l, HCO_3^- = 122mg/l, Cl^- =35.5 mg/l and SO_4^{2-}= 48 mg/l. Calculate total hardness and alkalinity present in water sample. Also calculate lime-soda required for softening one litre of this sample of hard water. **[RGPV 01]**

Solution

$$\text{Total Hardness} = [Ca^{2+} + Mg^{2+}]$$

$$= \left[30 \times \frac{100}{40} + 18 \times \frac{100}{24}\right] = \mathbf{150 \text{ ppm}}$$

$$\text{Alkalinity} = HCO_3^-$$

$$= 122 \times \frac{100}{122} = \mathbf{100 \text{ ppm}}$$

$$\text{Lime required} = \frac{74}{100}[Mg^{2+} + CO_2 + HCO_3^- \text{ all as } CaCO_3 \text{ equivalent}]$$

$$= \frac{74}{100}\left[18 \times \frac{100}{24} + 11 \times \frac{100}{44} + 122 \times \frac{100}{122}\right] = 148 \text{ mg/l}$$

$$L = 148 \frac{mg}{L} \times 1 \text{ Litre} = \mathbf{148mg/l}$$

$$\text{Soda required} = \frac{106}{100}[Ca^{2+} + Mg^{2+} - HCO_3^{-} \text{ as } CaCO_3 \text{ equivalent}]$$

$$= \frac{106}{100}\left[30 \times \frac{100}{40} + 18 \times \frac{100}{24} - 122 \times \frac{100}{122}\right]$$

$$S = 53 \frac{mg}{L} \times 1\,Litre = \mathbf{53\ mg.\ Ans.}$$

Problem 6

Calculate the amount of lime (88.3% pure) and soda (99.2% pure) required to soften 24,000 litres of water per day for a year containing the following.

$CaCO_3$: 1.85 mg/l, $MgCO_3$: 0.42 mg/I, $MgSO_4$: 0.90mg/l, SiO_2: 2.32 mg/1, $CaSO_4$: 0.34 mg/l, $MgCl_2$: 0.76 mg/l and NaCl: 2.34 mg/l. **[RGPV01, 06]**

Solution

NaCl and SiO_2 do not require lime and soda.

$$\text{Lime required} = \frac{74}{100}[CaCO_3 + 2 \times MgCO_3 + MgCl_2 + MgSO_4 \text{ as } CaCO_3 \text{ equivalent}]$$

$$= \frac{74}{100}\left[1.85 \times \frac{100}{100} + 2 \times 0.42 \times \frac{100}{84} + 0.76 \times \frac{100}{95} + 0.90 \times \frac{100}{120}\right]$$

$$= \frac{74}{100}[1.85+1.0+0.8+0.75]$$

$$= 3.256 \frac{mg}{L} \times 24{,}000 \times 365L \times \frac{1kg}{10^6 mg} \times \frac{100}{88.3}$$

$$= 3.256 \times \frac{24000 \times 365 \times 100}{10^6 \times 88.3} = 32.3 \text{ kg}$$

L = 32.3 kg Ans.

$$\text{Soda requirement} = \frac{106}{100}[CaSO_4 + MgCl_2 + MgSO_4 \text{ as } CaCO_3 \text{ equivalent}] \text{ mg/l}$$

$$= \frac{106}{100}\left[0.34 \times \frac{100}{136} + 0.76 \times \frac{100}{95} + 0.90 \times \frac{100}{120}\right] \text{mg/l}$$

$$= 1.06 \times [0.25 + 0.8 + 0.75] \times \frac{24000 \times 365 \times 100}{10^6 \times 99.2} = 16.848$$

S = 16.85 kg. Ans.

Problem 7

A Zeolite softener was 90% exhausted by removing the hardness completely when 10,000 litres of hard water sample passed through it. The exhausted zeolite bed required 200 litres of 3% sodium chloride solution for its complete regeneration. Calculate the hardness of water sample. **[RGPV 07]**

Solution

NaCl contained in 200 L of 3% NaCl solution.

= 30 gm/L × 200L = 6000 g NaCl

$$= 6000 \times \frac{50}{58.5}$$

= 5,128 gm equivalents of $CaCO_3$ 90% hardness of 10,000 L of water

$= 5{,}128$ gm equivalents of $CaCO_3$

$$1\text{L of water} = \frac{5128}{\left(10{,}000 \times \frac{90}{100}\right)} = \frac{5138}{9000}$$

$= 0.5698$ gm equivalents of Ca $CO_3 = 0.5698 \times 1000$ mg $CaCO_3$ equivalents

Hardness of water sample = **569.8 ppm Ans.**

Problem 8

Water sample using $FeSO_4.7H_2O$ as a coagulant at the rate of 139 ppm gave the following results for raw water.

Ca^{2+}= 320 ppm, Mg $^{2+}$= 120 ppm, CO_2 = 88 ppm and HCO_3^- = 732 ppm. Calculate the quantities of lime and soda required for softening 50,000 litres of hard water sample.

Solution

$$\text{Lime requirement} = \frac{74}{100}[\,Mg^{2+} + HCO_3^- + CO_2 + FeSO_4.7H_2O]\ \text{mg/l}$$

$$= 0.74\left[120 \times \frac{100}{24} + 732 \times \frac{100}{122} + 88 \times \frac{100}{44} + 139 \times \frac{100}{278}\right]$$

$= 0.74\ [500 + 600 + 200 + 50]$ mg/l $= 999$ mg/l

Now for 1000 Litres $= 999 \times 1000 = 999 \times 10^3$ mg

For 50,000 Litres $= 999 \times 50{,}000 = 4995 \times 10^4$mg $= 49950$ gm

L = 49.95 kg Ans.

$$\text{Soda requirement} = \frac{106}{100}[Ca^{2+} + Mg^{2+} - HCO_3^- + FeSO_4.7H_2O \text{ as } CaCO_3 \text{ equivalent}]$$

$$= \frac{106}{100}\left[320 \times \frac{100}{40} + 120 \times \frac{100}{24} - 732 \times \frac{100}{122} + 139 \times \frac{100}{278}\right] = 795 \text{ mg/L}$$

For 50,000 L of raw water $= 795 \times 50000$ L $= 795 \times 50 \times 10^3$ mg

$= 39750 \times 10^3$ mg

S = 39.75 kg Ans.

Problem 9

The hardness of 100000 litres of water sample was completely removed by a zeolite softener. The exhausted softener required 500 litres of sodium chloride solution, containing 110 g/litre of sodium chloride for regeneration. Calculate hardness of water in different units.

Solution

NaCl contained in 500 L of NaCl Solution = 110gm/1 × 500 L

$= 55000$ gm of NaCl $= 55000 \times \frac{50}{58.5}$

$= 47008.54$ gm equivalent of $CaCO_3$

1, 00,000 L of water $= 47008.54$ gm equivalent of $CaCO_3$

1 L of water $= \dfrac{4.7008 \times 10^7}{100000}$ mg/l

Hardness of water = 470.08 ppm = 47°F = 32.9°Cl

1ppm = 0.1°F = 0.07°Cl

470.08 ppm = 47°F = 32.9°Cl Ans

Problem 10

50 ml of sample contains 840 ppm of DO after 5 days. The DO value becomes 230 ppm. After the sample has been diluted to 80 ml, Calculate the BOD of sample. **[RGPV 06]**

Solution:

BOD = $[DO_b\text{-}DO_1] \times$ Dilution factor

$= (DO_b\text{-}DO_1) \times \dfrac{\text{ml of sample after dilution}}{\text{ml of sample after dilution}}$

$= (840\text{-}230) \times \dfrac{80}{50}$ = **976 ppm Ans.**

Problem 11

25 ml of a sewage water sample was refluxed with 10 ml of 0.25 N $K_2Cr_2O_7$ solutions in presence of dilute H_2SO_4, Ag_2SO_4 and $HgSO_4$. The unreacted dichromate required 6.5 ml of 0.1 N ferrous ammonium sulphate. 10 ml of the same $K_2Cr_2O_7$ solution and 25 ml of distilled water, under the same conditions as the sample, required 27 ml of 0.1 N ferrous ammonium sulphate solution. Calculate the COD of sewage water sample.

Solution:

V_b = 27 ml

V_t = 6.5 ml

N = 0.1 Normal

V_e = 25 ml

COD $= (V_b - V_t) \times N \times 8 / V_e \times 1000\, mg/l$

COD $= \dfrac{(27 - 6.5) \times 0.1 \times 8}{25} \times 1000$

$= \dfrac{20.5 - 0.8}{25} \times 1000$ = **656 ppm Ans.**

Problem 12

250 ml of sample water requires 4.5 ml of 0.1 Na_2SO_4 for complete neutralization using methyl orange as indicator. Another 250 ml of the sample of water was boiled with exactly 50 ml of 0.1 N Alkali mixtures. After filtering off the precipitation, the filtrate was made upto exactly 250 ml. 50 ml of this made up sample solution requires 8.5 ml of 0.1 N H_2SO_4 for complete neutralization Calculate the carbonate, non-carbonate and total hardness of water sample.

Solution:

(i) In the absence of OH^- alkalinity the CO_3^{2-} hardness was determined by titration against strong acid using methyl orange indicator. Thus titration upto methyl orange end point indicated the CO_3^{2-} hardness or carbonate alkalinity.

250 ml of water upto methyl orange end point = 4.5 ml of 0.1 N H_2SO_4

250 ml $\times N_M$ = 4.5 ml $\times$ 0.1 N

$$N_M = \frac{4.5 \times 0.1}{250} = 1.8 \times 10^{-3} \text{ N}$$

Now, strength of CO_3^{2-} hardness upto methyl orange end point in terms of $CaCO_3$ equivalent

$M = N_M \times 50 \times 1000$ ppm = 90 ppm

So CO_3^{--} hardness in terms of $CaCO_3$ equivalent = **90 ppm Ans.**

(ii) For estimation of non-carbonates hardness, Cl^- and SO_4^{2-} of Ca and Mg are precipitated by boiling the water sample with a known excess of a mixture of NaOH and Na_2CO_3 (known as alkalinity mixture or soda reagent.)

The involved reactions are

$$Ca^{2+} + CO_3^{2-} \rightarrow CaCO_3 \downarrow$$

$$Mg^{2+} + 2OH^- \rightarrow Mg(OH)_2 \downarrow$$

Then precipitates are filtered off and the unused alkali mixture is back titrated against standard acid. Note that even if the bicarbonates of Ca and Mg are present, they are converted into equivalent amount of Na_2CO_3

$$Ca(HCO_3)_2 + 2NaOH \rightarrow CaCO_3 \downarrow + Na_2CO_3 + 2H_2O$$

$$Mg(HCO_3)_2 + 4NaOH \rightarrow Mg(OH)_2 \downarrow + 2Na_2CO_3 + 2H_2O$$

Thus no alkali is consumed by the carbonate hardness present. However in practice the carbonate hardness is removed by boiling prior to the addition of alkali mixture.

Assuming there is no non carbonate hardness, as 50 ml of 0.1 N alkali mixture was made upto 250 ml, so the normality of this made up solution

$$= \frac{50\,\text{ml} \times 0.1\,\text{N}}{250\,\text{ml}} = 0.02 \text{ N} \ldots\ldots\ldots\ldots\ldots \text{(b)}$$

But given 50 ml of made up solution requires 8.5 ml of 0.1 N H_2SO_4.

Therefore normality of the made up solution

$$= \frac{8.5\,\text{ml} \times 0.1\,\text{N}}{50\,\text{ml}} = 0.017 \text{ N} \ldots\ldots\ldots\ldots\ldots\ldots \text{(c)}$$

Thus reduction in normality = b - c

= 0.02-0.017 = 0.003 N

We know that CO_3^{2-} hardness does not consume any alkali mixture, any consumption of the alkali (corresponding to 0.003 N) must be due to the non-carbonate hardness.

Hence normality with respect to non carbonates hardness = 0.003 N

(i) Non-carbonate hardness (in terms of $CaCO_3$ equivalent) = 0 .003 × 50 × 1000 = **50 ppm Ans**

(ii) Total hardness of water sample = Carbonate Hardness + Non-carbonate hardness

= 90 + 50 = **140 ppm** **Ans.**

Problem 13

Three samples A, B, C were analyzed for their salt contents.

(1) Sample A was found to contain 168 mg $MgCO_3$/litre

(2) Sample B was found to contain 820 mg $Ca(NO_3)_2$ and 2 mg of silica titer

(3) Sample C was found to contain 20 g of KNO_3 and 2 g of calcium carbonate/500 ml

Determine hardness in ppm and grains/gallon

Solution – Calculation of $CaCO_3$ equivalent

Sample	Constituent	Multiplication factor	$CaCO_3$ equivalent
A	$MgCO_3$ = 168 mg/l	$\frac{100}{84}$	$=168\times\frac{100}{84}$ = 200 mg/l
B	$Ca(NO_3)_2$ = 820 mg/l	$\frac{100}{164}$	$=820\times\frac{100}{164}$ = 500 mg/l
C	$CaCO_3$=2g/500 mg/l	$\frac{100}{100}$	$=4000\times\frac{100}{100}$ = 4,000 mg/l

Hardness of sample A = 200mg/l or 200 ppm
Hardness of sample B = 500mg/l or 500 ppm
Hardness of sample C = 4000mg/l or 4000 ppm

Now

1 ppm = 0.07° Cl = 0.07 grain/gallon
Hardness of sample A = 200 × 0.07 = **14 g/g Ans.**
Hardness of sample B = 500 × 0.07 = **35 g/g Ans.**
Hardness of sample C = 4000 × 0.07 = **280 g/g Ans.**

Problem 14

A water sample on analysis gives following data:
$MgCl_2$ = 95 ppm, $CaSO_4$ = 272 ppm, $MgSO_4$ = 120 ppm, H_2SO_4 = 49 ppm and SiO_2 = 4 ppm. Calculate the amount of (95% pure) lime and (97% pure) soda needed for treating 1 million liters of water. If the costs of lime and soda are Rs. 40 and Rs.2000 per 100 kg each respectively, calculate the total cost of chemical used for treating 1 million liters of water.

Solution:

Impurity	$CaCO_3$ equivalent
$MgCl_2$	$95\times\frac{100}{95}=100$ mg/l
$CaSO_4$	$272\times\frac{100}{136}=200$ mg/l
$MgSO_4$	$120\times\frac{100}{120}=100$ mg/l
H_2SO_4	$49\times\frac{100}{98}=50$ mg/l
SiO_2	Ignored

Amount of 95% pure lime requirement for softening 1 million litres of the water

$$L = \frac{74}{100}[MgCl_2 + MgSO_4 + H_2SO_4]\times Purity\ factor \times kg\ for 10^6\ Litre$$

$$L = \frac{74}{100}[100+100+50]\times\frac{100}{95}\times\frac{10^6}{10^6}$$

$$L = 194.74 kg$$

L $\therefore$ *Cost of the* lime *required at the rate of* $Rs.40/100\,kg. = \dfrac{194.74 \times 40}{100} = 77.90\,Rs.$

L = 77.90 Rs. Ans.

Similarly, amount of 97% pure soda needed for 1 million litre of the water

$$= \frac{106}{100}[100+200+100+50] \times \frac{100}{97} \times \frac{10^6}{10^6}$$

$$= \frac{491.75257}{100} \times 2000 = Rs.9835.05$$

$\therefore$ Total cost of the chemicals needed for softening 1 million litres of water :

$= Rs.(77.90 + Rs.9835.05)$

= **Rs. 9912.95 Ans.**

Problem 15

A water sample on analysis gave the following constituents in grains/gallon:

$MgCl_2$	= 9.5	$CaSO_4$	= 3.4
$CaCO_3$	= 5.0	$Mg(HCO_3)_2$	= 7.3
$MgSO_4$	= 6.0	SiO_2	= 2.4

Calculate the cost of the chemicals required for softening 20,000 gallons of water if the impurities of lime and soda are 95% and 90% respectively. The cost per 100 pounds each of lime and soda is Rs. 28 and Rs. 96 respectively.

Solution

Salt			$CaCO_3$ equivalent
$MgCl_2$	= 9.5	$9.5 \times \dfrac{100}{95}$	= 10 gpg
$CaSO_4$	= 3.4	$3.4 \times \dfrac{100}{136}$	= 2.5 gpg
$CaCO_3$	= 5.0	$5.0 \times \dfrac{100}{100}$	= 5.0 gpg
$Mg(HCO_3)_2$	= 7.3	$7.3 \times \dfrac{100}{146}$	= 5.0 gpg
$MgSO_4$	= 6.0	$6.0 \times \dfrac{100}{120}$	= 5.0 gpg
SiO_2	= 2.4	ignored	

Lime is required for = [Temporary Calcium Hardness + (2 × Temporary magnesium hardness + permanent magnesium hardness)]

= 5 + (2 × 5) + 10 + 5 = 30 gpg

$\therefore$ Cost of 95% pure lime required for softening 20,000 gallons at the rate of Rs. 28 per 100 lbs.

$\dfrac{74}{100} \times 30$	× 20,000 ×	$\dfrac{1}{7000}$	× $\dfrac{100}{95}$	× $\dfrac{28}{100}$
Lime required per gallon	gallons treated	1bs=7000 grains	purity factor	cost per 100 lbs

L = Rs 18.69 Ans.

Similarly, Soda required for Ca permanent hardness + Mg permanent hardness which generated equivalent quantity of Ca permanent hardness during lime treatment

$= 2.5 + (10+5) = 17.5$ gpg

$\therefore$ Cost of 90% soda required for treating 20,000 gallon at rate of Rs. 96 per 100 lbs.

$$\frac{106}{100}\times 17.5 \times 20{,}000 \times \frac{1}{7000} \times \frac{100}{90} \times \frac{96}{100}$$

Soda required per gallon	gallons treated	1 lb = 7000 grains	purity factor	cost per 100 lbls

S = Rs. 56.653 Ans.

Problem 16

The analytical report of a raw water sample is as follows:

$MgCl_2$ – 47.5 mg/L $CaCl_2$ – 55.5 mg/L

$CaSO_4$ – 4.06 mg/L Turbidity – 120 mg/L

10 mg/L alum dose was found to be sufficient to remove the entire turbidity of water sample. Calculate the total weight of the dry sediment in a lime soda softening plant for 20,000 litres of water. Alum contains 7% Al.

Solution

$$\underset{95}{MgCl_2} + Ca(OH)_2 \rightarrow \underset{58}{Mg(OH)_2}\downarrow + \underset{111}{CaCl_2}$$

95 mg of $MgCl_2$ yields 58 mg of $Mg(OH)_2$

$\therefore$ 47.5 mg of $MgCl_2$ yields $= \frac{58\times 47.5}{95}$ mg $= 29$ mg of $Mg(OH)_2$

Again 95 mg of $MgCl_2$ will produce 111 mg of $CaCl_2$ which gives 100 mg of $CaCO_3$ on treatment with soda.

$\therefore$ 29 mg of $MgCl_2$ will produce $= 29\times\frac{100}{95}$ mg of $CaCO_3$ $= 30.526$ mg of $CaCO_3$

(2) $$\underset{111}{CaCl_2} + Na_2CO_3 \rightarrow \underset{100}{CaCO_3}\downarrow + 2NaCl$$

111 mg of $CaCl_2$ yields 100 mg of $CaCO_3$

$\therefore$ 55.5 mg of $CaCl_2$ yields $= \frac{100\times 55.5}{111}$ mg of $CaCO_3$ $= 50$ mg of $CaCO_3$

(3) $$\underset{136}{CaSO_4} + Na_2CO_3 \rightarrow \underset{100}{CaCO_3}\downarrow + Na_2SO_4$$

136 mg of $CaSO_4$ gives 100 mg of $CaCO_3$

$\therefore$ 4.08 mg of $CaSO_4$ gives $= \frac{4.08\times 100}{136} = \frac{408}{136} = 3$ mg of $CaCO_3$

(4) Turbidity 120 mg/L

(5) $$\underset{27}{\underset{\text{(From Alum)}}{Al^{3+}}} \xrightarrow{\text{hydrolysed}} \underset{78}{Al(OH)_3}\downarrow$$

$\therefore$ 100 mg of alum contains 7 mg of Al^{3+}

10 mg of alum contains $= \dfrac{7 \times 10}{100} = 0.7$ mg of Al^{3+}

(Since it is given that alum contains 7% Al and the alum dose used is 10 mg/l)

Now 27 mg of Al^{3+} (from alum) give 78 mg of Al $(OH)_3$ $= \dfrac{78 \times 0.7}{27} = 2.222$ mg of $Al(OH)_3$

$\therefore$ Dry sediment obtained from 1 litre of the water sample
= (1a+1b) + (2) + (3) + (4) + (5)
= (29 + 30.526 + 50 + 3 + 120 + 2.222) mg = 234.748 mg

$\therefore$ Total weight of dry sediment obtained from softening 20,000 litres of the water sample
= (234.748 × 20,000) mg = **4.69496 kg** **Ans.**

Problem 17

The hardness of 1000 litres of water sample was completely removed by the zeolite. The zeolite required 30 litres of NaCl solution containing 1,500 mg/l of NaCl for regeneration. Calculate the hardness of the water sample. **[RGPV 06]**

Solution

30 litres of NaCl Solution contains = 1.5 × 30g = 45g of NaCl

$= 45 \times \dfrac{50}{58.5}$ g of $CaCO_3$ equivalent hardness

This much hardness seemed to be present in 1000 litres of water sample

$\therefore$ Hardness of water sample $= 45 \times \dfrac{50}{58.5} \times \dfrac{1000}{1000}$ mg/l = **38.46 ppm** **Ans.**

Problem 18

0.5 g of $CaCO_3$ was dissolved in HCl and the solution was made upto 500 ml with distilled water. 50 ml of the solution required 48 ml of EDTA solution for titration. 50 ml of hard water sample required 15ml of EDTA and after boiling and filtering required 10 ml of EDTA solution. Calculate the hardness. **[RGPV 06]**

Solution

Given 500 ml of standard hard water contain 0.5g or 500 mg $CaCO_3$

$\therefore$ 1 ml of standard hard water contains 1 mg $CaCO_3$

Now 48 ml of EDTA solution= 50ml of SHW = 1 × 50 mg of $CaCO_3$ equivalent

$\therefore$ 1 ml of EDTA solution $= 1 \times \dfrac{50}{48}$ mg of $CaCO_3$ equivalent

(i) Calculation of Total hardness of water

50 ml of hard H_2O = 15 ml EDTA

$= 15 \times \dfrac{50}{48}$ mg of $CaCO_3$ equivalent = 15.625 mg of $CaCO_3$ equivalent

$\therefore$ 1000 ml of hard water $= \dfrac{15.625 \times 1000}{50} = 312.5$ mg/L of $CaCO_3$ equivalent

Total Hardness = **312.5 ppm**

(ii) Calculation of non-carbonate hardness

50 ml boiled HW = 10 ml EDTA solution $= \left(10 \times \dfrac{50}{48}\right)$ mg of $CaCO_3$ equivalent

$= 10.417$ mg of $CaCO_3$ equivalent

$\therefore$ 1000 ml boiled HW $= \dfrac{10.417 \times 1000}{50}$ mg of $CaCO_3$ equivalent = 208.3 mg of $CaCO_3$ equivalent

$\therefore$ Non-Carbonate hardness = 208.3 mg/L = **208.3 ppm**

Hence Carbonate Hardness = (312.5 – 208.3) = **104.2 ppm Ans.**

Problem 19

One gm of $CaCO_3$ was dissolved in dilute HCl and the solution was made to one liter by dilution. 50 ml of the sample water required 25 ml of EDTA solution. Calculate total hardness of water sample.

[RGPV 07]

Solution

I) 1 gm $CaCO_3$ dissolved in 1 lit. of water

1 ml SHW	=	1 mg $CaCO_3$
II) 50 ml HW requied	=	25 ml EDTA =25 mg $CaCO_3$
50 ml HW	=	25 mg $CaCO_3$
1 ml HW	=	25/50 mg $CaCO_3$
1000 ml HW	=	25/50×1000 mg $CaCO_3$ =500 mg $CaCO_3$
Hardness	=	**500 ppm Ans.**

Problem 20

100 ml of a water sample required 20 ml of N/50 H_2SO_4 for neutralization to phenolphthalein end point. After this, methyl orange indicator was added to this and further acid required was 15 ml. Calculate the type and the extent of alkalinity.

[RGPV 07]

Solution

100 ml of water up to phenolphthalein end point = 20 ml of N/50 H_2SO_4

100 ml × Np = 20 ml × (N/50)

or Normality, Np =20 ml /100 ml ×N/50 = N/250 = 0.004N

Strength of alkalinity up to phenolphthalein end – point in terms of $CaCO_3$ eq.

P = 0.004 × (50g/l) = 0.2g/l = 200 mg/l = 200 ppm

Now, 100 ml of water up to methyl orange end point =20 ml+15 ml=35 mlof N/50 H_2SO_4

100 ml × Nm = 35 ml × (N/50)

Or Normality, Nm =35ml/100 ml× N/50=0.007N

Strength of total alkalinity in terms of $CaCO_3$ eq.

M =0.007× (50 mg/l) = 0.35 g/l = 350 mg/l = 350 ppm

Now, P = 200 ppm, M= 350 ppm

P>1/2 M

So, alkalinity is due to OH^- and CO_3^{2-} ions

Alkalinity due to CO_3^{2-} ions = 2(M–P) = 2(350 – 200) = 300 ppm

Total alkalinity = (50 + 300) ppm =**350 ppm Ans.**

Problem 21

25 ml of 0.1N Sodium Carbonate solution was added to 100 ml of a sample of hard water. The filtrate from the above required 30 ml of 0.05 N sulphuric acid for complete neutralization. Calculate the hardness of the water sample.

[RGPV 08]

Solution

Normality of Na_2CO_3 = N/10

Volume of hard water = 100ml

Volume of Na_2CO_3 neutralized by 30 ml of N/20 H_2SO_4 is calculated as

$N_1 V_1 = N_2 V_2$

$N/10 \times V_1 = N/20 \times 30$

$V_1 = 15$ ml

Therefore, effective volume of Na_2CO_3 used = 25ml–15ml = 10ml

Applying Normality equation:-

$N_1 V_1 = N_2 V_2$

$N_1 \times 100 = N/10 \times 10$

$N_1 = N/100$

Strength = N/100 × 50 × 1000mg/l

Therefore Hardness = **500 ppm Ans.**

Problem 22

0.292 g of a precipitate of calcium oxalate monohydrate was obtained from 200 ml water sample. Express the calcium content in ppm. **[RGPV 07]**

Solution

200 ml of water contains 0.292 gm calcium oxalate monohydrate

1000 ml of water contains 1.46 gm calcium oxalate monohydrate

Ca content in terms of ppm=1.46 ×100/146

=1ppm Ans.

Problem 23

100 ml of waste water containing (920 ppm dissolved oxygen) was diluted with 100 ml of distilled H_2O and kept in a bottle at 20°C for 5 days. The oxygen content of the resulting water was found to be 260 ppm. Calculate BOD of the sample. **[RGPV 06]**

Solution

BOD = [Original-final] dissolved O_2 content × Dilution factor

= [920-260] ppm × (200ml/ 100ml)

= **1320 ppm Ans.**

Problem 24

25 ml of sample of COD analysis was reacted with 15 ml of 0.25 N potassium dichromate solution and after the reaction, the unreacted dichromate required 18 ml of 0.1 N-FAS. 15 ml of the same $K_2Cr_2O_7$ solution and 25 ml of distilled water, under the same conditions as the sample, required 30 ml of 0.1 N ferrous ammonium sulphate. What is COD of sample?

Solution

Difference in volume of FAS required in the blank (distilled water) and the sample

= (30- 18) ml = 12 ml

Now 1000 ml of 1 N-FAS contains = 8 g of oxygen

Or 12 ml of 0.1 N-FAS contains = $\frac{8 \times 12 \times 0.1}{1000}$ g of oxygen

∴ 25 ml of H_2SO_4 sample consists of = $\frac{8 \times 12 \times 0.1}{1000}$ g of oxygen

Or 1000 ml of water sample consists of = $\frac{8 \times 12 \times 0.1 \times 1000}{1000 \times 25}$ of oxygen = 0.384 g of oxygen

= 384 mg of oxygen

Or Hence COD of sample = 384 mg/L = **384 ppm** **Ans.**

Unsolved Problems

1. Calculate the temporary and permanent hardness of water sample in different units having following analysis.

$Mg(HCO_3)_2$ – 73 mg/l $Ca(HCO_3)_2$ – 162 mg/l

$CaSO_4$ –136 mg/l $MgCl_2$ – 95 mg/l

$CaCl_2$ – 111 mg/l   NaCl – 100 mg/l

[**Ans. Temporary Hardness-150 mg/l, 15°F,10.5° Cl Permanent Hardness – 300 mg/l 30°F, 21°Cl**]

2. Water sample is not alkaline to phenolphthalein. However 100 ml of sample, on titration with N/50 HCl requires 16.9 ml of acid obtained the end point, using methyl orange as indicator. What are the types and amount of alkalinity present in the sample?

[**Ans. HCO_3^- type of alkalinity present=169 ppm**]

3. Water sample is alkaline to both phenolphthalein and methyl orange. 100 ml of water sample on titration requires 4.7 ml acid with N/50 HCl to phenolphthalein end point, then a few drops of methyl orange are added to same solution and the titration further continues, the yellow colour of the solution just turned red after addition of another 10.5 ml of acid solution. Elucidate type of alkalinity present.

[**Ans. CO_3^{2-} Alkalinity-94ppm, HCO_3^- Alkalinity - 58ppm Total Alkalinity – 152 ppm; Permanent Hardness – 300 mg/l 30°F, 21°Cl**]

4. Calculate the amount of lime required for softening 50,000 litres of hard water containing $CaCO_3$ = 25 ppm, $MgCO_3$ = 144 ppm, $CaCl_2$ = 111 ppm, $MgCl_2$=95 ppm, Na_2SO_4=15 ppm, Fe_2O_3=25 ppm

[**Ans.Lime=17.311 kg.**]

5. Calculate the lime and soda required to soften 10,000 litres of hard water having the following analysis Ca^{2+} - 250 ppm as $CaCO_3$; Mg^{2-} 100 ppm as $CaCO_3$ and HCO_3^--300 ppm as $CaCO_3$.

[**Ans. Lime-2.59 kg. Soda-0.53kg.**]

6. 5 g $CaCO_3$ was dissolved in HCl and the solution made upto 1 litre with distlled water. 50 ml of the solution required 98 ml of EDTA solution for titration. 50 ml of hard water sample required 30 ml of EDTA and after boiling and filtering required 15 ml of EDTA solution. Calculate the hardness.

[**Ans. Total Hardnes-1530.6 ppm Permanent Hardness-170 ppm Temporary Hardness- 780.6 ppm**]

7. What is the BOD of water containing 1.0 g of benzene per 10^6 litres? The reaction of benzene with oxygen is

$$C_6H_6(I) + 7.5O_2(aa) \rightarrow 6\ CO_2(aa) + 3\ H_2O$$

[**Ans. 3.02 mg/l**]

8. Calculate the COD of the effluent sample when 50 ml of an effluent required 16.6 ml of .001 M $K_2Cr_2O_7$ for oxidation [Given molecular mass of $K_2Cr_2O_7$=294].

[**Ans. 0.0159 ppm**]

9. The BOD of water in a certain river water is 6.2 mg/litre. Before reaction, the concentration of O_2 in the river is 8.9×10^{-3}g/litre. What is the concentration of O_2 in water when equilibrium is reached with the BOD?

[**Ans. 2.7×10^{-3}g/lit**]

10. Water sample is alkaline to both phenolphthalein as well as methyl orange. 200 ml of water sample on titration with N/50 HCl required 9.4 ml. of the acid to phenolphthalein end point. When a few drops of methyl orange are added to the same solution and the titration further continued, the yellow colour of the solution just turned red after addition of another 21 ml. of the acid solution. Elucidate on the type and extent of alkalinity present in the water in ppm

[Ans. CO_3^{2-} Alkalinity-94ppm, HCO_3 Alkalinity - 58ppm, Total Alkalinity – 152 ppm; Permanent Hardness – 300 mg/l 30°F, 21°Cl]

11. The hardness of 10000 litres of sample of water was completely removed by zeolite softener. The zeolite softener required 60 lit. of NaCl solution containing 1.5 kg/litre of NaCl for regeneration. Calculate the hardness of sample of water. **[Ans: 7.69 g/l]**

12. 100 ml of a water sample required 5ml of N/10 acid solution for titration while using phenolphthalein as indicator. 100 ml of the sample of water was again titrated and methyl orange was used as indicator. When 15 ml of the same acid solution was required for neutralization determine the type and extent of alkalinity. **[Ans: Total alklinity 750 ppm CO^{2-}_3 = 500 ppm, HCO^-_3=250ppm]**

[RGPV 09]

13. A sample of polluted water on analysis gives following result: **[RGPV 09]**

Suspended matter = 200 mg/l
$Mg(Cl_2)$ = 190 mg/l
$CaSO_4$ = 250 mg/l
H_2SO_4 = 98 mg/l
$MgSO_4$ = 240 mg/l
Organic matter = 750 mg/l

(i) Calculate total hardness of water.
(ii) Calculate amount of lime soda needed per liter for its treatment if purity of lime soda is 90% and that of soda is 98%. **[Ans: Total hardness = 583.82ppm, L=4.1 × 10^{-4} kg, S= 7.39 × 10^{-4}kg]**

14. Calculate the hardness of a water sample whose 20 ml required 30 ml EDTA. 10 ml of standard calcium chloride solution, whose strength is equivalent to 300 mg of $CaCO_3$ per 200 ml, required 20 ml of the same EDTA solution. **Ans: Hardness =1125mg/l** **[RGPV 09]**

15. Calculate the quantities of lime and soda required for softening 50,000 litres of water, containing the following salts per litre:

$Ca(HCO_3)_2$ = 8.1 mg; $Mg(HCO_3)_2$ = 7.5 mg
$CaSO_4$ = 13.6 mg. $MgSO_4$ = 12.0 mg.
$MgCl_2$ = 2.0 mg. **[Ans: L = 1.36 kg S = 1.17 Kg]**

16. How many grams of $MgCO_3$ dissolved per litre give 84 ppm of hardness? **[Ans 0.7056 gms]**

17. Calculate the lime and soda needed for softening 100000 litres of water containing the following: $MgSO_4$: 12.00 mg/lit, $Mg(HCO_3)_2$: 14.6 mg/lit. , $CaCl_2$: 22.2 mg/lit.and NaCl: 5.85 mg/lit.

[Ans: L=2.48 Kg.,S = 3.18 Kg.]

18. One gram of $CaCO_3$ was dissolved in HCl and the solution diluted to one litre. 100 ml. of this solution required 90 ml. of EDTA solution, while 100 ml. of the sample water required 40 ml. of EDTA. On the other hand, 100 ml. of the boiled water sample when titrated against EDTA consumed 20 ml. of solution. Calculation total permanent and temporary hardness of water sample in ppm.

[RGPV 10]

Ans. Total Hardness =440 mg/l, Temperory Hardness = 220 mg/l, Permanent Hardness=220 mg/l

19. A water sample is alkaline to both phenolphthalein as well as methyl orange. 100 ml. of the water sample on titration with N/ 50 HCl required 4.5 ml. of the acid to phenolphthalein end point. When a few drops of methyl orange are added to the same solution and titration further continued, the yellow colour of the solution just turned faint pink after addition of another 10.7 ml. of the acid solution. Elucidate on the type and extent of alkalinity present in the water sample. **[RGPV 10]**

Ans: Alkalinity due to CO_3= 90 ppm, HCO_3= 62 ppm

THEORETICAL QUESTIONS

1. Write short notes on: **[RGPV 01]**
   a. Complexometric titration b. Applications of coagulation in water purification.
   c. Phosphate conditioning of boiler feed water.
2. What are the various sources of water? What is the quality of water obtained from each of these sources? **[RGPV 01]**
3. What do you mean by soft and hard water? What are the causes of hardness of water? **[RGPV 01]**
4. What are the various units of measuring hardness? Give inter relationship between various units for hardness. Or **[RGPV 01,07]**
   Define hardness of water. What are its units? **[RGPV 02,06]**
5. Give chemical reaction involved in lime-soda process of softening hardware. **[RGPV 02,09]**
6. Discuss chemistry involved in zeolites process of softening hardware. **[RGPV 01, 04]**
7. Discuss about zeolites and their use for water softening. **[RGPV 03]**
8. How is water deionised by ion exchange process? **[MITS 03]**
9. What are natural and synthetic zeolites? Give chemical reaction involved in zeolite process of softening hard water. **[RGPV 2002, 2003]**
10. Write formulae and name of substances which impart temporary and permanent hardness of water. Give chemical reaction involved in softening hard water of lime soda process. **[RGPV 02, 03]**
11. What is calgon? How permanent hardness can be removed by calgon process? Give its reactions. **[RGPV 01,07,09]**
12. Discuss the phenomenon of corrosion in a boiler. **[RGPV 01]**
13. Explain the phosphate and carbonate conditioning of boiler feed water. Why carbonate conditioning is not used for high pressure boilers? **[RGPV 03,07]**
14. Discuss briefly the chemical reactions and methods used for the analysis of any two of the following parameters in water.
   1. Hardness 2. Dissolved Oxygen 3. Chlorides **[RGPV 03,07]**
15. How does the formation of sludge and scale affect boiler performance? **[RGPV 05,08,09]**
16. What is meant by 'Phosphate Conditioning of water'? **[RGPV 05,08]**
17. What is boiler corrosion? **[RGPV 06]**
18. What are the disadvantages of scale formation in the boiler? **[RGPV 06,09]**
19. At what stage and for which purpose hydrazine is added to high pressure boiler water? **[RGPV 01]**
20. What is Scale? How is it formed? **[RGPV 01, 02]**
21. Describe Scale and Sludge formation in boiler and its prevention. **[RGPV 02,07,09]**
22. How is water sterilized by chlorine? **[MITS 2005]**
23. Name the three substances used for sterilization of water. **[RGPV 2002]**
24. Explain the function of bleaching powder in water treatment. **[RGPV 01,08]**
25. Write a short note on applications of coagulant in the water. **[RGPV 01, 02,08]**
26. Describe with the help of a neat labeled diagram Ion-exchange process for purification of water. **[RGPV 05,09]**
27. Write short notes on

(a) Carry Over (b) Lime-soda process (Chemical reaction only) **[RGPV 04]**

28. Write a short note on the following –
 1. Internal conditioning of boiler feed water. **[RGPV 02,07, Guru Ghasidas 2003]**
 2. Ion exchange resins and their uses. **[RGPV 02]**
29. What is break point chlorination and its advantage. **[RGPV 2000, 02, 03,07]**
30. Write internal conditioning of boiler feed water? **[RGPV 03]**
31. Calculate hardness of water by using EDTA.
 In the determination of hardness of water by EDTA method, why NH_4OH-NH_4Cl buffer is used? **[RGPV 01]**
32. Write short note on complexometric titration. **[RGPV 01]**
33. Give chemical reaction involved in EDTA complexometric method of determining hardness of water. **[RGPV 04, 05]**
34. Explain the terms BOD and COD. **[RGPV 01,07]**
35. How can you determine the alkalinity of water sample containing hydroxide and carbonate ions? **[RGPV 02]**
36. Describe the significance and determination of Biological oxygen demand. **[RGPV 06,07]**
37. Discuss briefly the method used for the analysis of residual chlorine. **[RGPV 04]**
38. Explain Scale and Sludge Formation. Write disadvantages of Scale and Sludge Formation. **[RGPV 08,09]**
39. Compare Zeolite method and Ion exchange resin method of water softening. **[RGPV 08,09]**
40. Explain the function of the following in water treatment:
 i) Hydrazine ii) Hypo **[RGPV 08]**
41. Explain why:
 i) Hard water consumes a lot of soap.
 ii) Magnesium bicarbonate require double amount of lime for softening. **[RGPV 08]**
42. Name the various methods used for softening of water. Explain with various equations, which is the best method and why? **[RGPV 07]**
43. Give the reason of the following:
 i.) In the deionization process, water is usually passed through the cation exchanger and then through the anion exchanger.
 ii.) Alkalinity of water can't be due to the simulation presence of OH^-, CO_3^{--} and HCO_3^- ions. **[RGPV 07]**
44. Explain disinfection of the water. Suggest various methods and chemicals used for disinfection of water. **[RGPV 07]**
45. Explain the following terms:
 i) Blow down operation ii) Carry over **[RGPV 07]**
46. Write an informatory note on caustic embrittlement. **[RGPV 09]**
47. Discuss the demineralization of hard water by giving appropriate equations and diagram. **[RGPV 09]**
48. What are boiler scales? Write the formation and till effects of scales in boilers. How can scale formation be prevented by (i) Phosphate conditioning (ii) Calgon conditioning? **[RGPV 10]**
49. What are zeolites? How softening of hard water is carried out by zeolite process? Also write advantages and disadvantages of the process. **[RGPV 10]**

.......✱.......

Unit - II

Fuels and Combustion

2.1 INTRODUCTION

Fuel is any material which is capable of releasing energy when its chemical or physical structure is altered. Fuel releases its energy either through chemical means, such as combustion, or nuclear means such as nuclear fission or nuclear fusion. An important property of a useful fuel is that its energy can be stored to be released only when needed and that the release is controlled in such a way that the energy can be harnessed to produce work.

All carbon-based life forms—from microorganisms to animals and humans—depend upon fuels and everyone uses fuels as source of energy. Cells engage in an enzyme-mediated chemical process called metabolism that converts energy from food or solar power into a form that can be used to sustain life. Additionally, humans employ a variety of techniques to convert one form of energy into another, producing useful energy for purposes that go far beyond the energy needs of a human body.

Any source of heat energy is called as fuel-the term fuel includes all combustible substances that combine with oxygen of the atmosphere with the evolution of large amount of heat capable of being economically applied to domestic and industrial purposes. In short, fuel may be defined as any substance, which by oxidation, is made a source of heat energy for practical purpose. According to modern definition, a fuel is any fissionable material, chemical or reactant which produces energy in a form that can be used for producing power.

Fossil fuels are hydrocarbons, primarily coal and petroleum (fuel oil or natural gas), formed from the fossilized remains of dead plants and animals by exposure to heat and pressure in the Earth's crust over hundreds of millions of years. The theory that hydrocarbons were formed from these remains was first introduced by Mikhail Lomonosov in 1757. The term "fossil fuel" also includes hydrocarbons-containing natural resources that are not derived entirely from biological sources, such as tar sands. These later sources are properly known as mineral fuels.

Modern large-scale industrial development is based on fossil fuel use which has largely supplanted water-driven mills, as well as the combustion of wood or peat for heat. With global modernization in the 20th and 21st centuries, the growth in energy production from fossil fuels, especially gasoline derived from oil, is one of the causes of major regional and global conflicts and environmental issues. A global movement toward the generation of renewable energy is therefore under way to help us to meet the increased global energy needs.

Characteristics of a good fuel:

- **High calorific value:** A good fuel must have high calorific value since the amount of heat librated and temperature attained thereby depends upon the calorific value of fuel.
- **Low moisture content:** The moisture content should be low because it hinders the combustion process and reduces efficiency.
- **Moderated ignition temperature:** Ignition temperature is the lowest temperature to which the fuel must be preheated so that it starts burning smoothly. It should neither be too high nor to low.
- **Size of fuel:** For regular combustion of a solid fuel the size should be uniform.
- **High calorific intensity:** The calorific intensity of fuel should be high enough to melt the metal.

- **Low non combustible matter content:** Combustion of fuels provides non – combustible matter content which reduces the heating value and heat loss also occurs. So a good fuel should have low non- combustible matter content.
- **Efficiency:** Fuels on burning should not pollute the environment with any toxic gases as combustion products.
- **Low storage cost:** Storage cost in bulk should be low.
- **Low cost:** A fuel should be readily available in bulk at a low cost value.
- **Easy to transport:** The solid and liquid fuels can be easily transported from one place to another but the transportation of gaseous fuels is typical and costly and can even cause fire hazards. Therefore, a fuel should be easily transportable.

2.2 CLASSIFICATION OF FUELS

On the basis of their occurrence, fuels may be divided into:

1. Primary or Naturally Occurring Fuels.
2. Secondary or Artificial Fuels derived from primary Fuels.

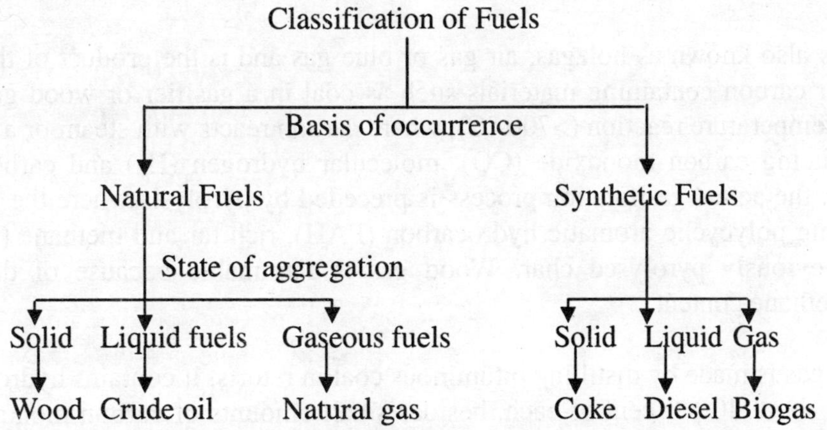

Fig. 2.1: Classification of Fuels

On the basis of state of aggregation, fuels are classified as follows:

Solid Fuels: They refer to various types of solid material that are used as fuel to produce energy and provide heating, usually released through combustion. Common solid fuels include wood, charcoal, peat, coal and pellets made from wood, corn, wheat, rye and other grains. Solid-fuel rocket technology also uses solid fuel. Solid fuels have long been used by humanity to create fire. Coal was the fuel source which enabled the industrial revolution, from firing furnaces to running steam engines. Wood was also extensively used to run steam locomotives. Both peat and coal are still used in electricity generation today.

Liquid Fuels: Liquid fuels are those combustible or energy-generating molecules that can be harnessed to create mechanical energy, usually producing kinetic energy, they also take the shape of container. Most liquid fuels, in widespread use, are derived from fossil fuels; however, there are several types, such as hydrogen fuel (for automotive uses), which are also categorized as liquid fuel. Fossil fuels which are also liquid fuels, come from dead animals and plants.

Gaseous Fuels: Gaseous fuels are the most convenient fuels. They require the least amount of handling and maintenance cost. Gas is delivered "on tap" via a distribution network and so is suited to a high population or industrial density. It is of following types.

Natural Gas: It is colorless and odorless in its pure form. Natural gas is combustible and when burnt, it gives off a great amount of energy. Unlike other fossil fuels, natural gas is clean burning and emits lower levels of potentially harmful air pollutants. Natural gas is a combustible mixture of hydrocarbon gases. While natural gas consists primarily of methane, it also includes ethane, propane, butane and pentane.

Water Gas: It is a method of hydrogen production that combines steam and coke gas in the following chemical reaction:

$$C + 2H_2O \rightarrow CO_2 + 2H_2$$

Water gas is more efficient heating fuel. The process was discovered by passing high pressure steam over hot coal, the major source of coke gas. Water Gas is a mixture of carbon monoxide and hydrogen obtained by passing steam over red-hot coke:

$$C + H_2O \rightarrow CO + H_2$$

The reaction is endothermic so the coke must be continually re-heated to keep the reaction going. This was usually done by alternating the steam stream with an air stream.

Wood Gas: It is also known as holzgas, air gas or blue gas and is the product of thermal gasification of biomass or other carbon containing materials such as coal in a gasifier or wood gas generator. It is the result of a high temperature reaction (>700 °C), where carbon reacts with steam or a limited amount of air or oxygen producing carbon monoxide (CO), molecular hydrogen (H_2) and carbon dioxide (CO_2). In several gasifiers, the actual gasification process is preceded by pyrolysis where the biomass or coal turns into char releasing polycyclic aromatic hydrocarbon (PAH), rich tar and methane (CH_4). Other gasifiers are fed with previously pyrolysed char. Wood gas is flammable because of the carbon monoxide, hydrogen and methane content.

Coal Gas: Coal gas is made by distilling bituminous coal in retorts. It contains hydrogen and marsh gas in large quantities, about 40 per cent of each, besides small amounts of carbon monoxide, carbon dioxide, nitrogen, oxygen and hydrocarbons of the C_nH_{2n} and C_nH_{2n-2} series, which impart illuminating properties. It has a limited use in domestic stoves and as a source of power in gas engines.

Table 2.1: Comparison of Fuel

S. No.	Property	Solid Fuel	Liquid	Gaseous
1.	Calorific value	Low	Higher	Highest
2.	Specific gravity	Highest	Medium	Lowest
3.	Ignition point	High	Low	Lowest
4.	Efficiency (thermal)	Poor	Good	Better than liquid fuel
5.(a)	Air required for Combustion	Large and excess of air	Less excess of air	Slight excess of air
(b)	Combustion rate	Slow process	Quick	Very rapid and efficient
(c)	Combustion control	Not easy	Controllable	Under control
6.	Risk of fire hazards	Least	Greater	Very high
7.	Use in I.C engine	Can not be used	Already in use	Can be used

8.	Mode of supply	Can not be piped	Can be piped	Can be piped
9.	Relative cost	Cheaper	Costly	Costly More costly than solid &liquid fuel
10.(a) (b) (c)	Special storage Storage Care in storage and transport	Large Easy Less care required	Less than liquid fuel Close container Care is necessary	Very high space Leak proof storage tanks and great care. Great care required
11.	Smoke	Depends upon quality of fuel	Generally smoke contains high carbon content & aromatic compound	No smoke production
12.	Ash	Production of ash depends on quality of fuel	No production of ash	No production of ash

2.3 CALORIFIC VALUE

The heating value or calorific value of a substance, usually a fuel or food, is the amount of heat released during the combustion of a specified amount of it. The calorific value is characteristic for each substance. It is measured in units of energy per unit of the substance, usually mass, such as: kcal/kg, kJ/kg, J/mol, Btu/m³. Heating value is commonly determined by use of a bomb calorimeter.

Gross and Net Calorific value

The heat of combustion of a fuel or the heat of reaction is the energy liberated in a chemical reaction when 1.0 g of the fuel is completely burnt into products and cooled to the initial temperature or it is defined as the total quantity of heat liberated when a unit mass of fuel is burnt completely in the presence of oxygen. The quantity known as higher heating value (or gross calorific value or gross energy) is determined by bringing all the products of combustion back to the original pre-combustion temperature and in particular condensing any vapour produced. The quantity known as lower heating value (or net calorific value) is determined by subtracting the heat of vaporization of the water produced by combustion from the higher heating value.

Units of heat: The units of heat generally employed are calories, kilogram calories, british thermal units and centigrade heat units.

(a) Calorie (cal) or gram calorie (g cal): For all practical purposes, the calorie or gram calorie may be defined as the amount of heat required to raise the temperature of 1 g of water through 1°C (more precisely from 15°C to 16°C).

$$1 \text{ calorie} = 4.185 \text{ Joules} = 4.185 \times 10^7 \text{ ergs.}$$

(b) Kilocalorie or kilogram calorie or kilogram centigrade unit (kcal or kg cal or K.C.U.): This is equal to 1000 calories and is thus, the amount of heat required to raise the temperature of 1 kg of water though 1°C (more precisely from 15°C to 16°C).

$$1 \text{ k cal} = 1000 \text{ cal}$$

(c) British thermal unit (B. Th. U. or B.T.U.): A British thermal unit is the amount of heat required to raise the temperature of 1 pound of water through 1°F (more precisely from 60°F to 61°F).

$$1 \text{ B. Th. U.} = 1{,}054.6 \text{ Joules} = 1{,}054.6 \times 10^7 \text{ ergs.}$$

(d) Centigrade heat unit (C.H.U.): The centigrade heat unit is the amount of heat required to raise the temperature of 1 pound of water through 1°C.

Interconversion of the various units of heat

The various heat units described above can be easily interconverted on the basis that 1 kg = 2.2 lb and 1°C=1.8°F. Accordingly,

1 k cal = 1000 cals = 3.968 B.Th.U. = 2.2 C.H.U.
1 B. Th. U. = 252 cals
100, 000 B.Th. U. = 1 Therm.

Units of Calorific Value: Calorific values of solid and liquid fuels are usually expressed in Calories per gram (cals/g) or Kilocalories per kilogram (kcals/kg) or British Thermal Units per pound (B.Th.U./Ib), whereas the calorific values of gases are expressed as Kilocalories per cubic metre (kcals/m^3) or British thermal units per cubic foot (B.Th.U./ft^3) or C.H.U./Ib or C.H.U./ft^3.

These units can be inter-converted as follows:
1 cal/g = 1 kcal/kg = 1.8 B.Th.U./Ib
1 kcal/m^3 = 0.1077 B.Th.U./ft^3
1 B. Th.U./ft^3 = 9.3 kcals/m^3

Determination of Calorific Value: Standard methods for measuring heating or calorific value are defined by the American Society for Testing and Materials, (ASTM). The heating value determined by bomb calorimeter is the higher heating value at constant pressure for liquid and solid fuels, it is more convenient to burn the fuel with oxygen under pressure at constant volume.

2.4 BOMB CALORIMETER

This instrument consists of the bomb, the container of water in which the bomb is placed and a surrounding compartment of temperature controlled water. The bomb is a small cylindrical pressure vessel with a tight fitting head clamped on the external face of the bomb by a screw cap, a port for a pressure relief valve and two ports for the two electrodes. The material (X gms) to be combusted is put in a metal cup that is suspended in the bomb by two supports which are also part of the electrical circuit containing the fuse wire. The fuse wire spans across the top of the metal cup and when current is passed through the fuse wire, it heats up rapidly and ignites the fuel.

The bomb is placed in a container with a known amount of water (W), together with an agitator and thermometer. The agitator is used to maintain a uniform temperature in the water and to aid heat transfer from the bomb. The thermometer measures the water temperature (T_1, its range is 24 to 30°C with 0.01°C precision). Between the container of water and the surrounding compartment of water (w), there is an air gap, which is an excellent heat insulator. When the calorimeter is running, the temperature of the calorimeter body is automatically maintained at the same temperature as the container of water holding the bomb (T_2). This provides an adiabatic condition and thus no heat transfers to or from the container of water, except from the heat released in the bomb.

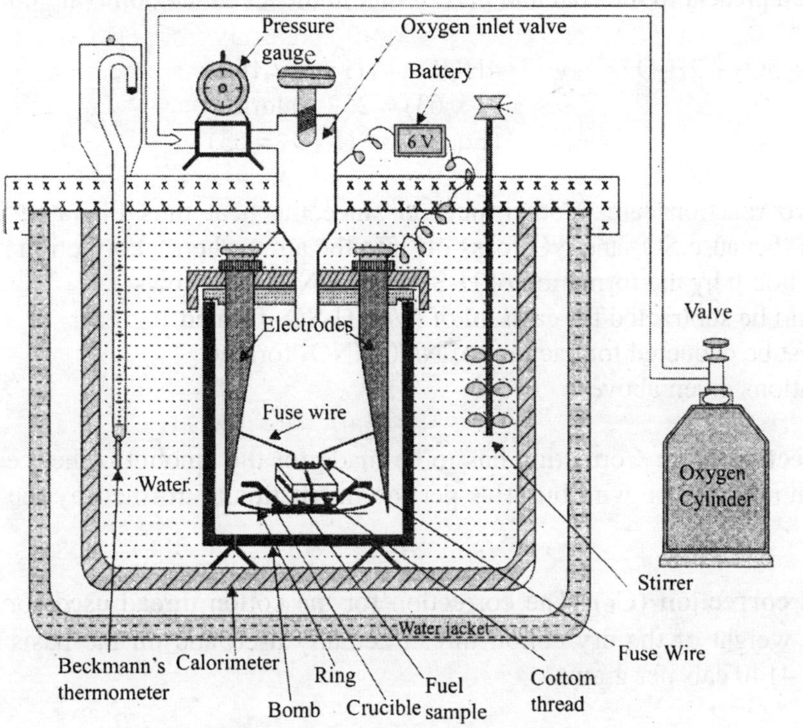

Figure 2.2: Bomb Calorimeter

Calculation: The calorific value of a fuel may be calculated by the following equation:

$$HCV = \frac{(W + w)(T_2 - T_1)}{X} cal/gm$$

where HCV = Higher calorific value of a fuel; W = Mass of water in calorimeter; w = Water equivalent of calorimeter; T_1 = Initial temperature of water in calorimeter; T_2 =Final temperature of water in calorimeter and X = Mass of fuel sample taken.

Thus, LCV = (HCV – 0.09H ×587) cal/gm

$$\text{HCV} = (W + w)\frac{(T_2 - T_1 + T_c) - (C_S + C_N + C_F + C_C)}{X}$$

where, T_C = Cooling Correction; C_S = Correction for H_2SO_4; C_N = Correction for HNO_3; C_F = Corrections for fuse wire and C_c = Corrections for cotton thread. The accurate value of calorific value can only be determined by applying a number of corrections such as acid correction, cooling correction, fuse wire correction, thread correction etc. otherwise inaccurate results are obtained by bomb calorimeter method.

Calculation of net calorific value: Net C.V. = Gross C.V. – Latent heat of water vapour formed during the combustion of X grams of the fuel

$$\text{NCV} = \text{GCV} - 0.09 \times H \times 587$$

where H is the percentage of hydrogen present in the fuel and latent heat of steam is 587cals/g.

Corrections

(i) Acids correction (C_S and C_N): The sulphur present in the coal is converted into H_2SO_4 in the bomb

$$S + O_2 \rightarrow SO_2$$

$$2SO_2 + O_2 + 2H_2O \rightarrow 2H_2SO_4;\ \Delta H = -144{,}000$$

3(4 × 49) = 39 calories

(Eq. wt. of H_2SO_4 = 49)

Similarly the nitrogen present in the coal and part of that in the air in the bomb are converted into HNO_3.

$$2N_2 + 5O_2 + 2H_2O \rightarrow 4HNO_3;\ \Delta H = -57{,}160$$

(4 x 63) = 252 calories

(Eq. Wt. of HNO_3 = 63)

Since the above two reactions are exothermic and since the heat thus liberated is not obtainable in practical use of coal (because SO_2 and NO_2 pass off into the atmosphere), correction must be made for the heat liberated in the bomb by the formation of H_2SO_4 and HNO_3 as follows:

(a) 3.6 calories should be subtracted for each ml of N/10 H_2SO_4 formed.

(b) 1.43 calories must be deducted for each ml of N/10 HNO_3 formed

(as per the equations given above)

(ii) Fuse wire correction (C_F): Correction has to be made for the amount of heat equivalent in calories derived from the amount of fuse wire burnt as per the instructions furnished by the supplier of the fuse wire.

(iii) Cotton thread correction (C_C): The correction for the cotton thread used for firing the charge is calculated from the weight of the dry cotton thread actually used and on the basis of that the calorific value of cellulose is 4140 cals per gram.

(iv) Cooling correction (T_c): If the time taken for the water in the calorimeter to cool from the maximum temperature attained to the room temperature is x minutes and the rate of cooling is dt°/minute, then the cooling correction = x. dt This should be added to the observed rise in temperature.

Theoretical Calculations of Calorific Value: Calorific value of a fuel is theoretically calculated by Dulong's formula. When a fuel is burnt, generally the fixed hydrogen is not available for combustion. The oxygen, if present in the fuel, is assumed to be present in combined form with hydrogen i.e. in the form of fixed hydrogen (H_2O).

$$\text{Since } Fixed\ hydrogen = \frac{Mass\ of\ Oxygen\ in\ the\ fuel}{8}$$

∴ The amount of hydrogen available for combustion = Total mass of hydrogen – Fixed Oxygen in fuel

$$= H - \frac{O}{8}$$

According to Dulong's formula,

$$HCV = \frac{1}{100}\left[\begin{matrix} Calorific\ value \\ of\ carbon \end{matrix} + \begin{matrix} Calorific\ Value\ of \\ available\ hydrogen \end{matrix} + \begin{matrix} Calorific\ value \\ of\ sulphur \end{matrix}\right]$$

$$HCV = \frac{1}{100}\left[8080C + 34500\left[H - \frac{O}{8}\right] + 2240S\right] kcal/kg$$

where C, H, O and S are percentages of carbon, hydrogen, oxygen and sulphur in the fuel respectively

$$LCV = \left[HCV - \frac{9}{100}H\,x587\right] Kcal/kg = \left[HCV - 0.09H\,x587\right] kcal/kg$$

The I.A. Davies formula can be expressed as $A = (3.635H + 235.9)\left[\frac{C}{3} + H - \frac{1}{8}(O+S)\right]$

Here the terms have the same meaning as in the Dulong's formula. This expression is based on the assumption that the heat emitted by a fuel is proportional to the air required for combustion. The heating values of gaseous and liquid fuels (which are easily vaporized) are experimentally determined by using Boy's gas calorimeter and Junker's gas calorimeter.

The main use of all these formulae is that they provide a means for calculating the calorific values of coals approximately when their compositions are known but of which the samples are not available.

2.5 COAL

Coal is a fossil fuel formed in swamp ecosystems where plant remains were saved by water and mud from oxidization and biodegradation. Coal is a readily combustible black or brownish-black rock. It is a sedimentary rock, but the harder form is anthracite coal and can be regarded as metamorphic rocks because of exposure to elevated temperature and pressure. It is composed primarily of carbon along with other elements, including sulfur. It is the largest single source of fuel for the generation of electricity world-wide, as well as one of the largest sources of carbon dioxide emission which is considered as the primary cause of global warming. Coal is extracted from the ground by coal mining, either underground mining or open pit mining (surface mining).

The word "coal" is of Aryan origin and appears in many languages (German language Kohle, Swedish language kol, Hindi Language "Koyla"), also giving the name for element carbon in those languages—charcoal is wood rendered to carbon and carbonic compounds by pyrolysis. There are many ways of classifying coal according to its chemical and physical properties. The most accepted system is the one used by the American Society for Testing and Materials (ASTM) which classified coals by grade or rank according to the degree of metamorphism (change in form and structure under the inferences of heat, pressure and water). Ranging from the lowest state, lignite to the highest, anthracite (ASTM D 388), these classifications are briefly described below in a descending order.

Anthracite: This is the highest grade of coal. It contains a high content 86-98 mass percent, of fixed carbon (the carbon content in the elemental state) on a dry mineral matter free basis and a low content of volatile matter, less than 2 to 14 mass percent (chiefly methane CH_4). The moisture content of fresh-mined anthracite generally is less than 15 percent. The heat content of anthracite ranges from 22 to 28 million Btu/ton (26 to 33 MJ/kg) on a moist, mineral-matter-free basis.

Anthracite is a shiny black dense, hard, brittle coal that borders on graphite at the upper end of fixed carbon. It is slow burning and has a heating value just below the highest for bituminous coal. Its use in steam generators is largely confined to bringing on stokers and rarely in pulverized form. In India it is mostly found in Kashmir and Eastern Himalayas. The anthracite rank of coal is subdivided into three groups. In descending order of fixed- carbon percent, they are meta-anthracite, greater than 98 percent; anthracite, 92 to 98 percent and semi anthracite, 86 to 92 percent.

Bituminous coal: Bituminous coal is a broad and largest class of coals containing 46 to 86 mass percent of fixed cărbon and 20 to 40 percent of volatile matter-more complex content than that found in anthracite. It derives its name from bitumen, an asphalted residue obtained in the distillation of some fuels. Bituminous coals range in heating value from 11,000 to more than 14,000 Btu/lb_m (about 25,600 to 32,600 kJ/kg). Bituminous coals usually burns easily especially in first pulverized form.

The bituminous rank is subdivided into five groups: low-volatile, medium-volatile and high-volatile A, B and C; the lower is the volatility, the higher is the heating value. The low-volatility group is grayish black and granular in structure, while the high volatility groups are homogeneous or laminar.

Sub bituminous coal: This is a class of coal with generally lower heating values than bituminous coal, between 8300 to 11,500 Btu/lb (about 19,300 to 26,750 kJ/kg.). It is relatively high in inherent moisture content, as much as 15 to 30 percent but often low in sulfur content. It is brownish black or black and mostly homogeneous in structure. Sub bituminous coals are usually burnt in pulverized form. The sub bituminous rank is divided into three groups: A, B, and C.

Lignite: The lowest grade of coal, lignite derives its name from the Latin lignum, which means "wood." It is brown and laminar in structure and remnants of wood fiber are often visible in it. It originates mostly from resin-rich plants and contains therefore high inherent moisture, as high as 30 percent and volatile matter. Its heating value ranges between 6300 to 8300 Btu/lb (about 14,650 to 9,300 kJ/kg.). Because of the high moisture content and low heating value, lignite is not economical to transport over long distances and it is usually burnt by utilities at the mine site. The lignite rank is subdivided into two groups: A and B.

Peat: It is not an ASTM rank of coal. It is, however, considered the first geological step in coal's formation. Peat is a heterogeneous material consisting of decomposed plant matter and inorganic minerals. It contains upto 90 percent moisture. Although not attractive as a utility fuel, it is abundant in many parts of the world. Several states in the United States have large deposits. Because of its abundance, it is used in few countries (Ireland, Finland and the Russia) in some electric generating plants and in heating.

Table 2.2: Properties of different type of coal

Coal Type	Depth of burial	Maximum temperature during burial	Moisture Content	Fixed Carbon Content
Lignite	0.2-1.5km	25-45 ^{0}C	30-50%	20-35%
Sub bituminous	1.5-2.5km	45-75 ^{0}C	10-30%	35-45%
Bituminous	2.5-6km	75-180^0 C	5-10%	45-80%
Anthracite	>6km	>180 ^{0}C	<5%	80-96%

2.6 ANALYSIS OF COAL

Chemical composition of the coal is defined in terms of its proximate and ultimate (elemental) analyses. The parameters of proximate analysis are moisture, volatile matter, ash and fixed carbon. Elemental or ultimate analysis encompasses the quantitative determination of carbon, hydrogen, nitrogen, sulfur and oxygen within the coal.

(A) Proximate Analysis / Qualitative / Physical Analysis: The basic method for proximate analysis is given by American National Standard Institute (ANSI), American Society for Testing and Material (ASTM standard D3172). It determines the mass percentages of carbon. Proximate analysis gives information about the practical utility of coal.

(i) Moisture content
(ii) Volatile matter
(iii) Ash content
(iv) Fixed carbon

Determination of constituents of coal:

(i) **Moisture Content**: Moisture is an important property of coal, as all coals are mined wet. Groundwater and other extraneous moisture are known as adventitious moisture and are readily evaporated. Moisture held within the coal itself is known as inherent moisture and is analysed. Moisture may occur in four possible forms within coal:

- **Surface moisture**: water held on the surface of coal particles or macerals
- **Hydroscopic moisture**: water held by capillary action within the microfractures of the coal
- **Decomposition moisture**: water held within the coal's decomposed organic compounds
- **Mineral moisture**: water which comprises part of the crystal structure of hydrous silicates such as clays.

It is determined by taking known weight of air dried coal sample in an accurately weighted silica crucible. Heat in open electric oven at 110^0C for about 1 hr. Then cool into dessicetor and weigh accurately. Repeat the above procedure until the two constant weights are obtained. Loss in weight of coal is reported as moisture content on percentage basis.

$$\text{Percentage of moisture} = \frac{\text{Loss in weight} \times 100}{\text{Weight of coal sample taken}}$$

Significance: Moisture reduces the calorific value of the coal and also promotes corrosion in storage and handling equipments in the industry. For every percent of moisture present, 1% of heat is lost. Hence lesser is the moisture content, better is the quality of coal as a fuel. However 5-10% moisture is desirable for uniform fuel bed and less of fly ash formation.

(ii) **Volatile Matter:** Volatile matter in coal is that component of coal except for moisture, which is liberated at high temperature in the absence of air. This is usually a mixture of short and long chain hydrocarbons, aromatic hydrocarbons and some sulphur. It is determined by heating a known weight of moisture free coal sample in a covered platinum crucible at $950 \pm 20^0 C$ for 7 min. in muffle furnace. At this temperature, hydrocarbons and hydrogen are driven off. The crucible is then taken out and cooled in air, then kept in dessicator and weighed. The loss of weight is noted as volatile matter.

$$\text{Percentage od Volatile matter} = \frac{\text{Loss of weight due to removal of volatile matter}}{\text{Weight of coal sample taken}} \times 100$$

Significance: High volatile matter content requires larger combustion space. As the fuel burns, it may create the pressure, so coal with higher percentage of volatile matter can not be used in locomotive boiler, as it has limited space for the combustion. The high volatile matter content gives long flames, high smoke and relatively low heating values. High volatile content is desirable in coal gas manufacture.

(iii) **Ash Content**: Ash content of coal is the non-combustible residue left after coal is burnt. During the combustion of coal, an inorganic mineral substance present in coal gets converted into ash by chemical reaction. Ash usually consists of Silica, Alumina, Iron oxide and small quantity of Lime, Magnesia etc. It represents the bulk mineral matter after carbon, oxygen, sulphur and water (including from clays) have been driven off during combustion. Analysis is fairly straightforward, with the coal thoroughly burnt and the ash material expressed as a percentage of the original weight.

There are two types of ash

Extrinsic Ash: It consists of anhydrous $CaSO_4$, $CaCO_3$, Fe_2O_3 etc.

Intrinsic Ash: The mineral matter originally present in vegetable matter forms intrinsic ash. It consists of Na, K, Mg, Ca and Si (2 to 3%). The minerals responsible for the formation of intrinsic ash can not be removed by mechanical method.

Determination: It is determined by heating the residue left after the removal of volatile matter at $700 \pm 50^0 C$ for half an hour without covering with lid. Weigh the cooled mass.

$$\text{Percentage of Ash} = \frac{\text{Weight of the residue} \times 100}{\text{Weight of coal sample taken}}$$

Significance: Ash creates many problems. It reduces the heating value of coal and causes cleaning and disposal problem. It has been estimated that one percent rise in coal ash is equivalent to 0.3 to 4 percent decrease in boiler efficiency. The ash content is important when the metallurgical operation is carried out because it may affect the metal and slag composition. However some ash is desirable since it protects the grate from direct contact with the incandescent coal, which might cause oxidation of the grate bar. However, now-a-days, ash is finding its application in cement. Good quality cements are manufactured by adding ash other wise ash is useless material.

(iv) Fixed Carbon: The fixed carbon content of the coal is the carbon found in the material which is left after volatile materials are driven off. This differs from the ultimate carbon content of the coal because some carbon is lost in hydrocarbons with the volatiles. Fixed carbon is used as an estimate of the amount of coke that will be yielded from a sample of coal. Fixed carbon is determined by removing the mass of volatiles determined by the volatility test from the original mass of the coal sample.

$$\% \text{ C} = 100 - \% \text{ of (moisture + volatile matter + ash)}$$

From the above determination, it appears that what is left after the amount of moisture, volatile matter and ash formed are subtracted, is equal to the fixed carbon. But this fixed carbon term is misnomer because it contains other non volatile elements also along with carbon.

Significance: Fixed carbon is directly proportional to calorific value. The percentage of fixed carbon helps in designing the furnace and shape of the fire box.

(B) Ultimate Analysis / Quantitative Analysis / Chemical Analysis : A more scientific test than proximate analysis is ultimate analysis which gives the mass percentages of the chemical elements that constitute the coal. These include –Carbon (C), Hydrogen (H), Sulphur (S), Nitrogen (N) and Oxygen. The ultimate analysis is required to determine the percentage of various components to classify the coal to fix its price along with putting the coal to different uses depending upon its composition. The methods are described below:

(i) Carbon and Hydrogen: Carbon and hydrogen are determined by Duma's Method. About 1-2 gm of coal sample is heated in especially designed apparatus in either gas heating furnace or electrically heated furnace. C and H of coal get converted into CO_2 and H_2O respectively. The gaseous products are absorbed respectively in anhydrous Calcium chloride and Potassium hydroxide tubes of known weights. The increase in weights of these tubes is determined.

$$C + O_2 \rightarrow CO_2$$
$$12 \qquad\qquad 44$$

[12 parts by mass of C give 44 parts by mass of CO_2]

$$2KOH + CO_2 \rightarrow K_2CO_3 + H_2O$$

$$H_2 + 1/2O_2 \rightarrow H_2O$$
$$2 \qquad\qquad 18$$

[2 parts by mass of H give 18 parts by mass of H_2O]

$$7H_2O + CaCl_2 \rightarrow CaCl_2 \cdot 7H_2O$$

$$\%C = \frac{\text{Increase in weight of KOH tube} \times 12 \times 100}{\text{Weight of coal sample taken} \times 44}$$

$$\%H = \frac{\text{Increase in weight of CaCl}_2\text{ tube} \times 2 \times 100}{\text{Weight of coal sample taken} \times 18}$$

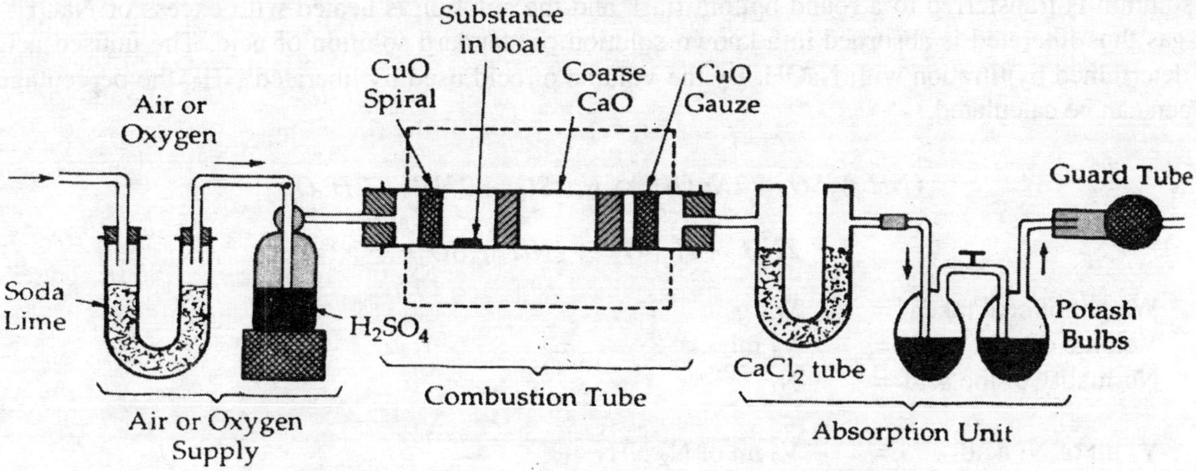

Fig. 2.3: Carbon and Hydrogen Determination

Significance: Carbon content is directly proportional to calorific value. Higher percentage of carbon also reduces the size of the combustion chamber. High percentage of hydrogen also increases the calorific value of coal. The content of hydrogen in coals varies from 4.5 to 6.5 percent from different types of coal. Hydrogen is responsible for the production of gaseous hydrogen, methane, carbonization of coal and gasification industries.

(ii) Nitrogen: It is determined by Kjeldahl's method. A known weight of coal sample is heated with concentrated H_2SO_4 along with K_2SO_4 and $HgSO_4$ which act as catalyst. Nitrogen present in coal gets converted into $(NH_4)_2SO_4$ quantitatively.

$$Nitrogen + H_2SO_4 \xrightarrow{\Delta} (NH_4)_2SO_4$$

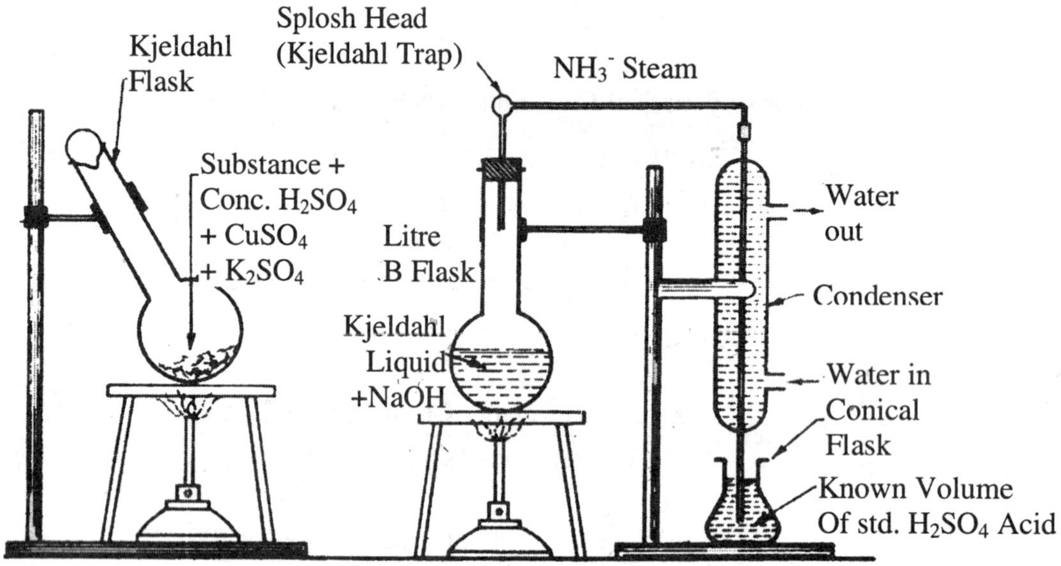

Fig. 2.4: Estimation of Nitrogen by Kjeldahl's Method

The solution is transferred to a round bottom flask and the solution is heated with excess of NaOH, the NH_3 gas thus liberated is absorbed in a known solution of standard solution of acid. The unused acid is then determined by titration with NaOH. By the volume of acid used by liberated NH_3, the percentage of nitrogen can be calculated.

$$(NH_4)_2SO_4 + 2NaOH \rightarrow Na_2SO_4 + 2NH_3 + 2H_2O$$

$$2NH_3 + H_2SO_4 \rightarrow (NH_4)_2SO_4$$

Let, Weight of coal taken = W_A g
Volume of acid used = V_1 ml
Normality of the acid = N_1

V_1 ml of N_1 acid = V_2 ml of N_2 NH_3

$\therefore V_2$ ml of 1N NH_3 = V_1 x N_1 ml of acid

But 1000ml of 1N Ammonia solution = 17g of NH_3 = 14g of Nitrogen

V_2 ml of 1 Normal ammonia solution $= \frac{14}{1000} \times N_1 \times V_1 g$ of Nitrogen

$$\therefore \text{Percentage of Nitrogen} = \frac{14}{1000} \times \frac{N_1 \times V_1 \times 100}{W} = \frac{1.4 \times N_1 \times V_1}{W}$$

Significance: It is an undesirable substance which is present in coal. It has no calorific value. It is useful in carbonization industries which recover a part of it as valuable bye product like NH_3, $(NH_4)_2SO_4$ and pyridine base.

(iii) Sulphur: It is determined by Eschka method. Known weight of coal sample is taken in platinum crucible and covered by 5 grams of Eschka mixture (2:1 mixture of porous calcinated magnesium oxide and anhydrous sodium carbonate) and heated to red hot until the mixture becomes brownish. Then transfer the cool mixture to 100 ml of boiling water and filter. Excess of barium chloride solution is added upto complete precipitation of sulphur as barium sulphate. The precipitate of $BaSO_4$ so obtained is filtered and heated to a constant weight from the weight of $BaSO_4$ obtained, the sulphur present in the coal is calculated by following formula:

$$\text{Percentage of sulphur} = \frac{\text{Weight of } BaSO_4 \times 32 \times 100}{233.3 \times \text{Weight of sample}}$$

where molecular wt of sulphur is 32 and molecular weight of $BaSO_4$ is 233.3.
Sulphur can also be determined by the washings obtained from the known mass of coal used in a bomb calorimeter for the determination of its calorific value. The washing contains sulphur in the form of sulphates from which it is precipitated as $BaSO_4$ by the addition of $BaCl_2$.

Significance: Sulphur contributes to the calorific value but it emits corrosive gases like SO_3, SO_2 and H_2S during carbonization of coal. These gases pollute the atmosphere and cause acid rain. The presence of sulphur in the coke used in iron industry affects the quality and properties of steel.

(iv) Ash: It is determined in the same way as in proximate analysis.

(v) Oxygen: The percentage of oxygen can be calculated by deducting the percentage of all the elements present in the coal from 100 by using following formula:

$$\% \text{ of Oxygen} = 100 - (\%C + \%H + \%N + \%S + \%\text{ash})$$

Significance: Oxygen present in coal decreases its calorific value. Better is the coal content, lesser is the percentage of oxygen. It combines with hydrogen and forms moisture, thus decreases the available hydrogen for combustion. The calorific value decreases by about 1.7% for every 1% increase in oxygen.

2.7 CARBONIZATION OF COAL

When the coal is heated strongly in absence of air, it loses volatile matter and is converted into white, lustrous, dense, strong, porous and coherent mass known as coke. The process of converting coal into coke is known as carbonization.

Caking and coking of coals: All types of coal can not be converted into coke. The coal having a tendency to soften, swell and stick together during combustion and to form solid coherent mass with porous structure is known as caking coke which can not be used in metallurgical process. If coke is hard, porous and strong than the coal from which it is formed, it is called coking coal, only bituminous coal can be coked.

Process of Carbonization

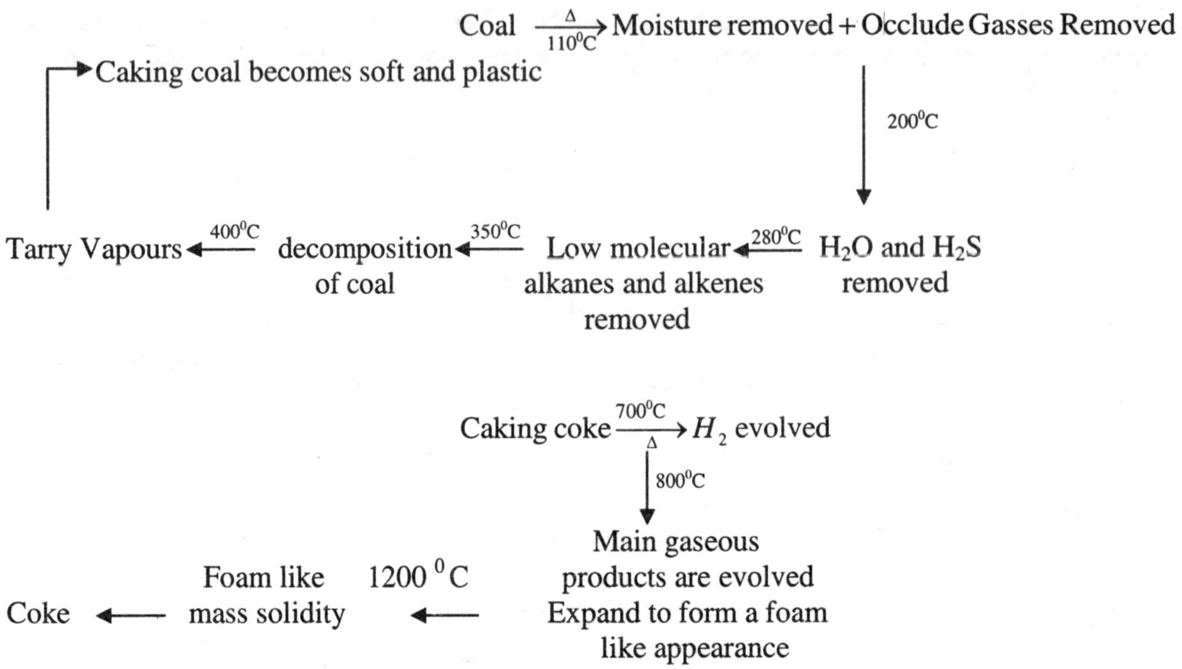

Types of Carbonization: The properties of coke produced mainly depend on the type of coal used, temperature of carbonization and the rate of carbonization. On the basis of temperature it is of two types:

1. Low Temperature Carbonization: In this process heating of coal is carried out at 500-700^{0}C. It is called low temperature carbonization. The coke obtained by this process is called soft coke or char. It contains 75-80% of carbon and 5-15% of volatile matter. The yield of gas is about 130-150 m^3/tonne. The tar obtained as bye product contains more of paraffins and small amount of aromatic hydrocarbons. There are two main commercial LTC plants in India - One is in Tamilnadu (Neyveli) and other is in Andhra Pradesh (Naspur).

2. High Temperature Carbonization: It is carried out at 900-1200^{0}C. It is used for the production of metallurgical coke. The yield of coke is 65 to 75% and the volatile matter is 1 to 3%. The bye product gas produced is about 370 to 480m^3/tonne. Its calorific value is less than LTC (5000-6000 K cal/m^3). This is used as an industrial as well as domestic fuel.

Merits:

1. The volatile matter is removed, so percentage of carbon is increased and thus calorific value.
2. Liquor ammonia is obtained as the bye product.
3. The coal gas produced during carbonization of fuel is used as gaseous fuel.
4. Carbonized coke can be used as domestic as well as industrial fuel.

Demerits:

1. Carbonization adds extra cost.
2. During carbonization gases are produced which create pollution.

Table 2.3: Comparison of the carbonization of coke at different temperatures

S.No	Characteristics	Lower temperature Carbonization	Higher temperature Carbonization
1	Carbonization temperature	500-700^{0}C	900-1200^{0}C
2	Percentage of coke produced	75-80%	65-70%
3	Volatile matter	5-15%	1-3%
4	Coal gas being produce mixture of CH_4, CO, NH_3	5-8%	17-20%
5	Calorific value of coal gas	6500-9500 Kcal/m^3	5400-6000 Kcal/m^3
6	Hardness of coke	Soft and smokeless	Hard and smoky
7	Percentage of straight chain hydrocarbon	Higher	Lower
8	Percentage of aromatic hydrocarbon	Lower	Higher
9	Use	Domestic Industrial	Industrial metallurgy

2.8 COKE

It is a solid carbonaceous residue derived from low-ash, low-sulfur bituminous coal from which the volatile constituents are driven off by baking in an oven at temperatures as high as 2,000° F (1,100° C) so that the fixed carbon and residual ash are fused together. Coke is used as a fuel and as a reducing agent in smelting iron ore in a blast furnace. Coke from coal is grey, hard and porous and has a heating value of 24.8 million Btu/ton (29 MJ/kg). Bye products of this conversion of coal to coke include coal-tar, ammonia, light oils and coal-gas. Coke can also be made from petroleum.

Metallurgical coke: It is also known as "Met" coke and is a carbon material manufactured by the destructive distillation of various blends of bituminous coal. Met coke has a very low volatile content. However, the "ash" constituents remain encapsulated in the resultant coke. Typical purities range from 88-92% fixed carbon. Metallurgical coke is used where a high quality, tough, resilient, wearing carbon is required. Applications include but are not limited to conductive flooring, friction materials, foundry coatings, and foundry carbon raiser, corrosion materials, drilling applications, reducing agents, heat-treatment, ceramic packing media, electrolytic processes and oxygen exclusion. Blast furnace coke is used in the blast furnaces of steel mills. It is the largest traded coke by volume and is produced in several countries with China being the largest producer and exporter.

Pet coke: It is a solid carbonization bye-product of high-boiling hydrocarbon fractions obtained in petroleum processing .There are many different variations and consistencies of petroleum from which the coke is derived. It is the general term for all special petroleum coke products such as green, calcined and needle petroleum coke. There are over 60 million tonnes of pet coke produced around the world annually. There are two methods of manufacturing metallurgical coke which are named according to the character of the oven in which the distillation is carried out.

1. Beehive ovens method.
2. Otto – Hoffman Ovens or By- product Ovens method.

1. Beehive Ovens method: Up to the end of 19th century, Beehive ovens were in use all over the world to manufacture the metallurgical coke. It is a dome shaped structure made up of fire bricks. It resembles to that of a beehive. The dimensions of oven are 4m wide and 2.5m high. The top is provided with a hole for charging the coal. Another hole, the discharging hole is provided in the circumference of the lower part of the wall. A number of ovens are built in row with common walls between neighbouring ovens.

The oven is charged with coal to produce a layer of about 60 to 90 cm deep. Sufficient air is introduced just to ignite the coal. Carbonization starts and volatile matter burns inside the partially closed side door. Carbonization takes place slowly from top to bottom and gets completed within 3 days. The exhausted gases are allowed to escape to the atmosphere and the hard metallurgical coke formed is quenched with water and taken out through the discharging door. The yield of the coke is about 60% of the coal charged. The capacity of each oven is about 5 tonnes. The process can be made economical by operating a series of ovens in such a manner that the hot oven gases escaping to the atmosphere are used to ignite the charge in the adjacent oven.

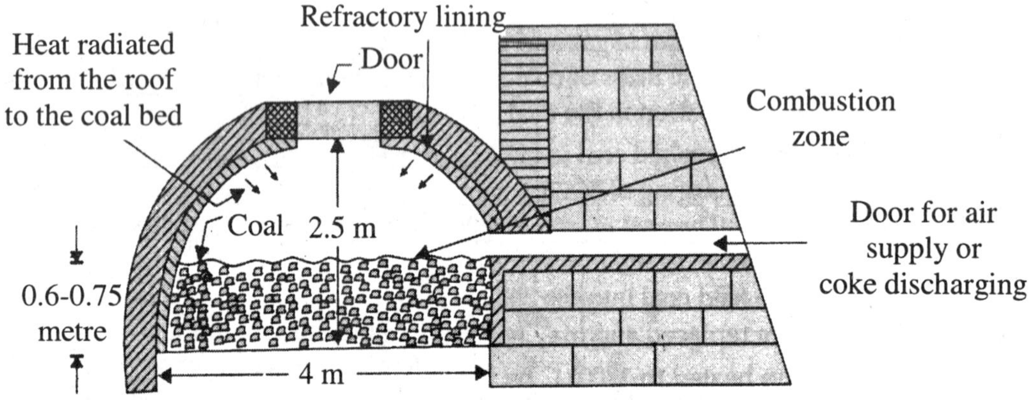

Fig. 2.5: Beehive Oven

Demerits of Beehive Ovens:

1. Valuable bye products escape out which are useful chemicals.
2. Yield of coke is less due to partial combustion.
3. Lack of flexibility of operation.

In spite of the above demerits, the Beehive ovens are still in use because of their low capital and running cost.

2. Otto Hoffmann's Ovens or By-product Ovens method: This method is based on regenerative principle of heat economy i.e. waste fuel gases are used for heating the checker work of bricks. These ovens consist of narrow rectangular chambers made of silica bricks having size 12m x 0.5m x 4m LBH respectively. They are tightly closed so that no air can enter. Each chamber is provided with a gas take off and refractory lined cast iron door at each end for discharging the coke. These carbonization chambers are erected side by side with vertical flues or inter space for combustion in between them. Generally, a battery of such ovens (consisting of about 25 to 1000 ovens) are used which are placed over the regenerator having a checker brick work which helps in utilization of the heat of the flue gases.

The wastes produced during combustion are passed through the regenerator and then let off to the atmosphere through a chimney. Regenerators are built underneath the ovens. The flue gases pass their sensible heat to the brick work of regenerators until the temperature rises to 1000^0C. The flow of heating flue gases is reversed and the inlet gases (flue gas and air) used for combustion are passed through the heated checker brickwork of regenerators. Thus inlet gases are preheated before entering. After some time the flow of gases is reversed so that the waste combustion gases again heat the checker brick work. Thus regenerator works on the principle of alternate heating and cooling cycles. This is achieved by periodically changing the flow direction of gases through the vertical flues by every 30 minutes or so.

The heating of the ovens is continued till the evolution of volatile matter ceases completely. The process of carbonization takes place layer by layer in the coal charge starting from the two side walls of the oven and moving towards the center. Each oven holds about 20 tonnes of coal charge and the time taken for carbonization is about 12 to 20 hrs. The temperature goes around 1100^{0}C and the yield of the coke is about 70% of the coal charged. 40% gas is used to heat the oven and the rest is sold out in steel plants. This gas has high calorific value and can be transported to distant places. After the process is complete, red hot coke is pushed outside by means of a ram which is electrically driven. The coke is collected into a quenching car. Dry quenching by inert gases is done to prevent the sensible heat of coke. Inert gases after quenching the coke become heated up and are circulated to boiler.

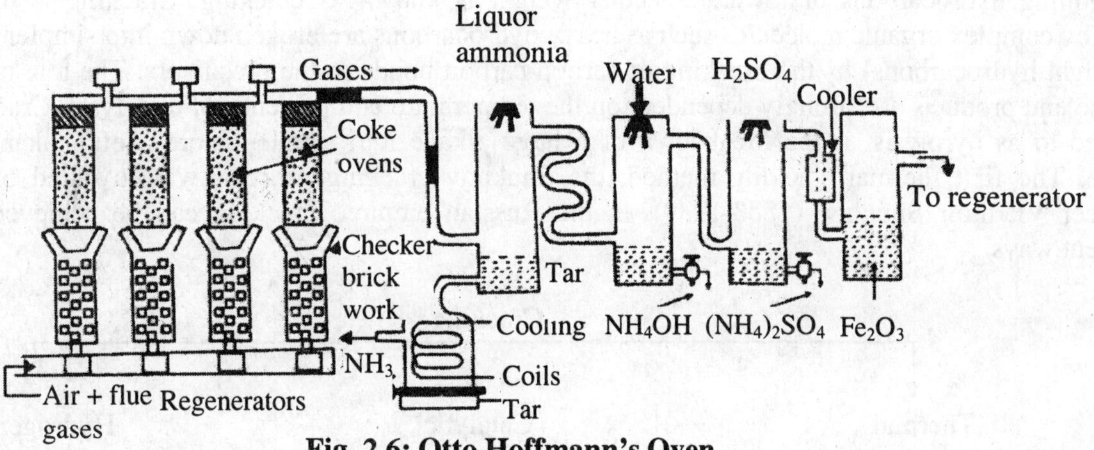

Fig. 2.6: Otto Hoffmann's Oven

Recovery of By-products: The gases and vapours evolved after combustion are collected separately.

i. **Recovery of Tar:** The gas from the coke ovens is passed through a tower in which liquor ammonia is sprayed. Tar and dust get collected in a tank. The tank is provided with heating coil to recover ammonia. From tar, number of bye products like crude benzene, phenolic compounds, pyridine bases, heavy naphtha, anthracene oil etc. are recovered.

ii. **Recovery of Ammonia:** In the next tower, ammonia is recovered by passing H_2SO_4 to form $(NH_4)_2SO_4$ which is used as a fertilizer. It is necessary to remove ammonia otherwise it may block the gas pipes in the form of $(NH_4)_2CO_3$.

iii. **Recovery of Benzol:** The gases are introduced in the next tower where benzene along with its homologues is removed by benzol scrubber or light oil. This oil contains low boiling hydrocarbons benzene, ethyl methyl benzene, tri-methyl benzene etc. By distillation, different products separate out and are recovered.

iv. **Recovery of H_2S:** It is essential to remove the sulfur compound from coke oven gas because its oxides SO_3 and SO_2 cause corrosion and H_2S has offensive odour. To remove H_2S gas and sulphur, the gas is passed through a chamber packed with moist Fe_2O_3 which reacts with H_2S to give Fe_2S_3.

$$Fe_2O_3 + 3H_2S \rightarrow Fe_2S_3 + 3H_2O$$

When Fe_2O_3 gets converted into Fe_2S_3, the purifier is exposed to the atmosphere where it is oxidized to the oxide. The SO_2 formed can be used in manufacture of sulphuric acid which is also used to absorb NH_3 from the coal gas.

$$Fe_2S_3 + 4O_2 \rightarrow 2FeO + 3SO_2$$
$$4FeO + O_2 \rightarrow 2Fe_2O_3$$

The purified coke oven gas is stored over water in holders. It is usually used as domestic fuel in such countries where coal is cheap. The main constituents of coal gas or coke oven gas are CH_4 and H_2 along with small quantity of CO_2, CO, N_2 and O_2.

2.9 CRACKING OF PETROLEUM PRODUCTS

With the rapid growth of automobile industry, the consumption of petrol has increased many folds, but the yield of this fraction is only 20% of the crude oil which is not of good quality. The yield of heavier petroleum fractions is quite high. Thus, it is necessary to make better use of these heavy fractions. This is achieved by cracking process. The process of breaking of higher hydrocarbons molecules into simpler, low boiling hydrocarbons of lower molecular weight is known as cracking. Cracking is the process whereby complex organic molecules such as heavy hydrocarbons are broken down into simpler molecules (e.g. light hydrocarbons) by the breaking of carbon-carbon bonds in the precursors. The rate of cracking and the end products are strongly dependent on the temperature and presence of catalysts. Cracking, also referred to as pyrolysis, is the breakdown of a large alkane into smaller, more useful alkanes and an alkene. The first thermal cracking method, the Shukhov cracking process, was invented by Russian engineer Vladimir Shukhov (1853-1939), in the Russian empire. Cracking can be achieved in three different ways.

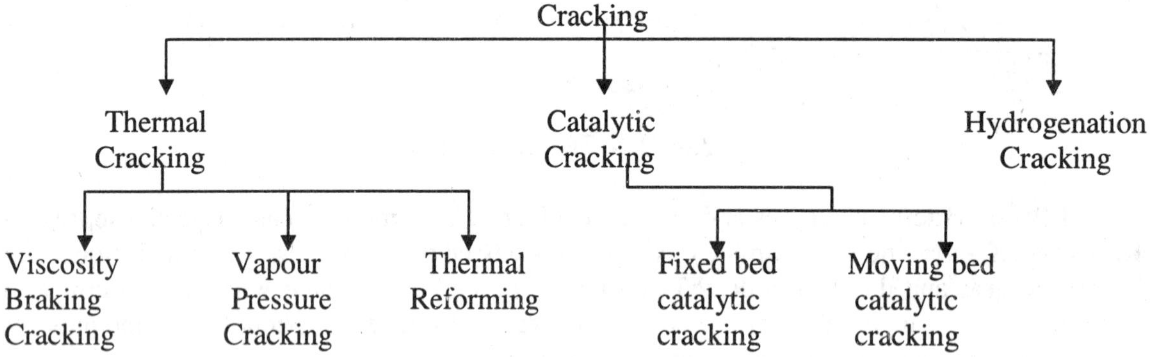

1. Thermal Cracking: It is carried out by applying heat (high temperature). It is also known as pyrolysis. In this process, higher hydrocarbons (more than 20-50 carbon atoms) are heated at 400-500^{0}C under 1000 psi pressure so larger molecules break down to the smaller molecules. In thermal cracking elevated temperatures (~800°C) and pressures (~700kPa) are used, a process first developed by William Merriam Burton. An overall process of disproportionation can be observed, where "light", hydrogen-rich products are formed at the expense of heavier molecules which condense and are depleted of hydrogen. The actual reaction is known as homolytic fission and produces alkenes, which are the basis for the economically important production of polymers.

$$C_{10}H_{22} \xrightarrow{\Delta} C_5H_{12} + C_5H_{10}$$

The cracked material is fed to the fractioner, where it is separated according to its boiling point. Thermal cracking can be done by three different ways.

(a) Viscosity Cracking: To produce the fuel oils of lower viscosity, the components are further subjected to cracking which is known as viscosity liquid phase cracking. It is carried out at 410-500^{0}C and 100 kg/cm^2 pressure. Smaller molecules have low viscosity.

(b) Vapour Pressure Cracking: In this process, at high temperature 600^{0}C and low pressure 20-25kg/cm^2 only vapour phase is obtained after cracking. By this process aromatic hydrocarbons and gaseous products are obtained. This is faster process than the liquid cracking. Heavy oil can not be cracked by this method.

(c) Thermal Reforming: This method is used for upgrading the fuel. By this method heavy gasoline of lower octane number is converted into higher gasoline of higher octane number. It is carried out at 500-550^{0}C temperature and 750 lbs per square inch pressure.

$$CH_3-CH_2-CH_2-CH_2-CH_2-CH_3 \rightarrow H_3C-\underset{CH_3}{\overset{CH_3}{\underset{|}{\overset{|}{C}}}}-CH_2-\underset{CH_3}{\underset{|}{CH}}-CH_2-CH_3$$

n-hexane Octane Number- (0) 2, 2, 4-Trimethylpentane Octane Number - (100)

2. Catalytic Cracking: This process is similar to the thermal cracking except the use of a suitable catalyst. This process is carried out at lower temperature and pressure so that it can be better controlled. Catalysts like aluminium silicates improve the yield and quality of gasoline.

(a) Fixed bed Catalytic Cracking: In this process, the catalyst is in the form of pellet of granules and the bed of the catalyst is fixed into the catalytic tower. Oil vapours to be cracked are passed through the tube at 420-450^{0}C temperature and 1.5 kg/cm^2 pressure. During this process larger molecules are converted into the smaller molecules and in this way cracking is achieved. After 8 to 10 hrs, the catalyst (zirconium oxide mixed with artificial clay) stops functioning because this is re-activated by burning off the deposited carbon.

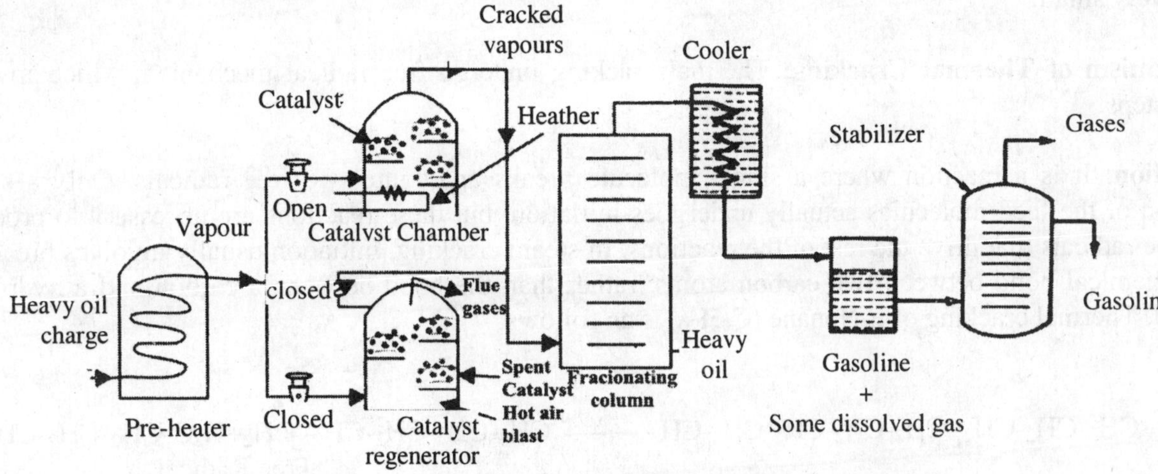

Fig. 2.7 Fixed bed catalytic cracking process

(b) Moving bed Catalytic Cracking: In this process, a fine powdered catalyst is used which flows down through a hopper into the reactor used for the cracking and oil vapour goes up in the reactor. Cracking takes place on the surface of the turbulent catalytic bed at 530^{0}C temperature and 3 to 5 kg/cm^2 pressure. When cracking of the vapour is completed, the catalyst is taken off from the bottom. It is regenerated again and the cracked vapour is separated from catalyst in dust separator and passed through fractioner where gas and gasoline are separated.

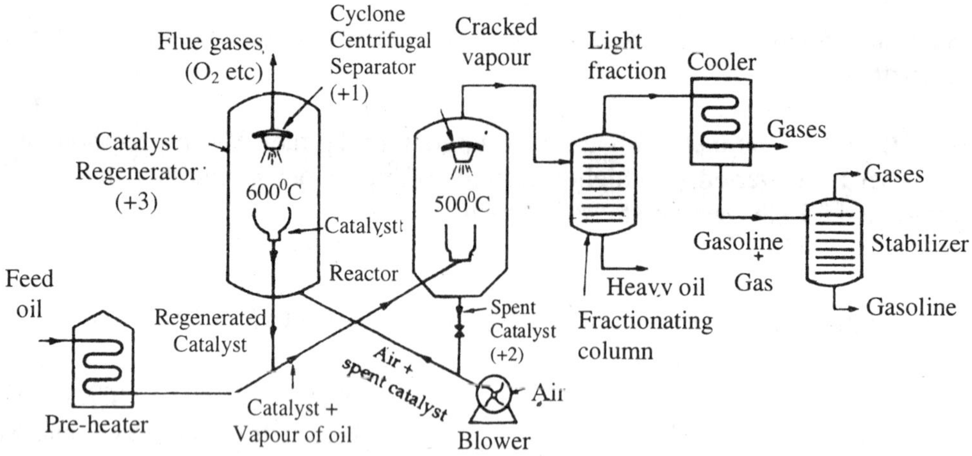

Fig. 2.8: Moving bed catalytic cracking process

(c) Hydrogenation Cracking: In this type of cracking, heavy oils are converted to gasoline by using hydrogen at high pressure and temperature in the presence of suitable catalyst.

Advantages of Catalytic Cracking:

- Unsaturated hydrocarbons are produced in small quantities.
- The petrol or gasoline obtained is of higher quality.
- Process is carried out at lower temperature and pressure so that it can be controlled easily.
- The process is fast.
- Sulphur, if present eliminates as H_2S. So sulphur contents present in gasoline and other products are very small.

Mechanism of Thermal Cracking: Thermal cracking undergo free radical mechanism which involes three steps.

Initiation: It is a reaction where a single molecule breaks apart into two free radicals. Only a small fraction of the feed molecules actually undergoes initiation, but these reactions are necessary to produce the free radicals that drive the rest of the reactions. In steam cracking, initiation usually involves breaking of a chemical bond between two carbon atoms, rather than the bond between a carbon and a hydrogen radical. Thermal cracking of n-Nonane (C_9H_{20}) is an follows:

$$CH_3\text{-}CH_2\text{-}CH_2\text{-}CH_2 \,\vdots\, CH_2\text{-}CH_2\text{-}CH_2\text{-}CH_2\text{-}CH_3 \xrightarrow{\Delta} CH_3\text{-}CH_2\text{-}CH_2\text{-}CH_2\text{-}\dot{C}H_2 + H_2\dot{C}\text{-}CH_2\text{-}CH_2\text{-}CH_3$$

Free Radical

Propagation: It is a reaction where a free radical removes a hydrogen atom from another molecule, turning the second molecule into a free radical. It is a reaction where a free radical breaks apart into two molecules, one an alkene, the other a free radical. This is the process that results in the alkene products of cracking.

$$CH_3\text{-}CH_2\text{-}CH_2 \,\vdots\, \underset{\beta}{CH_2}\text{-}\underset{\alpha}{\dot{C}H_2} \rightarrow \underset{\text{Free Radical}}{CH_3\text{-}CH_2\text{-}\dot{C}H_2} + \underset{\text{Ethene}}{CH_2{=}CH_2}$$

$$CH_3\text{-}CH_2 \,\vdots\, \dot{C}H_2 \rightarrow \dot{C}H_3 + CH_2{=}CH_2$$

Radical addition: It is the reverse of radical decomposition, in which a radical reacts with an alkene to form a single, larger free radical.

$$CH_3\text{-}(CH_2)_7\text{-}CH_3 + \dot{C}H_3 \rightarrow CH_3\ (CH_2)_3CH_2\text{-}CH_2\text{-}\dot{C}H\text{-}CH_2\text{-}CH_3 + CH_4$$

Free Radical

Free radical undergoes β scission to yield another free radical and an alkene.

$$CH_3(CH_2)_3CH_2\text{-}CH_2\text{-}CH\ \text{-}\dot{C}H_2\text{-}CH_3 \rightarrow CH_3\text{-}(CH_2)_3\text{-}CH_2\text{-}CH{=}CH_2 + \dot{C}H_2\text{-}CH_3$$

and soon free radical with no C-C bond in β position yields hydrogen free radical e.g.

$$CH_3\text{-}\dot{C}H_2 \rightarrow CH_2{=}CH_2 + \dot{H}$$

Termination reaction: It is a reaction when two free radicals react with each other to produce products that are not free radicals. Two common forms of termination are recombination, where the two radicals combine to form one larger molecule and disproportionation, where one radical transfers a hydrogen atom to the other, giving an alkene and an alkane.

$$\dot{C}H_3 + \dot{C}H_3 \rightarrow CH_3\text{-}CH_3$$

$$CH_3\dot{C}H_2 + CH_3\dot{C}H_2 \rightarrow CH_2{=}CH_2 + CH_3CH_3$$

Mechanism of Catalytic Cracking: Catalytic cracking is believed to follow cationic mechanism. This can be explained by taking the example of n–nonane.Due to thermal cracking, small amount of alkenes is produced. The alkenes produced are thus protonated by catalyst.

$$C_9H_{20} \xrightarrow{\text{Thermal Cracking}} CH_3 - CH_2 - CH = CH_2 + C_5H_{12}$$

$$CH_3 - CH_2CH = CH_2 + H^+ \rightarrow CH_3 - CH_2 - \overset{\oplus}{C}H - CH_3$$

$$CH_3 - (CH_2)_3 - \underset{|\atop H}{CH} - (CH_2)_3 - CH_3 + CH_3 - CH_2 - \overset{\oplus}{C}H - CH_3 \rightarrow$$

$$CH_3 - (CH_2)_3 - \overset{\oplus}{C}H - (CH_2)_3 - CH_3 + CH_3 - CH_2 - CH_2 - CH_3$$

The nonyl carbonium ion then undergoes β cleavage to yield an alkene and smaller caobonium ion.

$$CH_3 - CH_2 - CH_2 - CH_2 - \overset{\oplus}{C}H - CH_2 - CH_2 - CH_2 - CH_3 \rightarrow$$

$$CH_3 - CH_2 - \overset{\oplus}{C}H_2 + CH_3 - (CH_2)_3 - CH = CH_2$$

The primary carbonium ion rearranges to the more stable secondary carbonium ion by1:2 hybrid shift.

$$CH_3 - CH_2 - \overset{\oplus}{C}H_2 \rightarrow CH_3 - \overset{\oplus}{C}H - CH_3$$

Applications: In oil refinery, cracking processes allow the production of "light" products such as LPG and gasoline from heavier crude oil distillation fractions such as gas oils and residues. Fluid Catalytic Cracking (FCC) produces a high yield of gasoline and LPG while hydrocracking is a major source of jet fuel, gasoline components and LPG. Thermal cracking is currently used to "upgrade" very heavy fractions ("upgrading", "vis breaking") or to produce light fractions or distillates, burner fuel and/or petroleum coke. Two extremes of the thermal cracking in terms of product range are represented by the high-temperature process called steam cracking or pyrolysis (750 to 900°C or more) which produce valuable ethylene and other feedstocks for the petrochemical industry and the milder-temperature delayed coking (500°C) which can produce, under the right conditions, valuable needle coke, a highly crystalline petroleum coke used in the production of electrodes for the steel and aluminium industries.Fluid catalytic cracking is a commonly used process in a modern oil refinery.

2.10 COMBUSTION

A combustion reaction is known as the reaction where all components in a compound combine with oxygen, which then produce carbon dioxide and water. Combustion is commonly called burning. It is an exothermic reaction which means heat is produced and is easily distinguished. Combustion occurs predominantly in automobiles, homes and in factories. An example of a combustion reaction is as follows:

$$C_{(x)}\,H_{(y)} + O_2 \rightarrow H_2O_{(g)} + xCO_{2\,(g)} + \text{Heat / Light}$$

For the proper combustion, the substance must be brought to its ignition temperature. Ignition temperature is defined as the minimum temperature at which the substance ignites and burns without further addition of heat from outside.

Calculation of Air required for combustion: Following principles are used to find out the oxygen and air required for the combustion of fuel:

1) Substances always combine in definite proportions for complete combustion and these proportions are determined by the molecular masses of the substances and the products. In the formation of CO_2, 12 parts of carbon combine with 32 parts of oxygen to form 44 parts of CO_2.

$$C + O_2 \rightarrow CO_2$$

$$12 \quad 32 \qquad 44 \qquad \text{(By wt)}$$

$$1\,\text{vol} \quad 1\,\text{vol} \quad 1\,\text{vol} \quad \text{(By vol)}$$

Or 1 volume of carbon reacts with 1 volume of oxygen to produce 1 volume of carbon dioxide. Thus from the chemical equation, the amount of oxygen (by weight or by volume) can be calculated easily. The balanced chemical equations for the most common components of any fuel are given below:

$$H_2 + \frac{1}{2}O_2 \rightarrow H_2O$$

$$S + O_2 \rightarrow SO_2$$

$$CO + \frac{1}{2}O_2 \rightarrow CO_2$$

$$CH_4 + 2O_2 \rightarrow CO_2 + 2H_2O$$

$$2C_2H_6 + 7O_2 \rightarrow 4CO_2 + 6H_2O$$

$$C_2H_4 + 3O_2 \rightarrow 2CO_2 + 2H_2O$$

$$2C_2H_2 + 5O_2 \rightarrow 4CO_2 + 2H_2O$$

Nitrogen and ash present in fuel are non-combustible matters and hence do not consume any oxygen.

2) Composition and mean molecular weight of air: The composition of air is taken as 21% of O_2 and 79% of N_2 (by volume) and 23% of O_2 and 77% of N_2 (by weight). The mean molecular weight of air is taken as 28.95 g/mole. It may be noted that air consists of 21.00 mols of O_2, 78.06 mols of N_2 and 0.94 mols of Ar (argon). Since argon is inert, it is considered together with nitrogen for combustion calculations. That

is why the % N_2 in air by volume is taken as 79%. However, the mean molecular weight of air is taken as 28.95g/mole on the basis of the following:

$$\left[\frac{(21\times 32)+(78.06\times 28)+(0.94\times 39.34))}{100}\right]=28.9522 \text{ g/mole}$$

Further, 1 m^3 of O_2 is supplied by $\frac{1\times 100}{21}=4.76$ m^3 of air; and 1 kg of O_2 is supplied by $\frac{1\times 100}{23}=4.35$ kg of air.

3) Density of air: The density of air at N.T.P. is 1,290 kg. m^{-3} or 1.290×10^{-3} g cm^{-3}.

4) The composition of a solid or liquid fuel is usually expressed by weight whereas the composition of gaseous fuel is given by volume. The masses of gaseous substances can be calculated by Gas laws and Avogadro's Law.
(i) Avogadro's Law: 22.4 L (or 22,400 ml) of any gas at STP (i.e.0^0C and 760 mm pressure) have a mass equal to its 1mol. Thus 22.4 L of CO_2 at STP will have a mass of 44g, because 44g is its molar mass (Avogadro Law).
(ii) Gas Law: The mass of any gas can be converted to its volume at certain temperature and pressure by using gas equation.

$$PV = nRT$$

where P = Pressure, V = Volume, R = Gas constant and T = Temperature on Kelvin scale.
(iii) Boyle's Law and Charle's Law can be used for reducing the volume of a gas at a given temperature and pressure with the help of the equation.

$$\frac{P_1V_1}{T_1}=\frac{P_2V_2}{T_2}$$

where, P_1, V_1, T_1 are the initial pressure, volume, and temperature of the gas and P_2, V_2, T_2 are final pressure, volume and temperature of the gas.
(iv) The relative weights of the two or more gases are converted to the proportional volume by the relation.

$$\text{Proportional volume of the gases} = \frac{\text{Weight of the gas A}}{\text{Molar Mass of the gas A}} : \frac{\text{Weight of the gas B}}{\text{Molar Mass of the gas B}}$$

5) The minimum oxygen required should be calculated on the basis of complete combustion. In case of incomplete combustion, the products contain CO. In such a case, the excess oxygen is calculated after subtracting the amount of oxygen required to burn CO into CO_2.

Minimum oxygen required = Theoretical oxygen required – O_2 present in the fuel

6) For the efficient combustion excess air is always used in the furnace.

$$\%\text{Excess air} = \frac{\text{Actual air used Theoretical air required} \times 100}{\text{Theoretical air}}$$

7) Oxygen present in the fuel is present in combination with hydrogen. Thus this amount of hydrogen which is in combination with oxygen present in the fuel, does not take part in combustion. The rest of hydrogen is called available hydrogen which takes part in combustion reaction.

$$H_2 + \frac{1}{2}O_2 \rightarrow H_2O + heat$$

Since 1 part of hydrogen combines with 8 parts of oxygen or in other words every 8 parts of oxygen present get mixed with one part of hydrogen and are not available for combustion.

$$\therefore \text{available hydrogen} = \left[\text{Mass of hydrogen} - \frac{\text{Mass of Oxygen}}{8}\right]$$

Hence, theoretical amount of oxygen required for complete combustion of 1 kg of fuel

$$= \left[\frac{32}{12} \times C + \frac{16}{2}\left[H - \frac{O}{8}\right] + S\right] g$$

where C, H, O and S represent the percentages of carbon, hydrogen, oxygen and sulphur. Consequently theoretical amount of air required for complete combustion of 1kg of fuel is:

$$= \frac{100}{23}\left[\frac{32}{12} \times C + \frac{16}{2}\left[H - \frac{O}{8}\right] + S\right] g$$

2.11 KNOCKING

Knocking is also called pinking or pinging. It is the phenomenon of untreated liquid fuels. It is a sharp metallic sound similar to ratting of hammer which is produced in the internal combustion engine owing to immature ignition of the air gasoline mixture. There is a huge loss of energy and it causes damage to the piston and cylinder. Knocking increases with increasing compression ratio and an engine develops more power and consumes less fuel with increasing compression ratio. In internal combustion engine, a mixture of petrol vapors and air acts as a fuel. In the down stroke of the piston, a mixture of gasoline or petrol vapor and air is drawn from the carburretor into the cylinder and on the stroke the mixture is compressed. The ratio of the original volume of fuel mixture to that of the final volume obtained after compression is called compression ratio. Higher is the compression ratio, higher is the efficiency of engine.

When the compression ratio exceeds the limits, the ignition of fuel takes place before the piston head reaches the end of its stroke which lowers the ignition temperature of the end gas. As a result combustion of fuel takes place much rapidly and the end gas burns in an explosive and disorderly manner ahead the flame front and so produces the sound of knocking. Thus when ignition of mixture of air and gasoline takes place at the right moment, the fuel power generated is utilized in driving the engine, but if ignition occurs much earlier than the desired moment, the energy is lost in producing metallic sound produced against the position and walls of the cylinder. In many cases, a mixture of compressed liquid fuel vapor and air explodes in IC engine before the proper degree of compression is reached. This causes a decrease in the efficiency of the engine.

Disadvantages of Knocking:

1. It decreases the efficiency of engine.
2. It causes loss of energy.
3. Damages the piston and cylinder.

Relationship between Knocking and Structure of Hydrocarbon: Knocking and chemical structure are closely related. The knocking tendency decreases with increase in the compactness of the molecules, double bonds and cyclic structures. Thus, olefins of the same carbon chain length possess better antiknock properties than the corresponding paraffins.

1. The knocking increases with increase in the length of the hydrocarbon chain.
   n-heptane > n-hexane > n-pentane > n-butane

2. Anti knocking properties of branched chain paraffins is better than straight chain paraffins.
   n-heptane > 2-methyl hexane >2,2-dimethyl pentane.

3. Aromatic compounds like benzene and toluene have very high anti knocking properties.The constituent of fuel to knock is in the following order.

Straight chain paraffins> Branched chain paraffins > Olefins > Cycloparaffins (Naphthenes) > Aromatics. Cracked and reformed gasolines have higher octane number than the straight run gasoline. Straight run gasolines obtained from paraffinic crudes have lower anti-knocking properties as compared to those from naphthenic or aromatic crudes.

Prevention of Knocking: Knocking can be prevented by -

- The use of a fuel with higher octane rating .
- The addition of octane-increasing "lead", methylcyclopentadienyl manganese tricarbonyl (MMT), isooctane or other antiknock agents.
- Increasing the amount of fuel injected / inducted (resulting in lower Air to Fuel Ratio)
- Reduction of cylinder pressure by increasing the engine revolutions (lower gear), decreasing the manifold pressure (throttle opening) or reducing the load on the engine or any combination.
- Reduction of charge (in-cylinder) temperatures (such as thorough cooling, water injection or compression ratio reduction).
- Retardation of spark plug ignition.
- Improved combustion chamber design that concentrates mixture near the spark plug and generates high turbulence to promote fast even burning.
- Use of a spark plug of colder heat range in cases where the spark plug insulator has become a source of pre-ignition leading to detonation.
- Correct ignition timing is essential for optimum engine performance and fuel efficiency.

Consequences of Knocking: Engine knocking has disastrous consequences for the engine, since it leads to the catastrophical wear of the combustion chamber walls, through particle wear for moderate knocking, to welding for serious knocking. This is due to the contact between those walls and high temperature gases resulting from the unwanted explosion. The processes also lead to a 'knocking' noise for the engine, that gives its name to the phenomenon.

2.12 OCTANE NUMBER

The octane rating is a measure of the auto ignition resistance of gasoline (petrol) and other fuels used in spark-ignition internal combustion engines. It is a measure of anti-detonation of a gasoline or fuel. Octane number is the number which gives the percentage, by volume, of iso-octane in a mixture of iso-octane and normal heptane, that would have the same anti-knocking capacity as the fuel which is under consideration. For example, gasoline with the same knocking characteristics as a mixture of 90% iso-octane and 10% heptane will have an octane rating of 90.

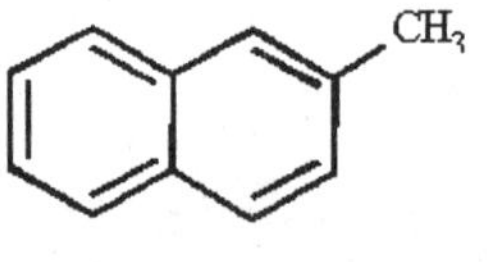

$H_3C-(CH_2)_{14}-CH_3$

2- Methyl naphthalene	n-hexadecane
100	0

Octane is measured relative to a mixture of iso-octane (2,2,4-trimethylpentane, an isomer of octane) and n-heptane. An 87-octane gasoline, for example, has the same octane rating as a mixture of 87 volume% of isooctane and 13 volume % of n-heptane. This does not mean, however, that the gasoline actually should contain these chemicals in these proportions. It simply means that it has the same auto ignition resistance as the described mixture. A high tendency to auto ignite, or low octane rating, is undesirable in a gasoline engine but desirable in a diesel engine. In order to classify fuels, an arbitrary scale for rating fuels was established by Edger in 1927. There are two commonly used octane scales, research octane number (RON) and motor octane number (MON). The operating conditions of both scales are different. For RON, the inlet temperature is about 52^0C, engine speed is 600 rpm, spark advance is 13^0 btc. The motor method MON is carried under more severe conditions; inlet temp 149^0C, engine speed 900 rpm, spark advance $19\text{-}26^0$ btc varying with the compression ratio. Since motor method uses more severe operating conditions, the motor octane number is usually lower than research octane number. The numerical difference between these values is called fuel sensitivity.

(Fs) Fuel sensitivity = RON- MON

It is possible for a fuel to have a RON greater than 100, because isooctane is not the most knock-resistant substance available. Racing fuels, Straight ethanol, Avgas and Liquified petroleum gas (LPG) typically have octane ratings of 110 or significantly higher e.g. ethanol's RON is 129 (MON 102, AKI 116). Typical "octane booster" additives include tetra-ethyl lead and toluene. Tetra-ethyl lead is easily decomposed to its component radicals, which react with the radicals from the fuel and oxygen that would start the combustion, thereby delaying ignition. That is why leaded gasoline has a higher octane rating than unleaded. Fuel sensitivity varies with source of crude petroleum and refining process used and it explains that fuel having higher sensitivity will have poor performance under severe conditions.

Two different grades of petrol are available from the same crude:
1. Regular unleaded – RON=90, MON=80
2. Premium unleaded – RON=95, MON=95

In most countries the "headline" octane that would be shown on the pump is the RON, but in the United States, Canada and some other countries the headline number is the average of the RON and the MON, sometimes called the Anti-Knock Index (AKI), Road Octane Number (RdON), Pump Octane Number (PON), or (R+M)/2. Because of the 8 to 10 point difference noted above, this means that the octane in the United States will be about 4 to 5 points lower than the same fuel elsewhere. 87 octane fuel, the "regular" gasoline in the US and Canada, would be 91-92 in Europe. However most European pumps deliver 95 (RON) as "regular", equivalent to 90-91 US (R+M)/2 and even deliver 98 (RON) or 100 (RON). The octane rating may also be a "trade name" with the actual figure being higher than the nominal rating.

Examples of octane ratings: The octane ratings of n-heptane and iso-octane are exactly 0 and 100 by definition. For other hydrocarbons, the octane ratings are as follows.

Table 2.4: Octane numbers of various hydrocarbons

n-octane	-10
n-heptane	0
2-methylheptane	23
n-hexane	25
2-methylhexane	44
1-heptene	60
n-pentane	62
1-pentene	84
n-butane	91
cyclohexane	97

The improvement in the anti-knocking rating of unleaded fuel and leaded fuel with its reduced lead content has been achieved by adding fuel components that have high octane rating such as benzene, methanol, ethanol etc. Knocking rating of fuel can also be identified by obtaining the highest useful compression ratio (HUCR). This is obtained by carrying a test on a variable compression engine under specified operating conditions when the spark timing and the air fuel ratio have been adjusted to give the maximum efficiency. The compression ratio is raised under specified conditions till knocking conditions are reached. It is impossible to assign HUCR to a given fuel except for particular engine running under specified conditions. To achieve RON of about 10^6, 0.5 g Pb/l should be added. On combustion $Pb(C_2H_5)_4$ forms Pb and PbO. Lead oxide and lead vapours so formed contaminate the atmosphere. At the time of explosive combustion, the lead oxide is rapidly reduced to metallic lead which is deposited on the spark plug points, the cylinder walls and the piston head. Ethyl bromide is added to convert lead to lead bromide. Lead bromide is volatile and escapes along with other exhaust gases.

$$Pb + 2C_2H_5Br \rightarrow PbBr_2 + 2CH_2 = CH_2$$

Now-a-days use of leaded petrol is minimized due to environmental pollution. The influence of the chemical structure on RON on great deal of research proves that RON decreases with increasing chain length, RON increases with increasing number of side chains and RON also increases with ring structure.

Gasoline from paraffinic crudes has low octane number. The octane number of cracked gasoline is higher than straight run gasoline. The octane number of aviation gasoline is very high due to highly branched hydrocarbon present in it. The octane number (ON) of regular gasoline is 74 and that of premium gasoline is 81. The superior is Triptane having 124. Because of high cost of pure iso-octane and n-heptane, sub standards having selected grades of spirits of good storage quality have been prepared by mixing with tetra ethyl lead having octane number greater than 100. The value is indicated by the colour of the mixture e.g. Spirit blends having octane number of 92, 91-96, 100-130, 118-135, have red/orange, blue, green and brown colour respectively. For spirit blends, having octane number greater than 100, the octane rating is expressed as:

$$\text{Octane Number} = \frac{\text{Power Number} - 100}{3 + 100}$$

where power number is the quantity proportional to the power supplied by the engine.

Performance number: It indicates maximum power that can be obtained with a fuel, without knock, relative to the maximum power that can be obtained with iso-octane, also without knock. Iso octane is arbitrarily assigned as PN of 100. It is based on the indicated power produced in a super charged standard engine operating under specified condition. A super charged engine using a fuel rated at 130 PN can produce approximately 1.3 times as much power as it can develop with a 100 PN fuel, namely iso-octane (without knock).

$$PN = \frac{\text{Knock limited indicated mean effective pressure of test fuel}}{\text{Knock limited indicated mean effective pressure of iso octane}}$$

If knock rate is below iso-octane, it is denoted by octane number. Fuels superior to iso-octane in anti knocking quality are denoted by PN octane number. Because of non linear variation, a new scale was derived which expresses the approximate relative engine performance and the units of this scale are known as PN octane number above 100 computed as:

$$ON(>100) = 100 + \frac{28.28A}{1.0 + .736A + \sqrt{1.0 + 0.736A - 0.035216A^2}}$$

2.13 DIESEL ENGINE FUEL

The diesel engines use cheaper paraffins only. In diesel engines the air alone is compressed with the result that the temperature is increased to 294-340^{0}C. The fuel is injected almost at the end of compression stroke. The fuel air mixture ignites spontaneously at the temperature of 290-340^{0}C due to high compression without electric spark from a battery as in petrol engines. Diesel fuel need not be volatile and hence branched chain alkanes and aromatics are less suitable for diesel engines. The diesel fuel generally consists of the fraction boiling between kerosene and the lubricating oils. The main property of diesel engine fuel is that it should ignite easily below compression temperature. The interval between the start of fuel injection and its ignition is termed as ignition delay or induction lag. For the efficient functioning of diesel engine, the induction lag should be brief. When the fuel has induction lag, large amount of the injected fuel gets accumulated in the cylinder before ignition and when ignition occurs, the accumulated fuel burns violently with a sudden increase in temperature and pressure. The uneven burning of the fuel is known as diesel knocking. The greater is the induction lag, higher is the diesel knock.

2.14 CETANE NUMBER

The ignition quality of fuel is expressed in terms of cetane number, which refers the mixture of cetane (n-hexadecane $C_{16}H_{34}$, (Value = 100) and 2- methyl naphthalene (value = 0). Cetane is a paraffin of high ignition quality. In a diesel engine, there is a definite time lag of 0.5-10 milli seconds between the injection of the oil and its ignition within the engine and this delay period is a constant for the fuel and is expressed as cetane number. The delay period is measured by cathode ray indicator or some other method. It has been found that low speed, medium speed and high speed diesel grades have cetane number as 25 or above, 35 or above and 45 or above respectively.

Low speed (150-500 rpm), medium speed (500-1500 rpm) and high speed (1500-2000 rpm) diesel fuels are respectively used for ships, locomotives (tractors) and buses (or trucks). Cetane, which ignites very readily, is given the rating 100 and 2-methyl naphthalene which ignites very cliquishly in a diesel engine, is given zero rating. The cetane number of a diesel fuel may be defined as the % of cetane in a mixture of cetane and n-methyl naphthalene that will have the same ignition characteristics as the fuel under examination. Diesel engines requiring a fuel of cetane number greater than 45 proposed that the amount of paraffins compounds in the fuel should be related to ignition quality. The evolution is made by measuring the aniline point or the temperature at which the fuel is completely soluble in aniline. Since aniline is an aromatic compound, paraffins are soluble at higher temperature than aromatic fuels.

The Diesel index is given by formula:

$$DI = \frac{\text{Aniline point } (^{\bullet} f) \times \text{API gravity } (60^{0} r)}{100}$$

The cetane number and the diesel index of the fuel for most high speed diesel oils should vary between 50 to 60.

Diesel fuel additives: To improve the cetane number, additives are used in diesel fuels, also referred as ignition accelerators. Typically an improvement of 6 on the cetane scale is obtained by adding 1% by volume of amyl nitrate, $C_5H_{11}ONO_2$. Other effective substances are ethyl nitrate ($C_2H_5ONO_2$) and ethyl nitrite (C_2H_5ONO), however the most widely used additive is currently 2 EHN (2-ethyl hexyl nitrate) because of its good resistance (response) in wide range of fuels and comparatively low costs. Adding 1000 ppm of 2 EHN will increase the cetane rating by about 5 units.

Anti waxing additives: These are copolymers of ethylene and vinyl acetate or other alkene esters copolymers, performance of these additives varies with different fuels and the improvement decreases as the dosage rate is increased. It is possible for 200 ppm of additive to reduce the cold filter plugging point (CFPP) temperature by about 10 K.

Detergents (amines and amides): These are used to inhibit the formation of combustion deposits. A typical dosage level is 100-200 ppm.

Anti-ices: Alcohol and glycol have a high affinity for water and are soluble in diesel fuels. Water is present through contamination humid air. If ice forms, it will block fuel pipes and filters.

Biocides: Anaerobic bacteria can form growth at the water/ diesel interface in storage tanks and these are capable of blocking fuel filters.

Antifoam ants: 10-20 ppm silicon based compounds facilitate the rapid and complete filling of vehicle fuel tanks.

Table 2.5: Difference between octane number and cetane number

S.No.	Octane Number	Cetane number
1.	The percentage of iso-octane in a mixture of n- heptane and iso-octane is called octane number.	The percentage of hexadecane in a mixture of hexadecane and 2-methyl naphthalene is called cetane number.
2.	It is used for identifying quality of petrol.	It is used for identifying quality of diesel.
3.	Octane number of gasolin can be raised by addition of TEL [$(C_2H_5)_4$ Pb] and diethyl telluride[($(C_2H_5)_2$ Te].	Cetane number of diesel can be raised by addition of ethyl nitrite, isoamyl nitrite,acetone peroxide etc.
4 (a)	$CH_3 - (CH_2)_5 - CH_3$ n- Heptane (Octane No. = zero) Knocks very badly	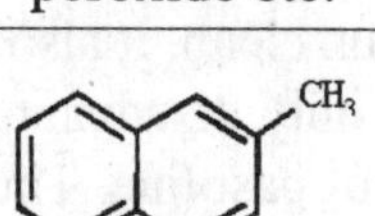 2- methyl naphthalene (Cetane No. = zero) knocks very badly

(b)	iso-octane (Octane No. 100) Knocks very little	n-Hexadecane (cetane No. = 100) Knocks very little
5	Straight chain hydrocarbon molecule are worst fuel , therefore low octane no.	branched chain hydrocarbon molecule are best fuel , therefore high cetane no.
6.	Relation between octane no. of hydrocarbon and structure is- aromatics > cyclo alkane > alkene >branched alkane>straight chain alkane	Relation between cetane no. of hydrocarbon of structure is- n- alkanes > cyclo alkane > alkenes >branched alkanes > aromatics.
7.	Standard requirement- octane number of petrol should be at least 85 for motorcycle & cars and above 100 for aeroplanes and helicopter.	Standard requirement- cetane number of diesel 25 for low speed engine, 35 for medium speed engine and above 45 for high speed engine.

2.15 ALTERNATIVE FUELS

Since the world reserves of petroleum are not ever lasting, a good deal of attention is being focused on the discovery of fuels which would prove to be an alternative to normal gasoline or diesel. Such fuels would be able to replace the conventional ones only when they have high energy density, good combustion quality, less corrosive tendency, they should be easily available and economically viable and do not produce excess pollution. These alternative fuels are divided in two categories:

1. Petroleum based fuels: These are the fuels which are obtained from distillation of crude oil obtained from earth crust. Examples: Kerosene, LPG etc.

2. Non petroleum base fuels : These may be liquid and gaseous, they may be synthetic or natural like benzol, alcohol types in liquid fuels or hydrogen, methane type gaseous fuels.

Important Fuels:

1. **Kerosene:** It is extensively used for lighting lamps and stoves. It is heavier distillate of gasoline and straight chain paraffin with initial boiling point 160^0C, end point 257^0C and has a very low aromatic content. It has low octane number (45 to 50) so it is not suitable for use in IC engines, having compression ratio more than 5:1. The main disadvantage is lower heating value than gasoline, higher viscosity carries more dirt to the fuse pump flow. Kerosene is being extensively used in aircraft gas turbines.

2. **LPG:** It contains mixture of propane and propylene and can be used in commercial vehicles with satisfactory results. Heating value is 48000 kJ/kg and motor octane number is 100, quite cheaper than gasoline, burns clean, does not pre ignite easily and very well mixes with air. LPG as a fuel has good ability to run clean, it also holds good during cold starting and fuel enrichment is automatically eliminated. The only disadvantage is that its storage requires more space, more over emissions are higher than that of gasoline. Thus to use it safely, quality standards and the specifications have to be prescribed and certification on exhaust emission is necessary.

3. **Benzol:** It is a distillate of coal tar. It contains 70% toluene, 10 percent xylene and a trace of sulphur bearing compounds having high anti-knock characteristics, but a lower heating value than gasoline.

The carbon deposit is more because of higher C/H ratio, but it can be used as a blending agent for convention in place of TEL because of its anti knocking property.

4. **Alcohol:** The pure alcohol is of organic origin and may be produced from different sources like grains, corn, sugar, potatoes or by fermentation. Alcohol is being considered as an engine fuel for more than 50 years. The main advantage of using alcohol is its high resistance characteristics which would permit engines to run at higher compression. The exhaust gas temperature will be lower. The main disadvantage is that lower heating values lead to a larger fuel tank and increased jet size of carburetor. Methanol or ethanol can also be used as blending components of gasoline because of its high anti-knocking property and will provide a lead free gasoline for cars and catalytic converters. For oxidation of CO and HC, a blend of methanol and ethanol can be used to increase the power output and efficiency by increasing the compression ratio. Vehicles running on pure ethanol would increase green house effect by 20% emission of green house gas for light duty vehicles and upto 50% for heavy duty vehicles.

5. **Hydrogen:** Hydrogen powered IC engines came into existence about 70 yrs ago. Currently hydrogen is used as SI engine fuel based on two facts: Hydrogen can be made from unlimited source and can be burnt easily and products of combustion do not contain HC, CO_2, CO and NO_x. Liquid hydrogen has great potential as an aviation fuel because of high energy content and cooling capacity and minimal environmental impact. Interest in hydrogen powered vehicles has increased due to long term source of hydrogen from water.

6. **Methane (CNG):** Methane has received very much attention as an alternative fuel to gasoline. Methane is a gas at atmospheric temperature and pressure and can be liquefied at a pressure of about 200 bar and -160^{0}C. The liquefied gas has to be stored in steel cylinders to be used as compressed gas (CNG). The advantages of using methane is its high heating value (abut 20% more than gasoline) and it is best for SI engines having compression ratio lying in the range 10.5:1 to 15:1. The gas is available from Sewage works (Bio-gas), Gobar (Gobar gas plants) which are being wasted. The gas available from these sources contains about 30% CO_2 which can be removed because CO_2 will corrode the steel cylinder. CO_2 is soluble in water. Methane has the advantage over gasoline that it does not dilute or destroy the oil film on the cylinder walls and therefore reduces wear of materials and maintenance costs.

7. **Nuclear Fuels:** The nuclear fuels are the isotopes of heavy elements capable of inducing a chain reaction of nuclear fission. At present, three isotopes are known to be suitable as nuclear fuels. These are natural uranium-235 and two artificially prepared isotopes plutonium-239 and uranium-233. These are the common materials that can sustain the fission reaction and therefore called nuclear fuels. The isotope U^{238} serves as raw material for the production of another nuclear fuel Pu^{239}. The isotopes U^{235} and U^{233} are fissionable materials. Nuclear reactors involve release of energy of the nuclei being fashioned under the action of neutrons and the fission neutrons accomplish the reaction with reproduction of the nuclear fuel.

$$_{90}Th^{232}(n,r)_{90}Th^{233} \rightarrow_{91} Pa^{233} \rightarrow_{92} U^{233}$$

Spent fuel elements are subjected to chemical processing in order to recover unconsumed uranium or thorium. Eight isotopes of thorium have been produced artificially, the most important of which is Th^{233} which undergoes β - decay producing Pa^{233}. This isotope is the precursor of the nuclear fuel, U^{238}. Thorium is a potential natural fuel. The nuclear fuels must be prepared for reactor use according to their physical as well as nuclear properties.

Bio fuel: "Bio-fuels" are the liquid or gas fuels that are not derived from petroleum based fossils fuels or which contain a proportion of non fossil fuels. Most of the fossil fuels we use are biological in nature. Perhaps we have to say that a biofuel is one that does not add to the stock of total carbon dioxide in the atmosphere. These are plant forms that typically remove carbon dioxide from the atmosphere and give up the same amount when burnt. Naturally, all the other fossil fuels have done the same, but we are talking about a time scale of one or two years for the biofuels, whereas the fossil fuels can only be considered on a time scale measured in millions of years. The biofuels are therefore considered to be "CO_2 neutral", not adding to the carbon dioxide level in the atmosphere. The type of biofuel used will depend on a number of factors, chief amongst them being the available feedstock and the energy that can be used locally. Bio-fuels can be used as road fuels in two ways:

a) It is used as a blend up to specified limits, with conventional motor fuels (petrol or diesel) in engines which need no modification.
b) It can use on their own but a conventional engine must first be modified – this use is confined to 'captive' fleets of vehicles.

OBJECTIVE QUESTIONS

1. The Calorific value of coal gas is:
   (a) 900 K-cal/m^3 (b) 270 K-cal/m^3
   (c) 4500-5900 K-cal/m^3 (d) 2700 K-cal/ m^3
2. Petrol gas is a mixture of
   (a) Air and petrol vapor (b) Air and kerosene
   (c) Petrol and nitrogen (d) None
3. Charcoal is constituent of:
   (a) Fuel (b) Gun powder
   (c) Discoloring agent (d) All
4. Purest form of carbon is:
   (a) Animal charcoal (b) Sugar charcoal
   (c) Petroleum coke (d) Lamp black
5. Natural Gas is composed of:
   (a) CH_4 (b) n-butane
   (c) n-octane (d) A mixtures of octane
6. Which of the following has more calorific value?
   (a) Water gas (b) Coal gas
   (c) Producer gas (d) Semi water gas
7. The soot formed by the burning of vegetables rich in carbon is called:
   (a) Carbon black (b) Gas Carbon
   (c) Lamp black (d) Coke
8. The component present in greater proportion in water gas is:
   (a) H_2 (b) CH_4
   (c) CO (d) CO_2
9. Which of the following has maximum calorific value?
   (a) Glucose (b) Fat
   (c) Protein (d) Mineral salts
10. Which of the following chemical product is not obtained by destructive distillation of Coal?
    (a) Bleaching agents (b) Synthetic fibers
    (c) Paints and inks (d) Mauveine and other drugs
11. The components present in producer gas are:
    (a) $CO + N_2$ (b) $CO + H_2$
    (c) $CO_2 + H_2$ (d) $CO + NO_2$
12. Charcoal is used to absorb poisonous gas in gas masks. It allows oxygen to pass through, but adsorbs the poisonous gas?
    (a) Cl_2 (b) CO_2
    (c) H_2S (d) CO
13. Which of the following is a silent killer gas which combines with haemoglobin in the blood?
    (a) CO_2 (b) CO
    (c) NO_2 (d) NO
14. Which alcohol is prepared from water gas?
    (a) C_2H_5OH (b) $CH_3CH_2CH_2OH$
    (c) CH_3OH (d) $C_6H_5CH_2OH$
15. The fuse wire used for supplying current to the fuel for heating it in bomb calorimeter is made of:
    (a) Aluminium (b) Magnesium
    (c) Copper (d) Silver

16. Increasing content of volatile matter in coal is:
(a) Anthracite < Bituminous < Lignite < Peat
(b) Anthracite < Lignite < Bituminous < Peat
(c) Peat < Lignite < Bituminous < Anthracite
(d) Peat < Bituminous < Lignite < Anthracite

17. Colloidal fuel is:
(a) Powdered Coal + tar + sterilizing agent
(b) Coal briquette + kerosene + sterilizing agent
(c) Powdered coal + fuel oil + sterilizing agent
(d) Coal briquette + gasoline + sterilizing agent

18. A fuel has 30% n-heptane and 70% iso-octane, its octane number should be:
(a) 130 (b) 100
(c) 70 (d) 40

19. In Liquid phase thermal cracking, which oils can be used?
(a) Heavy oils (b) Gas oils
(c) Both a and b (d) Other

20. What is the yield percentage in liquid phase thermal cracking?
(a) 30-40% (b) 40-50%
(c) 50-60% (d) 60-70%

21. What is the octane rating of petrol in LPTC?
(a) 50 (b) 60
(c) 70 (d) 80

22. Which catalyst is used in catalytic cracking?
(a) $Al_2(SiO_3)_3$ (b) $Al_3(SiO_3)_3$
(c) $Al_2(SiO_2)_3$ (d) $Al_3(SiO_3)_2$

23. Considerable amount of oxygen in flue gas indicates:
(a) Short supply of oxygen (b) Oxygen is in excess
(c) Both a and b (d) None

24. Octane rating of which one is 45?
(a) n-nonane (b) Benzene
(c) n-heptane (d) n-hexane

25. Octane rating of which one is 112?
(a) Benzene (b) n-Hexane
(c) n-heptane (d) n-nonane

26. Octane rating was introduced by:
(a) Edger (b) Heisenberg
(c) Dalton (d) Bohr

27. Quantity of bye product gas produced in low temperature carbonization is:
(a) 130-150 m^3/tonne (b) 300-390 m^3/tonne
(c) 200-250 m^3/tonne (d) 180-200m^3/tonne

28. Which of the following is not a unit of calorific value?
(a) K cal/kg (b) B.Th.U./ft^3
(c) K cal/m^3 (d) K cal/cm^2

29. Beckmann's thermometer can measure accurately up to:
(a) 1/10 th of a degree (b) a degree
(c) 1/100 th of a degree (d) 1/1000th of a degree

30. Which of the following is not a name of knocking?
(a) Pinking (b) Declotation
(c) Pinging (d) Detonation

31. Which of the following has octane number greater then 100?
(a) Regular gasoline (b) n-heptane
(c) Triptane (d) n-hexadecane

32. The temperature of diesel engine ranges:
(a) 150-200°C (b) 293-340°C
(c) 150-250°C (d) 195-284°C

33. Compression ratio is given by:
(a) Ratio of gaseous volume in the cylinder at the end of suction stroke to the volume at the end of compression stroke of the piston.
(b) Ratio of gaseous volume in the cylinder at the end of compression stroke to the volume at the end of suction stroke of the piston.
(c) None of these
(d) Other

34. Coke is pure variety of carbon which contains:
(a) 60% C (b) 50% C
(c) 80% C (d) 70-80% C

35. Calorific value of coal decreases because of:
(a) Carbon (b) Hydrogen
(c) O_2 (d) S

36. Anthracite contains:
(a) 60%C (b) 78%C
(c) 70%C (d) 90%C

37. The Cetane rating of hexadecane is:
(a) 100 (b) 0
(c) 50 (d) 120

38. A fuel having high ignition temperature is:
(a) Petrol (b) Wood
(c) Kerosene (d) LPG

39. Fuel suitable for use in motor engines is:
(a) Kerosene (b) Gasoline
(c) Diesel (d) Heavy Oil

40. Moisture is determined in proximate analysis of coal at temperatures:
(a) 75°C (b) 105°C
(c) 35°C (d) 55°C

41. HCV is also called as:
(a) NCV (b) GCV
(c) Both a and b (d) None

42. An example of secondary fuel is:
(a) Wood (b) Coal
(c) Natural gas (d) Gobar gas

43. The chemical name of tear gas is:
(a) Carbon disulphide (b) Sulphur dioxide
(c) Teflon (d) Chloropicrin

44. Power alcohol is:
(a) Ether + ethyl alcohol + petrol
(b) Ethyl alcohol + diesel
(c) Ethyl alcohol + petrol
(d) Ethane + ethyl alcohol

45. In Otto Hoffman's bye product oven, H_2S is recovered by using:
(a) Moist Fe_2O_3 (b) Dry Fe_3O_4
(c) Moist Fe_3O_4 (d) Dry Fe_2O_3

46. The catalyst present in catalytic converter to change harmful CO and NO to harmless CO_2 and N_2 is:
(a) Platinum (b) Rhodium
(c) Tungsten (d) Zirconium

47. Percentage of 'X' in coal determines the shape of fire-box and design of furnace. What is 'X' ?
(a) Hydrogen (b) Fixed carbon
(c) Sulphur (d) Ash Content

48. Favorable conditions for coal formation inside the earth surface arc:
(a) High pressure, Low temperature, O_2, bacteria
(b) Low pressure, Low temperature, absence of O_2 and bacteria
(c) High pressure, High temperature, absence of O_2 and presence of bacteria
(d) Low pressure, High temperature, pressure of O_2, presence of bacteria

49. The calorific value of fuel is expressed as:
(a) kcal cm (b) kcal cm^{-3}
(c) kcal /kg (d) cal m^{-3}

50. Which gas has least calorific value?
(a) Coal gas (b) Water gas
(c) Producer gas (d) Natural gas

51. Calorific value of carbon in Dulong's formula is:
(a) 34,500 Kcal/kg (b) 8080 Kcal/kg
(c) 2240 Kcal/kg (d) None of above

52. Ultimate analysis of fuel is determined by % of
(a) H_2O, Volatile matter, Ash and Carbon (b) C, H, S, N and H_2O
(c) S only (d) Fixed carbon only

53. Combustion is a:
(a) Endothermic process (b) Exothermic process
(b) Sublimation (d) None of the above

54. Latent heat of condensation of water vapour is:
(a) 287 kcal/kg (b) 387 kcal/kg
(c) 487 kcal/kg (d) 587 kcal/kg

55. Highest carbon content is found in:
(a) Peat (b) Lignite
(c) Sub – bituminous (d) Bituminous

56. When coal sample is kept in open lid crucible in muffle furnace at about 725°C temperature for ½ hour, the component determination will be:
(a) % moisture (b) % volatile matter
(c) % ash (d) % fixed carbon

57. Decomposition of higher molecule into simpler molecule is known as:
(a) Cracking (b) Knocking
(c) Polymerization (d) All of the above

58. Iso-octane has an octane rating of:
(a) 0 (b) 100
(c) 50 (d) Above 100

Answer Key

(1)c	(2)a	(3)d	(4)b	(5)a	(6)b	(7)c	(8)a	(9)b	(10)a	(11)a	(12)c	(13)b	(14)c
(15)b	(16)a	(17)c	(18)c	(19)b	(20)c	(21)b	(22)a	(23)c	(24)a	(25)a	(26)a	(27)a	(28)d
(29)c	(30)b	(31)c	(32)b	(33)a	(34)c	(35)c	(36)d	(37)a	(38)b	(39)b	(40)b	(41)b	(42)d
(43)d	(44)b	(45)a	(46)b	(47)b	(48)b	(49)c	(50)c	(51)b	(52)b	(53)b	(54)d	(55)d	(56)c
(57)a	(58)b												

SOLVED NUMERICAL PROBLEMS

Problem 1

In an actual test for determination of calorific value of fuel by bomb calorimeter the following data were obtained:

Weight of silica crucible, with nichrome fuse = 3.481 gm
Weight of crucible, nichrome fuse and fuel = 4.313 gm
Weight equivalent of calorimeter = 750 gm of water
Quantity of water in calorimeter = 1750 gm
Rise of temperature of water = 2.96° C
Calculate the calorific value of the fuel.

Solution:

Weight of fuel burnt (X) = 4.313 – 3.481 = 0.832 gm
Water equivalent of calorimeter (w) = 750gm
Quantity of water taken (W) = 1750 gm
Total water equivalent (W+w) = 2500 gm
Rise in temperature of water (T_2-T_1) = 2.96° C

$$HCV = \frac{(W+w)(T_2-T_1)}{X} \text{ cal/gm}$$

$$= \frac{(1750+750)\times(2.96)}{0.832}$$

$$\text{HCV} = \frac{7400}{0.832}$$

HCV = 8894.23 cal/ gm or 8.9 kcal /kg Ans.

Problem 2

The following data refer to a test in bomb calorimeter. From it find the lower and higher calorific values of the fuel if the sample of coal contains 4% hydrogen:

Weight of silica crucible = 3.28 gm
Weight of crucible + Fuel = 4.003 gm
Weight of water in the calorimeter = 1750gm
Water equivalent of the calorimeter = 510gm
Rise in temperature of water = 4.04°C
Cooling correction = 0.01°C

Solution:

Wt. of fuel = 4.003 – 3.28 = 0.723 gm
Water equivalent of the calorimeter (w) = 510 gm
Weight of water taken (W) = 1750 gm
Total water equivalent (W+w) = 2260gm

Rise in temperature (T_2-T_1) = 3.04°C
Cooling correction (Tc) = 0.01°C
Corrected temperature rise (T_2-T_1+ Tc) = 3.05°C

Heat gained by water = (W+w) × (T_2-T_1+ Tc)
= 3.05 × 2260

Let x be the higher calorific value of the fuel

Heat generated by fuel = Wt. of fuel × calorific value of the fuel
0.723 × x

Heat generated by fucl = heat gained by water
0.723 × x = 3.05 × 2260

$$\text{Therefore,}\quad x = \frac{3..05 \times 2260}{0.723}$$

= 9534 cal/gm

As $2H_2 + O_2 \rightarrow 2H_2O$
4 32 36

1 gm combustion of hydrogen gives 9 gm of water vapours.
1 gm fuel burnt will give
9 x 0.04 = 0.36 gm of water vapour

∴ Low calorific value of fuel = 9534 – 0.36 x 587
= 9534 – 211.32
= **9322.68 cal/gm** **Ans.**

Problem 3

In a test with bomb calorimeter 0.742 gm of petroleum was completely burnt. The calorimeter contained 2 kg of water in it, The water equivalent of the calorimeter was 0.720 kg. If the rise in temperature produced was 2.98°C, calculate the calorific value of the liquid fuel.

Solution:

Mass of fuel = 0.742 gm
Weight of water (W) = 2 kg = 2000 gm
Water equivalent of calorimeter (w) = 0.720 kg = 720 gm.
Rise in temperature = 2.98°C
Let the calorific value of the fuel = C cal/gm
Heat produced by fuel = 0.742 × C cal
Heat gained by water and calorimeter = (2000 + 720) × 2. 98
= 8105.6 cal

Heat produced by fuel = Heat gained by water and calorimeter
0.742 × C = 8105.6

$$C = \frac{8105.6}{0.742}$$ = **10923.98 cal/gm**

C = 10.92 kcal/kg Ans.

Problem 4

The following data is obtained in a bomb calorimeter experiment:
Mass of the fuel pallet = 0.85 gm
Mass of the water taken in calorimeter = 540 gm
Difference in final and initial temperature = 1.9° C

Cooling correction = 3.8 cal
Acid correction = 48.8 cal

Calculate the net calorific value of the fuel if it contains 3.6% hydrogen and 1.2% oxygen.

Solution:

$$L = \frac{(W+w)(t_2 - t_1 + \text{Cooling correction}) - (\text{Acid correction})}{\text{Mass of per fuel}(n)}$$

W = Mass of water taken in calorimeter
= 540gm
w = Water equivalent of calorimeter
$t_2 - t_1$ = Rise in temperature = 1.9°C
Cooling correction = 3.8 cal
Mass of fuel n = 0.85 gm
Acid correction = 48.8 cal
L= Gross calorific value of fuel

$$L = \frac{(540 \times 5.7 - 48.8)cal}{0.85}$$

= 3563.76 cal/gm

Net calorific value = Gross calorific value (L) – 0.09 H x 587 cal/gm
% of hydrogen = 3.6%
= 3563.76 – 0.09 x 3.6 x 587
= 3563.76 – 109.188
= **3373.57 cal/gm Ans.**

Problem 5

A sample of coal was analysed as follows: 1.0 gm of air dried coal sample was weighed in a silica crucible. After heating for 1 hour at 105 - 110°C, the dry coal residue weighed 0.985 gm. The crucible was covered with a vented lid and then heated strongly for exactly 7 minutes at 950 $\pm$20°C. The residue weighed 0.800 gm. The crucible was then heated strongly in air until a constant weight was obtained. The last residue was found to weight 0.100 gm. Calculate the proximate analysis results on (a) air dry basis, (b) oven dry basis (c) moisture and ash free basis.

Solution:

Mass of moisture in the coal samples
= 1.000 – 0.985 = 0.015 gm
Mass of volatile matter = 0.0985 – 0.800 = 0.185 gm
Mass of ash = 0.10 gm

(a) Proximate analysis on air dry basis

Percentage of moisture $= \frac{0.015 \times 100}{1.000} = 1.5\%$

Percentage of volatile matter $= \frac{0.185 \times 100}{1.000} = 18.5\%$

Percentage of ash $= \frac{0.10 \times 100}{1.000} = 10.0\%$

∴ Percentage of fixed carbon % C=100 – % of (moisture + volatile matter + ash)
= 100 – %(1.5+18.5+10.0)
Fixed carbon = **70% Ans.**

(b) Proximate analysis on oven dry or moisture free basis

Percentage of volatile matter $= \dfrac{0.185 \times 100}{0.985} = 18.78\,\%$

Percentage of ash $= \dfrac{0.10 \times 100}{0.985} = 10.15\,\%$

$\therefore$ Percentage of fixed carbon = 100 – (18.78+10.15)

= 71.07 % Ans.

(c) Proximate analysis on moisture and ash free basis percentage of volatile matter

$= \dfrac{0.185 \times 100}{4.985 - 0.100} = 20.90\,\%$

Percentage of fixed carbon = 100 – 20.90

= 79.10 % Ans.

Problem 6

Calculate the value of air required for complete combustion of one liter of producer gas, the combustion of which by volume is: **(RGPV 2002)**

CO = 20%

H_2 = 40%

CH_4 = 8%

N_2 = 38%

Solution:

For hydrogen

$H_2 + 0.5\ O_2 \rightarrow H_2O$

Quantity of oxygen required

0.4 x 0.5 = 0.2

For carbon monoxide

$CO + 0.5O_2 \rightarrow CO_2$

Quantity of oxygen required

0.2 x 0.5 = 0.1

For methane

$CH_4 + 2O_2 \rightarrow CO_2 + 2H_2O$

Quantity of oxygen required

= 0.08 x 2 = 0.16

Nitrogen being non-combustible will not consume oxygen

Total quantity of oxygen used = 0.2 + 0.1 + 0.16

$= 0.46\text{m}^3$

Quantity of air required (as air contains 21% O_2)

$= \dfrac{0.46 \times 100}{21}$

= 2.190 m^3 Ans.

Problem 7

A sample of coal contains 89% C, 8% H, 3% ash. When this coal was tested in the laboratory for its calorific value in the bomb calorimeter, the following data were obtained:

Weight of coal burnt(x) = 0.89 gm

Weight of water taken (W) = 650gm

Water equivalent of bomb and calorimeter (w) = 2500 gm

Rise in temperature ($T_2 - T_1$) = 2.5° C

Cooling correction (Tc) = 0.03°C

Fuse wire correction = 10 cal

Acid correction = 50 cal.

Assuming that the latent heat of condensation of steam as 587 cal/ gm, calculate the (i) gross and (ii) net calorific values of the coal in cal/gm.

Solution:

(i) G.C.V. or (H.C.V.)

$$= \frac{(W+w)(T_2 - T_1 + \text{Cooling correction}) - (\text{Acid} + \text{Fuse correction})}{x}$$

$$= \frac{(650+2500)(2.5+0.03)-(50+10)}{0.89}$$

G.C.V = 8887 cal/gm Ans.

(ii) N.C.V. or (L.C.V.) = G.C.V. – 0.09 H + 587

= 8887 – 0.09 × 8 + 587

= 8464.36 cal/gm Ans.

Problem 8

A coal has following composition by weight: C= 90%, 0=3.0% , S=0.5%, N=0.5% and ash = 2.5. Net calorific value of coal was found to be 8,490.5 Kcal/g. Calculate the percentage of hydrogen and higher calorific value of coal. **[RGPV 05]**

Solution:

HCV = (NCV + 0.09H × 587) kcal/kg

= 8,490.5 + 0.09H × 587) kcal/kg---------------- (i)

$$HCV = \frac{1}{100}\left[8080C + 34500\left[H - \frac{O}{8}\right] + 2240S\right] kcal/kg$$

$$\text{HCV} = \frac{1}{100}\left[8{,}080 \times 90 + 34500\left(H - \frac{3.0}{8}\right) + 2{,}240 \times 0.5\right]$$

= 0.01[727200 + 34500 H- 12937.5 + 1120]

= [7272 + 345 H – 129.37 + 11.2]

= [7153.84 + 345 H] kcal/kg---------------------- (ii)

From (i) and (ii) we get

7153.84 + 345 H = 8490.5 + 52.74 H

345H – 52.74H = 8490.5 – 7153.84

292.26 H = 1,336.66

$$\therefore \ \% \text{ of H} = \frac{1336.66}{292.26} = 4.5735 = 4.57\%$$

HCV = 8490.5 + 0.09 × 4.57 × 587 = **8731.9 kcal/kg Ans**

Problem 9

A sample of coal was analyzed as follows: Exactly 2.500g was weighed into a silica crucible after heating for one hour at 110°C the crucible weighed 2.415g which was covered with a vented lid and strongly heated for exactly seven minutes at 950 ± 20°C. The residue weighed 1.528 g. The crucible was then heated without the cover until a constant weight was obtained. The last residue was found to weight 0.245g. Calculate the percentage of the above analysis.

[RGPV 06]

Solution:

Mass of Moisture in Coal sample: = 2.500g – 2.415 g = 0.085 g

Mass of Volatile matter: = 2.415 – 1.528 = 0.887 g.

Mass of ash = 0.245 g

$$\text{Percentage of Moisture} = \frac{0.085 \times 100}{2.500} = 3.4\%$$

$$\text{Percentage of volatile matter} = \frac{0.887 \times 100}{2.500} = 35.48\%$$

$$\text{Percentage of ash} = \frac{0.245 \times 100}{2.500} = 9.8\%$$

Percentage of fixed carbon = 100 – % of (moisture + volatile + ash matter)

= 100 – % (3.4 + 35.48+9.8) = 100 – 48.68

= 51.32 % Ans.

Problem 10

A sample of coal was analysed as follows:

Exactly 1.5 gm of coal was weighed into a silica crucible. After heating for one hour at 100°C, the residual weighed 1.415 gm. The crucible was then covered with a vented lib and strongly heated for exactly seven minutes at 950 ± 20°C. The residual weighed 0.528 gm. The crucible was then heated without the cover, until a constant weight was obtained. The last residue was found to weight 0.254 gm. Calculate:

(i) The percentage results of the above analysis

Solution:

$$\text{(a) Moisture (\%)} = \frac{\text{Loss in Weight}}{\text{Weight of coal sample taken}} \times 100$$

$$= \frac{1.5 - 1.415}{1.5} \times 100$$

$$= \mathbf{5.67\%}$$

$$\text{(b) Volatile matter (\%)} = \frac{\text{Loss in weight due to removal of volatile matter}}{\text{Weight of coal sample taken}} \times 100$$

$$= \frac{1.415 - 0.528}{1.5} \times 100$$

$$= \mathbf{59\%}$$

$$\text{(C) Ash (\%)} = \frac{\text{Weight of ash left}}{\text{Weight of coal taken}} \times 100$$

$$= \frac{0.254}{1.5} \times 100$$

= **16.93%** **Ans.**

(d) Fixed carbon (%) = 100-% of (moisture + volatile + ash matter)

= 100- (5.67 + 59+ 16.93)

= **18.4%** **Ans.**

Problem 11

A sample of coal was found to contain the following:

C: 80%, H: 5.0%, O: 1.0%, N: 2% remaining being ash. Calculate the amount of minimum air required for complete combustion of 1 kg of coal sample. **[RGPV 07]**

Solution:

1 kg of coal contains: C= 800 g, H= 50 g, N=20g, O=10g

$$\text{Theoretical wt. of air required} = \frac{100}{23}\left[\frac{32}{12}\times C+\frac{16}{2}\left[H-\frac{O}{8}\right]+S\right]g$$

Theoretical or minimum wt. of oxygen required for combustion of 1 kg of coal:

$$=\left[\frac{32}{12}\times C+\frac{16}{2}\left[H-\frac{O}{8}\right]+S\right]g=\left[800\times\frac{32}{12}+50\times\frac{16}{2}-10\right]g$$

$$= [2133.33 + 400 - 10] = 2523.33\text{gm}$$

Theoretical wt. of air required for combustion of 1 kg of coal:

$$2523.33\times\frac{100}{23} = 10971\text{gm}$$

10.971 kg Ans.

Problem 12

A liquid hydrocarbon fuel contains C: 89.4% and H: 10.6% by weight of 100 kg and is burnt. Calculate theoretical amount of air. **[RGPV 07]**

Solution:

100 kg of fuel contains: C= 89.4kg, H= 10.6 kg

$$\text{Theoretical wt. of air required} = \frac{100}{23}\left[\frac{32}{12}\times C+\frac{16}{2}\left[H-\frac{O}{8}\right]+S\right]g$$

Theoretical or minimum wt. of oxygen required for combustion of 1 kg of coal:

$$=\left[89.4\times\frac{32}{12}+10.6\times\frac{16}{2}\right]kg = [238.4 + 84.8]\text{ kg} = 323.2\text{ kg}$$

Theoretical or minimum wt. of air required for combustion of 1 kg of coal

$$323.2\times\frac{100}{23} = \mathbf{1405.21\ kg\ Ans.}$$

Problem 13

A sample of coal was found to have the following percentage composition:
C= 75%, H = 5.2 %, O= 12.1%, N = 4.5 % and ash = 3.2%. Calculate the minimum amount of air required for complete combustion of 1 kg of coal. **[RGPV 07]**

Solution:

1 kg of coal contains:
C= 750 g, H= 52 g, N=45g, ash = 32g, O= 12.1 g

$$\text{Theoretical wt. of air required} = \frac{100}{23}\left[\frac{32}{12}\times C+\frac{16}{2}\left[H-\frac{O}{8}\right]+S\right]kg$$

$$=\left[750\times\frac{32}{12}+52\times\frac{16}{2}-12.1\right]\times\frac{100}{23}$$

$$=[2000+416-12.1]\times\left(\frac{100}{23}\right)g$$

= 10451.7 gm or 10.45 kg Ans.

Problem 14

A gas used in internal combustion engine had the following composition by volume: H_2 = 45%, CH_4 = 36%, CO=15%, N_2=4%. Find the volume of air required for the combustion of $1m^3$ of the gas.**[RGPV 04]**

Solution:

1 m^3 of gas contains: $H_2 = 0.45\ m^3$, $CH_4= 0.36\ m^3$, CO= $0.15\ m^3$, $N_2=0.04m^3$

Combustion reaction	Volume of Oxygen required (m^3)
$H_2 + 0.5O_2 \rightarrow H_2O$ $1m^3$ $0.5\ m^3$ $1m^3$	$0.45 \times 0.5 = 0.225\ m^3$
$CH_4 + 2O_2 \rightarrow CO_2 + 2H_2O$ $1m^3$ $2m^3$ $1m^3$ $2m^3$	$0.36 \times 2 = 0.720\ m^3$
$CO + 0.5O_2 \rightarrow CO_2$	$0.15 \times 0.5 = 0.075\ m^3$

Total Volume of oxygen required = $(0.225 + 0.720 + 0.075)\ m^3 = 1.020\ m^3$

$\therefore$ Volume of air required per m^3 of the gas = $1.020 \times \frac{100}{21}$

= **4.857 m^3 Ans.**

Problem 15

Find the volume of oxygen and air required at 27°C and 740 mm pressure for complete burning of 200 gms of coal which has C= 72% , hydrogen=62%, sulphur =7.8%, oxygen=4%, ash=3% and moisture=3%.

Solution:

200 gm of Coal contains,

$$C = \frac{72}{100} \times 200 = 144gm$$

$$H = \frac{6.2}{100} \times 200 = 12.4gm$$

$$S = \frac{7.8}{100} \times 200 = 15.6gm$$

$$O = \frac{4}{100} \times 200 = 8gm$$

Ash and moisture are not combustible and hence require no oxygen.

Equation for combustion:

$C + O_2 \rightarrow CO_2$

12gm + 32gm 22400 ml at N.T.P.

$2H_2 + O_2 \rightarrow 2H_2O$

4gm 32 gm 22400 ml at N.T.P.

$S + O_2 \rightarrow SO_2$

32 gm 32 gm 22400 ml at N.T.P.

Volume of oxygen required for 144 gm carbon

$$= \frac{22400}{12} \times 144$$

= 268800 ml at N.T.P.

Volume of oxygen required for 12.4 gm hydrogen

$$= \frac{22400}{4} \times 12.4$$

= 69440 ml at N.T.P.

Volume of oxygen required for 15.6 gm sulphur

$$= \frac{22400}{32} \times 15.6$$

= 10920 ml at N.T.P.

Total volume of oxygen required

= 268800 + 69440 + 10920

= 349160 ml at N.T.P. Ans.

Volume of oxygen already present

$$= \frac{22400}{32} \times 8$$

= 5600 ml at N.T.P.

∴ Net volume of oxygen required 343560 ml at N.T.P.

= 343.56 litre at N.T.P.

To convert the volume of oxygen 343.56 litre at N.T.P. to 27°C and 740 mm pressure

$V_1 = 343.56$ litre

$V_2 = ?$

$T_1 = 273$ K

$T_2 = 27 + 273 = 300^o$

$P_1 = 760$ mm

$P_2 = 740$ mm

For gas equation

$$\frac{P_1V_1}{T_1} = \frac{P_2V_2}{T_2}$$

$$\frac{760 \times 343.56}{273} = \frac{740 \times V_2}{300}$$

$$V_2 = \frac{760 \times 343.56}{273} \times \frac{300}{740}$$

= 387.74 litre Ans.

Hence the volume of oxygen required at 27°C and 740 mm Pressure

= 387.74 litre

Volume of air required $= \frac{387.74 \times 100}{21}$

= 1846.39 litre Ans.

Problem 16

A gas used in internal combustion engine had the following composition by volume: H_2= 45%, CH_4=36%, CO=15% and N_2=4%. Find the volume of air required for combustion of per m^3 of the gas.

Solution:

For hydrogen

$$H_2 + 0.5O_2 \longrightarrow H_2O$$

Quantity of oxygen required

$0.45 \times 0.5 = 0.225$

For CH_4

$$CH_4 + 2O_2 \rightarrow CO_2 + 2H_2O$$

Quantity of oxygen required

$$= 0.36 \times 2$$
$$= 0.72$$

For CO

$$CO + 0.50_2 \rightarrow CO_2 \uparrow$$

Quantity of oxygen required

$$= 0.15 \times 0.5$$
$$= 0.75$$

Total quantity of oxygen required

$$= 0.225 + 0.72 + 0.75$$
$$= 1.695 \text{ m}^3$$

Air contains 21% of oxygen so% of air

$$= \frac{1.695}{21} \times 100$$

$$= \mathbf{8.0714\ m^3} \quad \textbf{Ans.}$$

Problem 17

A sample of coal gas was found to contain the following C = 81%, H_2=4%, O_2=2% and N_2=1%, the remaining being ash. Estimate the quantity of maximum air required for complete combustion of 1kg of the sample, if 40% of the excess air is supplied.

Solution:

$$C = 810 \text{ kg.}$$
$$H = 40\text{gm}$$
$$O = 20 \text{ gm}$$

Their combustion equations are

$$C + O_2 (g) \longrightarrow CO_2(g)$$
$$12 + 32$$

$$H_2 + \frac{1}{2} O_2 (g) \longrightarrow H_2O (l)$$

Theoretical amount of oxygen required for combustion of 1kg of coal:

$$= \left[C \times \frac{32}{12} + H \times \frac{16}{2} - O\right]$$

$$= \left[810 + \frac{32}{12} + 40 \times \frac{16}{2} - 20\right]$$

$$= [2160 + 320 - 20]$$
$$= 2460 \text{ gm}$$
$$= 2.460 \text{ kg}$$

Theoretical amount of ar required for combustion of per kg of coal

$$= \text{Amount of oxygen} \times \left(\frac{100}{23}\right)$$

$$= 2.460 \text{ kg} \times \left(\frac{100}{23}\right)$$

$$= 10.6957 \text{ kg}$$

Hence actual amount of air used per kg of coal

$$= \text{Theoretical amount} \times \left(\frac{140}{100}\right)$$

$$= 10.6957 \times \left(\frac{140}{100}\right)$$

= 14.9740 kg Ans.

Problem 18

Calculate the weight and volume of air needed for complete combustion of 5 kg of a coal containing 85% carbon, 10% hydrogen and rest oxygen.

Solution:

5 kg of coal contains

C = 4.25 kg
O = 0.25 kg
H = 0.500 kg

∴ Minimum weight of oxygen needed for combustion of 5 kg of coal

$$= 4.25\times\frac{32}{12}+0.50\times\frac{16}{2}-0.25kg$$

$$= 11.33 \ + \ 4.000 - 0.25$$

$$= 15.083 \text{ kg}$$

∴ Minimum weight of air needed for complete combustion

$$= 15.083 \times \frac{100}{23}$$

= **65.558 kg or [65,558 gm] Ans.**

Now molecular weight of air is 28.94 gm

∴ 28.94 gm of air occupied a volume

= 22.4 litre at N.T.P.

$$\therefore 65558 \text{ gm} = \frac{22.4}{28.94}\times 65558$$

= 50,742.9 litre

= **50.7429 m^3 Ans.**

Problem 19

A sample of coal was found to have the following % composition by weight: C=75%, H=5.2%, O=12.1%, N=3.2% and ash=4.5%. Calculate (i) the minimum amount of O_2 and air by weight necessary for complete combustion of 1 kg of coal (ii) weight of air required; if 40% excess air is supplied (iii) gross and net calorific value of coal sample using Dulong's formula.

[RGPV 01]

Solution:

(i) 1 kg of coal contains: C= 750 gms, H = 52 g, O_2= 121 g, N= 32 g

∴ Minimum wt. of O_2 required for complete combustion of 1 kg of coal:

$$= \left[750\times\frac{32}{12}+52\times\frac{16}{2}-121\right]g \quad = [2000 + 416 - 121] \text{ g} \quad = 2,295 \text{ g}$$

∴ Minimum wt. of air required $= 2.295 \text{ kg} \times \frac{100}{23}$

= 9.978 kg Ans.

(ii) Wt. of air required with 40% excess $= 9.978 \times \frac{140}{100}$ = **13.969 kg Ans**

(iii) $$\text{HCV} = \frac{1}{100}\left[8080C + 34500\left[H - \frac{O}{8}\right] + 2240S\right] kcal/kg$$

$$\text{HCV or GCV} = \frac{1}{100}\left[8{,}080 + 75 + 34{,}500\left(5.2 - \frac{12.1}{8}\right)\right] kcal/kg$$

$$= \frac{1}{100}[606{,}000 + 179400 - 52181.25]$$

= 7332.19 kcal/kg Ans.

NCV $= \text{HCV} - 0.09H \times 587$

$= (7332.19 - 0.09 \times 5.2 \times 587)$

$= 7332.19 - 274.716$ **= 7057.474 kcal/kg Ans.**

Problem 20

The percentage composition of sample of anthracite coal is C=90, H=3.5, O=3.0, N=1.0, S=0.5 and the remainder being ash (by weight). Estimate (i) minimum weight of air required for combustion of 1 kg of this fuel, (ii) the composition of dry products of combustion by volume, if 50% excess air is supplied.

[RGPV 04]

Solution:

1 kg of coal contains C = 900 g H= 35g, O=30g, N=10g, S=5g and ash (by difference) =20g

S.N.	Constituent	Amount	Combustion reaction	Wt. of oxygen required (g)
1	C	900 g	$C + O_2 \rightarrow CO_2$ 12g 32g 44g	$900 \times \frac{32}{12} = 2{,}400$
2	H	35 g	$H_2 + 0.5O_2 \rightarrow H_2O$ 2g 16g 18g	$35 \times \frac{16}{2} = 280$
3	S	5 g	$S + O_2 \rightarrow SO_2$ 32g 32g 64g	$5 \times \frac{32}{32} = 5$
4	O	30 g	Oxygen present in fuel	30

Minimum wt. of O_2 required for 1 kg of coal:

$$= \left[900 \times \frac{32}{12} + 35 \times \frac{16}{2} + 5 \times \frac{32}{32} - 30\right]$$

$= 2655g$

(i) Minimum wt. of air required for 1 kg of coal

$$= 2{,}655 \times \frac{100}{23} g$$

= 11543.48 g = **11.543 kg Ans.**

Excess air $= 11.543 \times 150/100$

$= 17.315$ kg

Difference of excess air $= 17.315 - 11.543$

= 5.772 kg or 5772 g Ans.

(ii) Calculation of weight of dry products of combustion with 50% excess air. Dry products obtained during the reaction are CO_2, SO_2, N_2, O_2

$$CO_2 = 900\times\frac{44}{12} = 3{,}300\text{ g}$$

$$SO_2 = 5\times\frac{64}{32} = 10\text{ g}$$

$$N_2 = 10\text{ g(in fuel)}+11543.48\times\frac{150}{100}\times\frac{77}{100}\text{g(of air)} = 10\text{g} + 13332.72\text{ g} = 13342.72\text{ g}$$

$$O_2 = 5772\times\frac{23}{100} = 1327.56\text{ g}$$

Calculation of volumetric composition of dry products of combustion:

Wt. of dry product	Mol. mass	Relative Vol. of dry product
$CO_2 = 3{,}300$ g	44	$\frac{3300}{44} = 75.000$
$SO_2 = 10$ g	64	$\frac{10}{64} = 00.156$
$N_2 = 13342.72$ g	28	$\frac{13342.72}{28} = 476.53$
$O_2 = 1327.56$ g	32	$\frac{1327.56}{32} = 41.49$

Total = 593.18 m^3

$\therefore$

$$CO_2 = 75\times\frac{100}{593.18} = 12.64\%$$

$$SO_2 = 0.156\times\frac{100}{593.18} = 0.026\%$$

$$N_2 = 476.53\times\frac{100}{593.18} = 80.33\%$$

$$O_2 = 41.46\times\frac{100}{593.18} = 6.99\%$$

Problem 21

A producer gas has following composition by volume: CH_4 = 4%, CO=26.0%, H_2=10%, CO_2 = 10%, N_2=50%. Calculate minimum quantity of air required for complete combustion of 1 m^3 of the fuel gas and percentage composition of dry products of combustion by volume when 20% excess air is used.

[RGPV 03, 02]

Solution:

1m^3 of fuel gas contains: CH_4 = 0.04 m^3, CO= 0.26 m^3, H_2=0.10m^3, CO_2=0.10m^3, N_2=0.50m^3.

Combustion reaction	Vol. of O_2 required	Vol. of dry products (CO_2)
$CH_4+2O_2\rightarrow CO_2+2H_2O$	0.04 × 2 = 0.08 m^3	0.04 × 1 = 0.04
$CO + ½ O_2\rightarrow CO_2$	0.26 × 0.5 = 0.13	0.26 × 1 = 0.26
$H_2 +½ O_2\rightarrow H_2O$	0.10 × 0.5 = 0.05	
Total	= 0.260 m^3	CO_2 = 0.30 m^3

$\therefore$ Minimum air required $= 0.260\ m^3 \times \dfrac{100}{21} = 1.238\ m^3$

$\therefore$ Vol. of air required per m^3 of gaseous fuel using 20% excess air.

$$= \left[0.260\,m^3 \times \frac{100}{21} \times \frac{120}{100}\right] = 1.4857\ m^3 \qquad \text{or}$$

Excess air = $1.486\ m^3$

Remaining air = Excess air – air used

$1.486 - 1.238 = 0.248\ m^3$

Calculation of volume of dry product of combustion $CO_2 = 0.30\ m^3$,

$$O_2 \text{ (of excess air)} = \frac{21}{100} \times 0.248 = 0.052\ m^3$$

$$N_2 = 0.50\ m^3 \text{ (fuel gas)} + 1.486 \times \frac{79}{100} \text{(of air)}$$

$$= 0.50 + 1.1739 = 0.50 + 1.174 = 1.674\ m^3$$

Total volume of dry products = $(0.30 + 0.052 + 1.674) = 2.026\ m^3$

$$\therefore \quad CO_2 = \frac{0.30 \times 100}{2.026} = 14.81\%$$

$$O_2 = \frac{0.052 \times 100}{2.026} = 2.57\%$$

$$N_2 = \frac{1.674 \times 100}{2.026} = 82.62\%$$

Problem 22

A sample of coal has the following composition by weight C = 84.9%, H=11.4%, S=3.2%, O=0.4%, ash =0.1% Calculate the minimum quantity of air required for complete combustion of 1 kg of coal.

[RGPV 05]

Solution:

1 kg of coal contains: C= 849 g, H= 114 g, S=32 g, 0=4g

Theoretical or minimum wt. of air required for combustion of 1 kg of coal:

$$= \frac{100}{23}\left[\frac{32}{12} \times C + \frac{16}{2}\left[H - \frac{O}{8}\right] + S\right] g$$

$$= \frac{100}{23}\left[849 \times \frac{32}{12} + 114 \times \frac{16}{2} + 32 \times \frac{32}{32} - 4\right] g$$

$$= [2264 + 912 + 32 - 4]\ g \times \frac{100}{23}$$

= 13,930g = **13.930 kg Ans.**

Problem 23

The % analysis by volume of producer gas is: H_2=18.3%, CH_4=3.4%, CO=25.4%, CO_2=5.1%, N_2=47.8%. Calculate the volume of air required for combustion of $1 m^3$ of the gas. **[RGPV 05]**

Solution:

1 m^3 of producer gas contains: $H_2 = 0.183 m^3$, $CH_4 = 0.034 m^3$, $CO = 0.254 m^3$, $CO_2 = 0.051 m^3$, $N_2 = 0.478 m^3$

Combustion reaction	Vol. of O_2 needed m^3
$H_2 + 0.5\ O_2 \rightarrow H_2O$	$0.183 \times 0.5 = 0.0915$
$CH_4 + 2O_2 \rightarrow CO_2 + 2H_2O$	$0.034 \times 2 = 0.0680$
$CO + 0.5O_2 \rightarrow CO_2$	$0.254 \times 0.5 = 0.1270$
	Total = 0.2865

Hence, volume of air required for complete combustion of $1m^3$ of producer gas:

$= 0.2865 \times \frac{100}{21}\ m^3$ **$= 1.3643m^3$ Ans.**

Problem 24

A petrol sample contains 84% carbon and 16% hydrogen by weight. Its flue gas composition data by volume is as under CO_2=12.1%, CO= 1.1%, Oxygen=1.3%, N=85.5%. Calculate: (i) minimum air for complete combustion of 1.0 kg of petrol (ii) actual air supplied per kg of petrol and the (iii) the calorific values of petrol sample. **[RGPV 01]**

Solution:

(i) 1 kg of petrol contains: C = 840 g, H=160 g

Combustion reaction	Wt. of O_2 req. (g)	Wt. of dry products (g)
$C + O_2 \rightarrow CO_2$	$840 \times \frac{32}{12} = 2240$	$CO_2 = 840 \times \frac{44}{12} = 3080$
$H_2 + \frac{1}{2} O_2 \rightarrow H_2O$	$160 \times \frac{16}{2} = 1280$	
Total	3520	

Minimum wt. of air required for complete combustion of 1 kg

$= 3520 \times \frac{100}{23} = 15304$ g = 15.304 kg

(ii) 1 m^3 of flue gas contains: $CO_2 = 0.121\ m^3$, $CO = 0.011 m^3$, $O_2 = 0.013\ m^3$, $N_2 = 0.855 m^3$

Conversion of volumetric analysis to mass analysis:

Vol. of Gas	Mol. Mass (m)	v × m	Mass/kg of flue gas
$CO_2 = 0.121/m^3$	44	5.324	$\frac{5.324}{29.988} = 0.1776$ kg
$CO = 0.011/m^3$	28	0.308	$\frac{0.308}{29.988} = 0.0103$ kg
$O_2 = 0.013/m^3$	32	0.416	$\frac{0.416}{29.988} = 0.0139$ kg

$N_2 = 0.855/m^3$	28	23.940	$\frac{23.94}{29.988} = 0.7983$ kg
		Total = 29.988	Total = 1.0000 kg

Mass of excess O_2 per kg of flue gas

= Mass of O_2 (in flue gas – required to convert 0.0108 kg CO to CO_2)

$$= [0.0139 - 0.0103 \times \frac{16}{28}] \text{ kg} = [0.0139 - 0.0059] \text{ kg} = 0.0080 \text{ kg}$$

Mass of C/kg of flue gas =

$$= \text{Mass of} \left[CO_2 \times \frac{12}{44} + CO \times \frac{12}{28} \right]$$

$$= \left[0.1776 \times \frac{12}{44} + 0.0103 \times \frac{12}{28} \right] \text{kg} = 0.0484 + .00441 = 0.0528\text{kg}$$

Mass of flue gas formed by forming 1 kg petrol

$$\frac{wt. of\ C/kg\ of\ petrol}{wt. of\ C/kg\ of\ flue\ gas} = \frac{0.84\text{kg}}{0.0528\text{kg}} = 15.909\text{kg}$$

∴ Excess O_2/kg of petrol burnt

= (Mass of excess O_2/kg of flue gas) × (Mass of flue gas/kg of petrol burnt)

= 0.008 × 15.909 kg = 0.1273 kg

Excess air per kg of petrol burnt

0.12730 × (100/23) = 0.5535kg

Hence actual air supplied per kg of petrol burnt = Mass of air (for combustion + excess in Flue gas)

= 15.304 + 0.5535 = **15.858 kg Ans.**

(iii) HCV $= \frac{1}{100}[8080 \times 84 + 34500 \times 16]$ kcal/kg

$= \frac{1}{100}[678{,}720 + 552000] = 12{,}307]$ kcal/kg

12,307 kcal/kg Ans.

NCV = HCV – 0.09 H × 587

12,307 – 0.09 × 16 × 587

NCV = **11461.72 kcal/kg Ans.**

Problem 25

A sample of coal was found to have the following composition C=81%, H=5%, S=0.5%, N=3.0% and ash 10.5%. Calculate the percentage composition by volume of the fuel gas, when 30% excess air by weight is supplied for combustion. **[RGPV 06]**

Solution:

1. 1 kg of coal contains:

C= 810 g, H= 50 g, S=5g, N=30g, ash 105 g

Minimum mass of air required for 1 kg of Coal:

$$= \left[810 \times \frac{32}{12} + 50 \times \frac{16}{2} + 5 \times \frac{32}{32} \right] \times \frac{100}{23}$$

$$= [2160 + 400 + 5] \times \left(\frac{100}{23} \right) g = 11{,}152\text{g} = \mathbf{11.152\ kg\ Ans.}$$

2. Calculation of masses of dry product of combustion with 30% excess air

$CO_2 = 810 \times 44/12 =$ 2,970g

$SO_2 = 5 \times 64/32 = 10g$

Excess air $=11.152 \times \frac{130}{100} = 14.4976$ kg

Difference in excess air = 14.4976 – 11.152 = 3.3456kg

Amount of O_2 present in excess air = 3.3456 × 23/100 = 0.769 kg or 769 g

$N_2 = 30\ g + 11,152 \times \frac{130}{100} \times \frac{77}{100} = 11193g$

Calculation of volumetric composition of dry products of combustion

Mass of dry products	Mol. Mass	Relative volume of dry produces
CO_2 = 2,970 g	44	$\frac{2970}{44} = 67.5$
SO_2 = 10 g	64	$\frac{10}{64} = 0.1563$
O_2 = 769 g	32	$\frac{769}{32} = 24.03$
N_2 = 11193 g	28	$\frac{11193}{28} = 399.75$
	Total	491.436

$\therefore CO_2 = \frac{67.2727 \times 100}{491.436} = 13.73\%$

$SO_2 = \frac{0.1563 \times 100}{491.436} = 0.032\%$

$O_2 = \frac{24.03 \times 100}{491.436} = 4.89\%$

$N_2 = \frac{399.75 \times 100}{491.436} = 81.34\%$

Problem 26

A sample of petrol was found to contain 15.2% H and 84.8% C by weight. Calculate the weight of oxygen needed for the combustion of 1.15 liter of petrol. (Given density of petrol= 0.87 g/ml). **[RGPV 07]**

Solution:

Density (p) of petrol = 0.87g/ml = 0.87kg/l

Mass of petrol=V × p = 1.15L × 0.87kg/l

= 1.0005kg

Wt. of oxygen required for combustion of 1 kg of petrol

= [848 (32/12) +152 (16/2)]

= 2261.34+1216 = 3477.34 g

=3.47 kg

Wt. of oxygen required for combustion of 1.0005 kg of petrol

= 3.47 × 1.0005 kg

= 3.471 kg Ans.

Problem 27

A hydrocarbon fuel on burning gave a flue gas having the following volumetric analysis: O_2 = 3.56%, CO_2 = 13.53% and N_2 = 82.91%. Determine the following: **[RGPV 08]**

i.)The composition of fuel by weight

ii.) The % of excess air used

Solution

i) As the flue gas contains CO_2 so one of the constituent in fuel must be carbon.

Moreover, combustion reaction for carbon is:

$$C + O_2 \rightarrow CO_2$$

This indicates that moles of CO_2 = moles of O_2 = moles of C

Assuming total amount of dry flue gas = 100 k mol,

So moles of CO_2 = 13.53 k mol

Thus, amount of O_2 in flue gas=13.53 (from CO_2) + 3.56(from free O_2 in flue gas)

= 17.09 k mol -- (i)

Given amount of N_2 in the flue gas = 82.91 k mol

We know that, in 100 k mol air, 79 k mol N_2 is present (i.e. 79% N_2 by volume)

Thus, amount of air supplied for combustion

=100/79 × 82.91 k mol=104.95 k mol--- (iia)

Amount of O_2 supplied =104.95 × 21/100

=22.039=22.04 k mol--- (iib)

From (i) and (iib), it can be concluded that

Amount of O_2 that has combined with H_2

= 22.04 – 17.09 = 4.95 k mol

The combustion reaction for H_2 is:

$$2 H_2 + O_2 \rightarrow 2H_2O$$

Thus, amount of H_2 burnt = 2 × 4.95 = 9.90 k mol

And weight of H_2 burnt = 9.9 × 2 = 19.8 kg-- (iii)

As 100k mol of flue gas containing 13.53 k mol of CO_2 or 13.53 k mol of C

Therefore, amount of C in fuel

= 13.53 × 12 = 162.36 kg--- (iv)

Total wt of C + O_2 + H_2 +N_2

162.36 + 19.80 + 82.9 +22.04 = 287.11kg

Now,

% C = 162.36 / 287.11 × 100 = **56.5 % Ans .**

% H = 19.80 / 287.11 × 100 = **6.8% Ans.**

% N = 82.91 / 287.11 × 100 = **28.8 % Ans.**

%O_2 = 22.04 /287.11 × 100 = **7.6% Ans.**

ii) Theoretically, amount of O_2 required for producing 13.53 k mole of CO_2 = 13.53 k moles

Moreover, amount of O_2 required for burning H_2 =4.95 k moles

Thus, total amount of O_2 theoretically required =13.53 + 4.95 = 18.48 k mole

From (ii), amount of O_2 supplied = 22.04 k moles

So, % of excess air = 22.04 – 18.48/18.48 ×100

= **19.264 % Ans.**

THEORETICAL QUESTIONS

1. Differentiate between octane number and cetane number. **[RGPV 06, 07, 09]**
2. Write the significance of proximate analysis of coal. **[RGPV 06]**
3. Describe the Otto- Hoffman's process for preparing coke. What are its advantages over the Beehive Oven method? **[RGPV 06, 09, 10]**
4. Discuss in brief cracking. **[RGPV 06, 07]**
5. Distinguish between the coal and coke. **[RGPV 09]**
6. Write the significant factors for selecting coal for different uses. **[RGPV 09]**
7. Write short note on: **[RGPV 07, 08]**
   (i) Gross and net Calorific values
   (ii) Octane number
   (iii) Metallurgical coke and its characteristics **[RGPV 05,10]**
8. Discuss:
   (i) Octane number (ii) Cracking **[RGPV 05, 07]**
9. Why is octane number of 2, 3-dimethyl heptane higher than n-heptane? **[RGPV 01]**
10. What is knocking in an IC engine? "How is it related to the structure of the constituent hydrocarbons?" Define octane number. **[RGPV 03]**
11. Define and classify fuels. Describe the formula for calculating calorific value of fuel from its ultimate compositional data. **[RGPV 02, 07]**
12. Discuss Beehives Oven method for manufacture of coke. **[RGPV 04]**
13. Why is $C_2H_4Br_2$ added, when TEL is used as an anti knock? **[RGPV 01]**
14. Why is peat not considered as an economical fuel? **[RGPV 01]**
15. Explain proximate analysis of coal. How is it carried out? What is its significance? **[RGPV 01, 07, 08]**
16. What is meant by calorific values of fuel? **[RGPV 01, 07]**
17. Discuss in brief the ultimate analysis of coal. **[RGPV 03, 08]**
18. How is gross calorific value of solid fuel determined by bomb calorimeter? Write Dulong's formula for calculating calorific value of the fuel from its ultimate analysis date. **[RGPV 04, 08]**
19. Define and classify fuels.
    a) Describe the proximate analysis of coal and discuss its significance. **[RGPV 07]**
    b) What is knocking in IC engine? How is it related to the structure of the constituent hydrocarbons? Define octane number. **[RGPV 02]**
20. (a) How can you determine % C and % H in a coal sample?
    (b) Explain various bye- products recovered in Otto-Hoffman's coke oven process. **[RGPV 06]**
21. (a) How octane rating of petrol sample can be determined?
    (b) i) Explain cracking with its mechanism.
    ii) Write the significance of proximate analysis of coal. **[RGPV 06, 09]**
22. Give the advantages and disadvantages of pulverized coal. **[RGPV 07]**
23. Define the term CV, HCV and LCV. **[RGPV 07]**
24. Why ethylene dibromide is added with TEL while using as antiknocking agent? Explain with chemical equations involved in it. **[RGPV 07]**
25. What is cracking? Explain various types of cracking with neat labeled diagram. **[RGPV 07, 09]**
26. Draw a well labeled diagram of Bomb Calorimeter for determination of calorific value of a solid fuel. **[RGPV 07, 09]**
27. Define proximate and ultimate analysis of fuel. Give the name of parameters analysed under proximate and ultimate analysis. **[RGPV 07, 09, 10]**
28. State the characteristics of a good fuel. **[RGPV 07]**
29. Explain why: **[RGPV 07]**
    i.) A good fuel must have low ash content?

ii.) It is advantageous to convert cattle dung into gobar gas than to burn it in dried state?

30. Differentiate between thermal and catalytic cracking. **[RGPV 07, 09]**
31. What is Octane Number of gasoline? How the Octane Number of gasoline may be improved? **[RGPV 08]**
32. Calculate the weight and volume of air required for the combustion of one kg of graphite. **[RGPV 08]**
33. What is Carbonization? Describe Otto-Hoffmann method for manufacturing of metallurgical coke. **[RGPV 08]**
34. Differentiate between:
    i.) Cracking and Reforming. **[RGPV 08]**
35. Define Fuel. What are the criteria for selecting a fuel? **[RGPV 09]**

Unsolved Problems

1. A sample of petrol was found to contain 15.4% hydrogen and 84.6% carbon by weight. Calculate the volume of oxygen at N.T.P. required for the complete combustion of 1kg of this fuel.
   [Ans. 2441.6 Lit]

2. Calculate the volume of air required for complete combustion of one cubic meter of produced gas the composition of which (by volume) is H_2 = 30%, CO = 10%, CH_4= 4%, N_2= 56%
   [Ans. 1.333 m^3]

3. A sample of a fuel on analysis gives the follows results:
   C = 86%, H=4%, N=1.3%
   S=3%, O=4%, Ash=1.7%
   Calculate the minimum weight of air (containing 23% of oxygen by weight) required for complete combustion of 500g of this fuel.
   [Ans. 5.65 kg]
4. Calculate the amount of theoretical air by weight and volume for complete combustion of 2 kg of coke (Air contains 21% by volume of oxygen and 23.2% by weight of oxygen).
   [Ans. 17.792 Litre at NTP]

5. The following data was obtained in a Boy's gas calorimeter experiment -
   Volume of gas used = 0.1 m^3 at STP
   Wt. of water heated = 25kg
   Temp. of inlet water = 20°C
   Temp. of water = 33°C
   Wt. of steam condensed = 0.025 kg
   Calculate HCV and LCV per m^3 at STP.
   Take the heat liberated in condensing water vapour and cooling the condensate at 580 K cal/kg.
   [Ans. 3,105 K cal $m^{3]}$

6. The ultimate analysis of coal gives carbon = 84%, S=1.5%, N=0.6%, H=5.5%, O_2=8.4% Calculate the gross and net calorific values using Dulong's formula.
   [Ans. 8065.44 K cal/kg]

7. When 0.84g of sample of fuel was completely burnt in excess of oxygen, the increase in temperature of water in a calorimeter containing 1060g of water was 25° C. Calculate the HCV of fuel, if water equivalent of calorimeter is 135g.
   [Ans. 3556.55k cal/g]

8. Calculate the weight and volume of air required for combustion of one kg of carbon.

[Ans.8.89m^3]

9. A gas has following composition by volume: H_2 =30%, CH_4 = 5%, CO = 20%, CO_2=6%, O_2=5%, N_2=34%. If 50% excess air is used, find the weight of air actually per m^3 of this gas. Mean molecular wt. of air =28.97gms/mol.

[Ans. 277 gms]

10. A gaseous fuel has following composition by volume H_2=20%, CH_4=5%, CO=20%, CO_2=5%, N_2=45%. If 50% excess air is used, find the weight of air actually supplied per m^3 of the gas.

[Ans. 2768.4 litre]

11. Find the volume of O_2 and air required at 27°C and 740 mm Pressure for complete burning of 200 gms of coal which has C=70%, H=6.2%, S=7.8%,) ash= 3% and moisture=3%.

[Ans. 349160ml at NTP 387.74 Litre 1846.39 Litres]

12. Caclulate the volume of air required for complete combustion of five Litres of CO. Given percentage of Oxygen in air = 21.

[Ans. 11.9 Litres]

13. A gas used in I.C.E. had the following composition by volume H_2=45%, CH_4=36%, CO=15% and N_2=4%. Find the volume of air required for combustion per m^3 of the gas.

[Ans. 8.0714m^3]

14. A sample of coal containing 92%C, 5%H, 3% ash was tested in the laboratory for its calorific value in the bomb calorimeter, the following data were obtained. **[RGPV 2010]**

Wt. of coal burnt	= 0.95g
Wt. of water taken	= 700g
Water eq. of bomb calorimeter	= 2,000g
Rise in temperature	= 2.48°C
Cooling correction	= 0.02°C
Fuse wire correction	= 10.0 cal
Acid correction	= 60.0 cal

Calculate the GCV and NCV of the coal in cal/g (Assume the latent heat of condensation of steam as 580 cal/g).

[Ans. GCV = 7031.6 cal/g, LCV=6.770 cal/g]

15. A sample of Gondawana Coal of Jharia was analysed as follows:
Exactly 2,500g was weighed into silica crucible. After heating for 1hr. at 110°C the residue weighted 2.414g. the crucible was then covered with lid and strongly heated for exactly 7 min. at 950 ± 20°C. The residue weighted 1.528g. The Crucible was then heated without cover until a constant weight was obtained. The last residue was found to weight 0.245g. Calculate the % results of the above analysis.

[Ans. Moisture: 3.4%, Volatile matter = 35.48%, ash = 9.80%, Fixed Carbon = 51.32%.]

16. 0.945g of fuel on complete combustion in excess of oxygen increased the temperature of water in a calorimeter from 13.25 to 19.2°C, the mass of water in a calorimeter was found to be 1,458g . Calculate the GCV if the water equivalent of calorimeter is 144g.

[Ans. 10,087cal/g.]

17. Calculate the gross and net calorific value of coal sample having the following composition C=80%, H=7%, O=3%, S=3.5%, N = 2.1% and ash 4.4%.

[Ans. GCV = 8828 K cal/kg, NVC= 8,458 K cal/kg]

19. A gas has following composition by volume H_2 = 20%, CH_4= 6%, CO=22%, CO_2=4%, O_2=4%, N_2=44%, 20% excess air is used. Find the weight of air actually supplied per m^3 of the gas. Mol. Wt of air = 28.97g/mole.

[Ans. 2,143g]

20. A sample of coal has the following analysis C=83%, S=1.5%, N=0.6%, H=7.5% and O=8.4%. Find the gross calorific value using Dulong's formula.

[Ans. 8,885 K cal/kg]

21. A gaseous fuel has the following composition by volume:
H_2 = 25%, methane=30%, ethane=11% ethene= 4.5%, butene = 2.5%, CO = 6.0%, CO_2=8%, O_2=2% and N_2 = 12%, Calculate the air fuel ratio and fuel ratio and volumetric analysis of dry products of combustion using 40% excess air.

[Ans. (i) 9.333:1 (ii) CO_2=9.49%, N_2=86.71%, O_2=3.80%]

22. What amount of air would be required for the complete combustion of 10 kg fuel containing 85% ethanol and 15% methanol?

[Ans. 95.6 kg]

23. Calculate the theoretical quantity of air that will required for the complete combustion of a liquid fuel weighting 1kg. It contains 80% by weight benzene and 20% wt ethanol (Assume the composition of air to be 80% N_2 and 20% O_2 by wt.

[Ans. 14.7kg]

24. A sample of fuel gave on analysis 85% C, 6% H, 4.5% S, 2% O and 2.5% ash. This oil was employed for heating in a furnace with 30 % excess air. Calculate (a) Theoretical amount of air used per kg of fuel (b) the actual amount of air used per kg of fuel.

[Ans. (a) 12.13kg (b) 15.77 kg]

25. Calculate the amount of air required for the complete combustion of 1 m^3 of the gaseous fuel having the following composition by volume H_2= 50%, CH_4=36%, N_2=1.5%, CO=6%, C_2H_4=4%, Water vapour=2.5%.

[Ans. 5.33m^3]

26. Calculate the volume of air at STP needed for the complete combustion of 1kg of methane.

[Ans. 13.33m^3]

27. A sample of coal contains C= 60 %, H= 4%, O_2 = 6%, N_2 = 2% and ash = 28%. Calculate the percentage composition of the dry products of combustion, assuming that 40 % excess air is used.
[RGPV 2010][Ans. Total air = 11321.73 g, % O_2 = 6.36 %, % N_2= 74.79 %, %CO_2 = 18.83 %]

.......*.......

Unit - III

Lubricants

3.1 INTRODUCTION

Lubricants are essential parts of every machinery. Everything from home lock to computer, hard disk drive to jet and space aircrafts requires lubrication for their moving parts. In addition to automobiles and industrial applications, lubricants are used for many other purposes including biomedical applications for artificial joints, R-Y jelly, often for personal lubricant and others. Lubricant is a substance which is capable of reducing the friction between two surfaces which are sliding, moving, or rolling over each other. It reduces the coefficient of friction between two rubbing surfaces of the machinery. The loss of energy due to friction is reduced by the process of applying these substances and is known as lubrication. Petroleum is the main source of lubricants but synthetic lubricants have also been prepared in recent years for specific purposes.

Functions of Lubricant

1) Lubricant reduces the friction, for example-Steel surfaces have minute peaks and valleys. When the surfaces slide over each other, they get interlocked. When these surfaces are separated by some lubricating substance, the small peaks and valleys do not interlock and the top surface slides very freely over the bottom surface.
2) Lubricants avoid direct contact between the rubbing surfaces, as a result reduce wear and tear, surface deformation, minimize heavy damage, breakdowns and save the cost.
3) It acts as a coolant, hence reduces loss of energy in the form of heat. E.g. in the machine parts, when the surfaces rub, then heat is produced at the point of contact and that heat is adsorbed by the cool oil flowing over the heated surface and returns it to the reservoir at much lower temperature. Thus lubricant reduces the waste of energy, as a result efficiency of the machine increases.
4) It keeps out dirt, lubricant entraps the foreign particles of dirt and thus prevents the damage of smooth surface of the journal and bearing.
5) It acts as cleaning agent and as a scavenger to wash off and transport solid particles produced in combustion or wear.
6) It acts as sealing agent. E.g. in the internal combustion engines, lubricants are applied between piston and cylinder and they act as sealing agent.
7) It prevents rust and corrosion and thus reduces the maintenance and running cost of the machines.
8) It minimizes the liberation of the frictional heat and hence stops seizure of moving surfaces.
9) It transmits fluid power. In automobile service stations, hydraulic lift is used to raise plunger or piston inside a cylinder for transmitting power or face by means of petroleum oil. The petroleum oil acts as anti wear, anti oxidant and rust inhibitor. It also protects the sliding and contacting surfaces.

Characteristics of Lubricant: Lubricant must possess the following characteristics:

Viscosity: Good viscosity is essential to ensure cushioning and quiet operation. An oil viscosity that is too high will result in excess friction and degradation of oil properties associated with high oil operating temperature. In cold climates lubricants should flow easily at low temperature. Oils should have a minimum pour point of 5° C (9° F) lower than the lowest expected temperature. The pour point for mineral oil is typically -7° C (20° F). When lower pour points are required, synthetic oils with pour points of -40° C (-40° F) may be necessary.

Film strength: Good film strength helps prevent metal contact and scoring between the gear teeth.

Lubricity (oiliness): Lubricity is necessary to reduce friction.

Adhesion: Helps prevent loss of lubrication due to throw-off associated with gravity or centrifugal force especially at high speeds.

Temperature: Ambient and operating temperatures also determine the selection of lubricants. Normal oil operating temperature ranges from 50 to 55° C (90 to 100 °F) above ambient. Oils operating at high temperature require good viscosity and high resistance to oxidation and foaming. Caution should be exercised whenever abnormally high temperatures are experienced. High operating temperatures are indicative of oils that are too viscous for the application, excess oil in the housing, or an overloaded condition. All of these conditions should be investigated to determine the cause and correct the condition. Oil for gears operating at low ambient temperatures must be able to flow easily and provide adequate viscosity. Therefore these oils must possess high viscosity indices and low pour points.

Chemical stability and oxidation resistance: Prevents thickening and formation of varnish or sludge. This requirement is especially significant in high-speed gears because the oil is subjected to high operating oil and air temperatures.

Extreme pressure protection: Provides additional galling and welding protection for heavily loaded gears when the lubricant film thickness fails. Extreme pressure lubricants are available for mild and severe (hypoid) lubricant applications.

3.2 MECHANISM OF LUBRICATION

Mechanism of lubrication is simple and it can be classified into three types:

1. Fluid film / hydrodynamic/ thick film mechanism: The modern period of lubrication began with the work of Osborne Reynolds (1842-1912). Reynold's research was concerned with rotating shafts rotating in bearings and cases. When a lubricant was applied to the shaft, Reynolds found that a rotating shaft pulled a converging wedge of lubricant between the shaft and the bearing. He also noted that as the shaft gained velocity, the liquid flowed between the two surfaces at a greater rate. This, because the lubricant is viscous, produces a liquid pressure in the lubricant wedge that is sufficient to keep the two surfaces separated. Under ideal conditions, Reynolds showed that this liquid pressure was great enough to keep the two bodies from having any contact and that the only friction in the system was the viscous resistance of the lubricant.

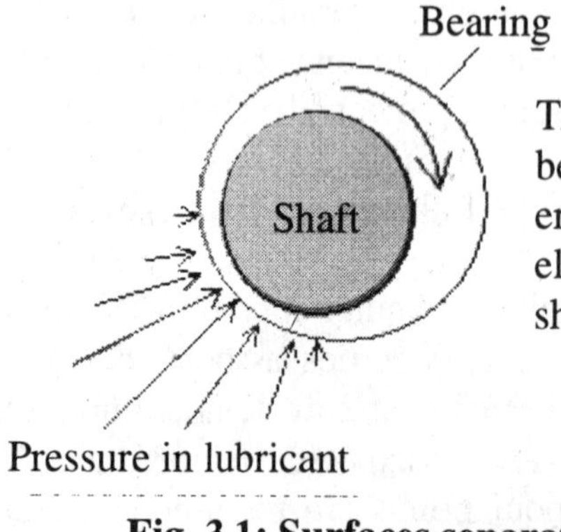

The rotating shaft drags a wedge of fluid beneath it that develops a pressure great enough to support the shaft and eliminate contact friction between the shaft and the bearing in ideal situations

Fig. 3.1: Surfaces separated by Bulk Lubricant film

There are four essential elements in hydrodynamic lubrication - the first two are obvious, a liquid (hydro-) and relative motion (-dynamic). The other two are the viscous properties of the liquid and the geometry of the surfaces between which the convergent wedge of fluid is produced. While considering hydrodynamic lubrication, we must be very careful about how we treat the viscous properties of our lubricant. The less viscous is a liquid, lower is the friction. Too low of a viscosity jeopardizes our system.The distance between the two surfaces decreases with higher loads on the bearing, less viscous fluids and lower speeds. The surface geometry is also very important. The surfaces have to be such that a converging wedge of fluid can develop between the surfaces, allowing the hydrodynamic pressure of the lubricant to support the load of the shaft or moving surface. This is obtained in a number of ways, a common design other than the shaft and bearing configuration is the tilted pad bearing, where a tilted pad skims over a sheet of fluid.

In this type of mechanism, the moving /sliding surfaces are separated from each other by a thick film of liquid fluid (at least 1000 A° thick).The lubricant fills the irregularities of the sliding or moving surfaces and thus prevents direct contact between the material surfaces and wear is minimized. Coefficient of the friction for unlubricated surface is 0.5 -1.5 which reduces to 0.001 – 0.03 for lubricated surface. This small friction is only due to the internal resistance between the particles of lubricants moving over each other.

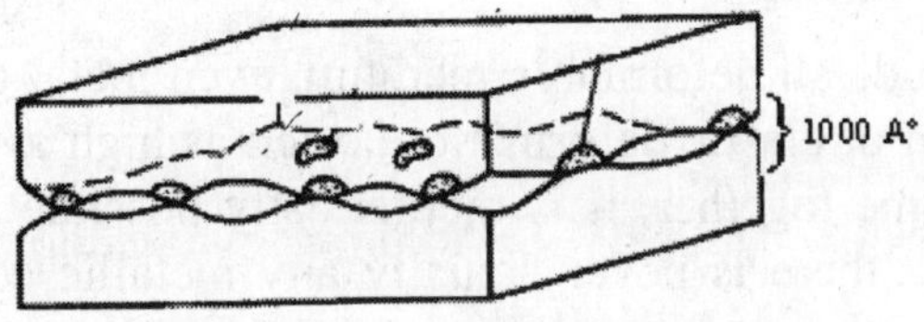

Fig. 3.2: Hydrodynamic lubrication

Examples: Delicate instruments like watches, light machines such as sewing machines, scientific instruments, clocks, guns etc.

Types of oil used: The lubricants used for this purpose are hydrocarbon oil blended with selected long chain polymer. In order to maintain suitable viscosity, anti oxidants like amino phenols are also added. Organometallic detergents are added to keep the carbon particles in hydrodynamic lubrication. It is an excellent method of lubrication since it is possible to achieve coefficients of friction as low as 0.001 and there is no wear between the moving parts. Special attention must be paid to the heating of the lubricant by the frictional force since viscosity is temperature dependent. One method of accomplishing this is to cycle the lubricant through a cooling reservoir in order to maintain the desired viscosity of the fluid. Another way of handling the heat dissipation is to use commercially available additives to decrease the viscosity's temperature dependence. We also have to pay special attention to the extremes of motion, when using hydrodynamic lubrication: starting and stopping. When the surfaces are at rest with respect to each other or at very low speeds, the distance of separation is theoretically zero.

Aerodynamic Lubrication: Aerodynamic lubrication is a recent extension of the theory of hydrodynamic lubrication. The theory is the same that a converging wedge of high pressure is formed between two surfaces, supporting one surface from coming into contact with the other surface. Extra attention has to be paid to the system. Instead of using a thin fluid lubricant, a gas of 1,000 times less viscosity is used. The distance of separation is minute, requiring close to perfectly smooth surfaces. Besides the surfaces have to be virtually free of defects, using aerodynamic lubrication requires very high speeds and low loads.

The benefits of aerodynamic lubrication are obvious. There is no need to cool the air that is the lubricant because heat built up is minimal, no waste and air is cheap. The amount of precision required to allow this

method to work properly is tremendous, making the applicability of aerodynamic lubrication limited.
Elasto-hydrodynamic Lubrication: Consider a shaft of metal resting on a sheet of rubber as shown below:

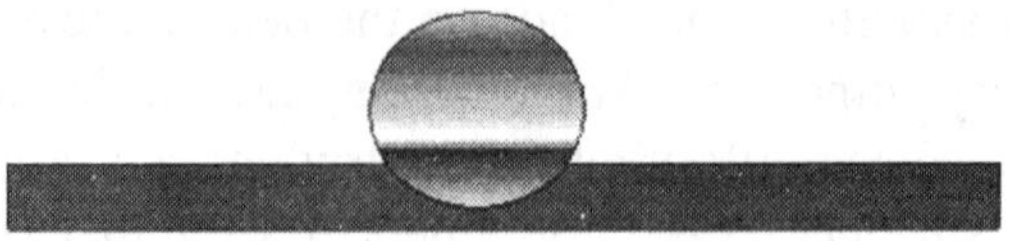

With lubrication of some sort, let us use the generic case, oil. The pressures of the hydrodynamic film will complicate the picture. It will exert pressure on the deformable medium and the shaft lifting it upward. The shape of the rubber will be changed as suggested below. Actually however, the shaft will be shifted to one side depending on its direction of spin.

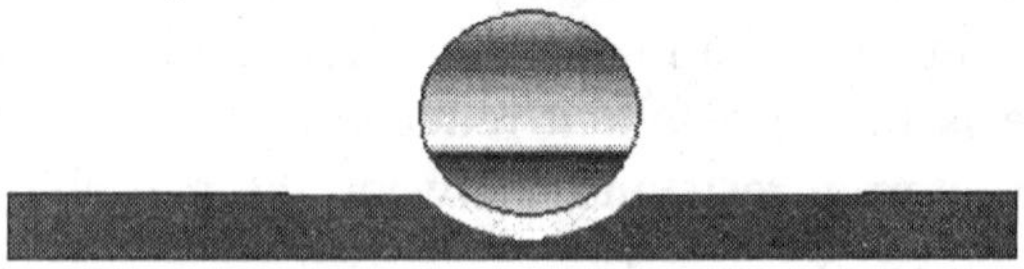

Let us extend this model to include all deformable medium, even metal gear teeth. Because metal is very hard, it has a very high threshold of elastic deformation, often as high as 100,000 psi in gear teeth. When these two deformable media come together, it is theoretically possible to capture a hydrodynamic film between the two faces such that there is never actually any metallic contact occurring. In this case of extreme pressure, the viscosity of the oil film may increase as much as 10,000x, behaving virtually like a solid between the two surfaces. This explains why many mechanisms are able to operate under much harsher conditions than would classically be expected. There is a catch though, this type of elasto-hydrodynamic lubrication works only when the thin film is in the order of 10-40 millionths of an inch. This requires the surfaces to be extremely smooth and carefully aligned a machinist's nightmare. This is what keeps elasto-hydrodynamic lubrication from becoming an everyday lubrication answer. It is however, very applicable and necessary in high pressure situations.

A paradox arises though. Why, if the harder a liquid is pressed, the more like a solid it becomes, would lubricants ever fail under these enormous pressures? The answer is not at all clear or accessible yet. It is believed that tremendous heat generated through atomic level interactions fractures the lubricant.

2. Boundary lubrication/Thin film lubrication: Fluid or hydrodynamic lubrication is effective only if the lubricant film is at least 1000 A° thick. Film thickness, however, is often very much smaller than this value under conditions of high loading and slow rate of rotation and lubrication must be maintained by a 'boundary' film, whose thickness may not exceed one or two molecular layers. If the maximum pressure is so great that the oil film is only two or three molecules thick. Hydrodynamic or fluid lubrication is replaced by boundary lubrication. Some of the hills or asperities in the surfaces may be higher than the film thickness.

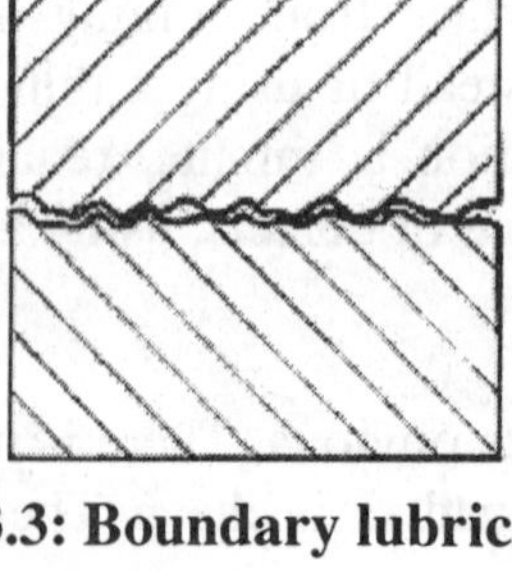

Fig. 3.3: Boundary lubrication

In this type of lubrication, lubricant molecules adsorbed on an interface between two asperities in contact, which is rough on the atomic scale, can switch the interface from the strong to weak pinning regime, resulting in a large reduction in the static friction. Boundary lubrication is the most common type of lubrication in day-to-day usage because it finds its applicability where hydrodynamic and elasto-hydrodynamic lubrication fail at relatively slow speeds, high contact pressures and with less than perfectly smooth surfaces. As running conditions become more severe such as with rough surfaces and high contact pressures, wear becomes a severe problem to the system. To combat this wear it is necessary to prepare the surface of the metal accordingly. Taking basic mineral oil as the basis of lubrication, which in most cases it is, it is possible to create a lubricant that forms a surface film over the surfaces strongly adhering to the surface. These films are often only one or two molecules thick but they provide enough of a protection to prevent metal to metal contact. This type of boundary protection is known as boundary lubrication.

A brief explanation of what needs to be added to basic mineral oil in order to create an effective boundary lubricant is that the best additives are active organic compounds with long chain molecules and active end groups. These compounds bind tightly and intricately with each other, forming a film that builds up on the surface of the metal itself binding strongly to the metal. This results in a thin film that is very difficult to penetrate. When two surfaces, each covered with a boundary layer, come in contact with each other, they tend to slide along their outermost surfaces, with the actual faces of the surfaces rarely making contact with each other. Liquids are rarely good boundary lubricants. The best boundary lubricants are solids with long chains of high inter-chain attraction, low shear resistance so as to slip easily and a high temperature tolerance. The boundary lubricant should also, obviously, be able to maintain a strong attachment to the surfaces under high temperatures and load pressures.

The most common boundary lubricants are probably greases. Greases are so widely used because they have the most desirable properties of a boundary lubricant. They not only shear easily, they flow. They also dissipate heat easily; form a protective barrier for the surfaces, preventing dust, dirt and corrosive agents from harming the surfaces.

It is suitable for the condition when continuous film of the lubricant can not persist and direct metal to metal contact is possible because of various reasons, e.g. when a shaft starts moving from rest or its speed is very low or load is very high or viscosity of oil is extremely low. In these conditions, friction between the lubricated surfaces lies on absorbed or boundary layers of the lubricants. The load is carried by the lubricant on both the metal surfaces. Coefficient of the friction is 0.05 to 0.15. The friction is dependent mainly upon the nature of the material of the surfaces and also on some characteristics that can be determined by the chemical properties of the lubricant. The effectiveness of the boundary lubrication primarily depends on the structure and chemical properties of the oil to be used for boundary lubrication. The lubricants used in this type of lubrication should have long hydrocarbon chains, polar groups to enhance spreading and orientation over the metallic surfaces at high pressure, lateral attraction between the chain and active atoms or groups capable of forming linkages with the metals or other surfaces. Other important properties of boundary lubricants are good oiliness, low pour point, high resistance to oxidation and heat and high viscosity index. Lubricants used for boundary lubrication are:

1) Graphite and MoS_2
2) Mineral oils mixed with 0.1-5% of boundary agents like fatty acids, alcohol and amines.
3) Vegetable and animal oils and their soaps can be used as boundary agent.

Lubrication takes place under following conditions:

a) In low speed cases or starting and stopping of rotating or sliding motion (hinge joints, low speed sleeve bearing etc.)

b) In high temperature cases (e. g. steam engine or IC engine cylinders)

c) In high pressure cases (in roller bearings, gears etc.)

The coefficient of friction in boundary lubrication generally varies from 0.08 to 0.15. When the boundary lubrication has to work under vacuum, the lubrication film goes out. Hence, friction increases because of the direct contact of the metal. The presence of the air increases the efficiency of the boundary lubrication because of the formation of protective iron oxide film on the surfaces. When lubricants are fatty acids, the presence of moisture has been found to increase the effectiveness of the boundary lubrication.

3. Extreme pressure lubrication: If the load or pressure is too high, the contact between the metal surfaces increases and if the temperature is also too high, deformation, seizures, welding etc. take place to a large extent. The temperature is dependent upon the sliding velocity between the surface and the pressure. Hence, when there is high load and high temperature generated between the sliding surfaces, extreme pressure lubricants are used. This type of lubricants contains organic compounds containing sulphur, phosphorous, lead, chlorine etc. as extreme pressure additives. Sulphur and chlorine present in these additives react with metal to form sulphides and chlorides. These have high M.P. and act as good lubricants under extreme temperatures. The organic compounds decompose and form high melting lubricating films on the metal surfaces. These additives form a more durable film on the metal surfaces and thus film is capable of withstanding high loads and high temperatures. These additives are the organic compounds having active radicals or groups such as chlorine (as in chlorinated esters), sulphur (as in sulphurized oils) or phosphorous (as in tri cresyl phosphate). Some examples of extreme pressure additives are compounds containing oxygen (fatty acids, ketones, esters etc.), compounds containing sulphur or sulphur and oxygen, chlorinated wax, sulphurized fats, sulphurized olefins, organic compounds containing lead and both chlorine and sulphur. These additives form layers of films having low shear strength (which does not allow the metal to tear away) and they also act as fluxing agents which contaminate the metal surface and hence prevent welding.

Wire drawing of titanium requires chloride containing additives which react with the stable oxide film on the useful metal surface. In cutting fluids, lubricants used may contain a hydrocarbon, small amount of fatty acids of organic chloride or sulphide. In heavy duty automobiles, automotive hypoid gears high pressure and rubbing action are encountered, lubricant may contain EP additives like chlorine, sulphur and phosphorus.

3.3 CLASSIFICATION OF LUBRICANTS

Lubricants are classified into four types depending upon physical state:

- Liquid Lubricants
- Semi solid Lubricants
- Solid Lubricants
- Synthetic Lubricants

CLASSIFICATION OF LUBRICANTS

- Liquid Lubricants (or Lubricating oils)
  - Animal Or Vegetable oil
  - Mineral oil
  - Blended oil
- Semisolid Lubricants (or greases)
  - Calcium based greases
  - Soda based greases
  - Lithium based greases
  - Axle greases
- Solid Lubricants
  - Structural Lubricants
  - Mechanical Lubricants
  - Soap
  - Chemically Active Lubricant
  - Refractories
- Synthetic Lubricants

3.4 LIQUID LUBRICANTS / LUBRICATING OILS

Good lubricating oil possesses following properties:

- High boiling point.
- Low freezing point.
- Adequate viscosity for particular work.
- High resistance to heat and corrosion.
- Stable to decompose at high temperature.

Lubricating oils are further classified as

i) Animal or Vegetable oil: These are primarily triglyceride esters derived from plants and animals. For lubricant base oil use, the vegetable derived materials are preferred. Common ones include high oleic canola oil, palm oil, sunflower seed oil and rapeseed oil from vegetable sources and tall oil from animal sources. Many vegetable oils are often hydrolyzed to yield the acids which are subsequently combined selectively to form special synthetic esters.

Preparation of Animal oil / Vegetable oil: Animal oils are extracted from crude fat by rendering process in which the tissue is broken by treatment with steam or combined action of steam and water. Vegetable oils such as cotton seed oil and castor oil are obtained by crushing the seeds. Before use, both animal and vegetable oils require further treatment :

1) Cooling of oil to remove sterarine.
2) Filtration through animal carbon to remove colour and brightening the oil.
3) Neutralization of free fatty acids by requisite amount of alkali.
4) Coagulation with sulphuric acid to remove suspended impurities.
5) Filtration.

Characteristics of animal and vegetable oils: They possess oiliness and hence they stick to the surface of machine parts, under high temperature and load.

Limitations

1) They are costly.
2) They get oxidized easily and form acids and gummy compounds.
3) They get thickened in presence of air.
4) They get hydrolyzed in presence of water and moisture.

PREPARATION OF

ANIMAL OIL → Rendering and Crushing: Animal tissue + H_2O/steam

VEGETABLE OIL → Rendering and Crushing: Seed +H_2O/steam

↓

Filtration
The oil obtained is filtered through active carbon due to which it gets decolorized

↓

Neutralization
The acid produced due to rendering is neutralized by NaOH

↓

Treatment with H_2SO_4
To convert the suspended impurities By converting them into coagulants

↓

Filtration through Fuller's Earth

↓

[The filtered oil is known as Animal and Vegetable oil]

Examples

Animal oil: Lard oil, neet foot oil and sperm oil. They are normally used in ordinary machine parts, sewing machines etc.

Vegetable oil: Castor oil is generally used in racing cars and palm oil is used in delicate instrument such as scientific instruments.

ii) Mineral or petroleum oils: These are basically lower molecular weight hydrocarbons with 12-50 carbon atoms. Their viscosity increases with the length of the hydrocarbon chain.

Purification: Impurities like wax asphalt etc. must be removed from crude liquid petroleum oils before they are used. They are obtained by distillation of crude petroleum. Before use, certain treatment is required.

Removal of wax from the oil by following processes:

De-waxing

1) Wax is removed by mixing the oil with propane or trichloroethylene.
2) Refrigerate to precipitate the wax.
3) Centrifuge to remove the oil wax suspension.
4) Filter.
5) Distill to remove the solvent from oil.

Acid Refining

1) Dewax oil by treating with conc. H_2SO_4 so that the impurities are dissolved or converted to tarry sludge.

2) Tarry sludge is removed by filtration.
3) Neutralize with NaOH to remove excess acid.
4) Decolorize by passing the oil through Fuller's Earth.

Solvent Refining

1) Oil is mixed with nitrobenzene to remove the asphaltic impurities.
2) This mixture is kept undisturbed for sometime. After sometime it separates out into layers- Oil layer and Solvent layer (impurities + solvent)
3) Distill oil layer to remove the solvent.

It is essential to remove these impurities before mineral oil is used otherwise it creates number of problems like:

1) Wax raises the pour point and makes lubricating oil unfit for use at low temperature.
2) Asphalt undergoes decomposition at high temperature and causes carbon deposition and sludge formation.
3) Certain constituents get oxidized under working conditions and form sludge.

iii) Blended Oils / Compounded Oil: To produce the desired characteristics of lubricating oil, various additives are added in small quantity. The oils thus obtained are known as blended or compounded oils.

There are two types of lubricant additives

I. Chemically active additives
II. Chemically inert additives.

I. Chemically active additives: Such additives chemically react with metals and form metal protective films.

Examples

- **Antioxidants:** These are molecules that slow down or prevent the oxidation of other molecules. Oxidation is a chemical reaction that transfers electrons from a substance to an oxidizing agent. Oxidation reactions can produce free radicals, which start chain reactions that damage cells. Antioxidants terminate these chain reactions by removing radical intermediates and inhibit other oxidation reactions by being oxidized themselves. As a result, antioxidants are often reducing agents such as thiols or polyphenols and aromatic amines

- **Corrosion inhibitors:** These are chemical compounds which when added in small concentration, stop or slow down corrosion of metals and alloys. Some corrosion inhibitors are hexamine, phenylenediamine, dimethylethanolamine, sodium nitrite, cinnamaldehyde, condensation products of aldehydes and amines (imines), chromates, nitrites, phosphates, hydrazine, ascorbic acid and others.Organic compounds of phosphorous and antimony are used as corrosion and rust inhibitors.

- **Anti wear or EP agents:** These are additives for lubricants to prevent metal-to-metal contact between parts of gears. EP additives are usually used in applications such as gearboxes, while AW additives are used with lighter loads such as bushings. AW additives typically contain zinc and phosphorus compounds.

- **Friction Modifiers:** These are added to lubricants to reduce the surface friction of the lubricated parts. Typically these are polar chemical compounds having high affinity for metal surfaces and possessing long alkyl chains. Glycerol mono-oleate , Phosphoric acid esters and Organic fatty acids are used as friction modifiers. They change the coefficient of friction by absorption on metal surface.

- **Dispersants:** Alkyl thio phosphonates are used as dispersants. They keep insoluble contaminants dispersed in the lubricants.

- **Antifoamants:** Silicon polymers are used as antifoamant. They reduce the surface tension to collapse the foam and thus prevent the formation of persistent foams.

- **Metal Deactivators:** These are fuel and lubricant additives used to stabilize fluids by deactivating (usually by sequestering) metal ions, mostly introduced by the action of naturally occurring acids in the fuel and acids generated in lubricants by oxidative processes with the metallic parts of the systems. Metal deactivators inhibit the catalytic effects of such ions, especially copper, retarding the formation of gummy residues (e.g. gels containing copper mercaptide). An example of a metal deactivator used for gasoline and jet fuels is N,N'-disalicylidene-1,2-propanediamine. It is used in turbine and jet fuels, diesel, heating oil and greases. It is approved for military and commercial aviation fuels.

II. Chemically Inert Additives: These additives improve the physical properties that are critical to the effective performance of the lubricant.

Examples

- **Viscosity Modifiers:** Polymers and co-polymers of the olefins when added to oil, reduce the rate of viscosity change with temperature and thus improve the viscosity of oil.

- **Pour point depressants:** Polymethacrylates, phenolic polymers and alkylated naphthalenes are used as pour point depressants. They reduce interlocking by modifying the wax crystal formation and thus enable lubricant to flow at low temperature.

3.5 GREASES / SEMI SOLID LUBRICANTS

When the thickening agent is added to the lubricating oil, the substance so obtained is known as grease. The lubricating oil may be petroleum oil or synthetic oil and thickness consists of special soap of sodium, calcium, barium, aluminium or lithium etc. Non soap thicknesses are carbon black, silica gel, poly urea, synthetic polymer, bentonite clay etc. which improve the heat resistance of a lubricant.

Preparation of Greases

Greases are prepared by saponification of fat with alkali (like caustic soda, lime etc.) followed by mixing hot lubricating oil. Consistency of the finished grease is determined by the total amount of the mineral oil.

Properties of Greases

1) Greases have higher shear or frictional resistance than oils so that they can support much heavier loads at lower speeds.
2) Coefficient of friction of greases is more than that of oils, so it is better to use oil instead of greases.
3) Greases normally work at low temperature and they cannot effectively dissipate heat from bearing. That is why the grease lubricated bearing works at relatively low temperature as compared to the oil lubricated bearing.

Applications

1) Greases are used where oil cannot retain its place due to high load, low speed, intermittent operation, sudden jerks etc. for example Rail axel boxes.
2) In bearings and gears that work at high temperature.
3) Greases are more resistant to contamination by dirt or moisture. They are used when bearing needs to be sealed against entry of dust, dirt etc.
4) Greases are used where dripping or spurting of oil is undesirable e.g. paper, textile, edible etc.

Classification of Greases

On the basis of soap used, greases are classified into four types.

a) Soda based Grease: It is prepared by adding sodium soap as thickening agent in petroleum oil.

Properties

a. It is water soluble because it is prepared by adding sodium carbonate (which is soluble in water) as thickening agent.
b. These greases can be used up to 175°C.
c. These are economic grease and mostly used in ball bearings which generate frictional heat.

b) Calcium based Grease or Cap Grease: It is prepared by adding small amount of calcium hydroxide to hot oil.

Properties

a. These are most economic greases and most commonly used.
b. They are resistant to water.
c. They can be used up to 80 °C.
d. They are generally used in caterpillar treads, tractors, water-pumps etc.
e. Servorex greases are calcium-lead base, short fibrous structure greases with appropriate EP and anti-rust properties. These greases are recommended for both anti-friction and plain bearings operating at medium speed under heavy and severe shock loads. Due to their excellent water repellent characteristics, these greases are successfully used for bearing lubrication of steel mills, cane crushers and mill rolls of sugar factories. These greases are used by various steel plants in centralized grease lubrication systems and are also recommended for grease lubricated gear couplings.

c) Lithium-based Grease: It is prepared by mixing lithium soaps in petroleum oil.

Properties

a. They are resistant to water and can work at high temperature.
b. They are stable on storage.
c. They have high oxidation and mechanical stability.
d. They are costly.
e. They are specially used in aircrafts at extreme heights, where low temperature (-55°C) can exist.
f. They have high melting points (150°C).
g. Servo gem EP greases are lithium-base greases having extreme pressure properties. These possess excellent shear stability, high load carrying capacity, high oxidation stability and anti-rust/anti-corrosion properties. These greases prevent welding and seizure of moving parts often caused by shock loading and resist water washout. These greases meet IPSS:1-09-005 specification and are recommended for both plain and anti-friction bearing in a wide variety of applications such as automotive, earth moving equipment and general industrial machinery.

d) Axle Grease: It is prepared by adding lime (or any heavy metal hydroxide) to resin and fatty oils. Fillers like mica talc etc. are also added to grease.

Properties

1) They are water resistant.
2) They are generally used for equipments working at low speeds and high loads.

3.6 SOLID LUBRICANTS

Solid lubricants are used in following conditions:

1) Machines operating at very high loads and low speeds.
2) Where a liquid or a semi solid lubricant film cannot be maintained.
3) Contamination (by the entry of dust or dirt particles) of lubricating oil is undesirable as in the case of commutator bleads of electric motors and generators.
4) Where the lubricated parts are not easily accessible.
5) Where the operating temperatures and pressures are too high.

They are used either in the dry powder form or mixed with water or oil. The coefficient of friction between solid lubricants is between “0.005 to 0.01”. There are five types of solid lubricants.

(i) **Structural Lubricants:** These are widely used lubricants. They include graphite, molybdenum disulfide, talc, vermiculite etc. Their property is due to their layer lattice structure. They cleave themselves and fix themselves on or into the bearing surface. E.g. Graphite is soapy to touch, non inflammable and works up to 375°C without oxidizing in air. It is mostly used in air compressor, lathes, general machine shop work , food stuff industry, railway track joints, open gear chains, IC engines, cast iron bearing etc.

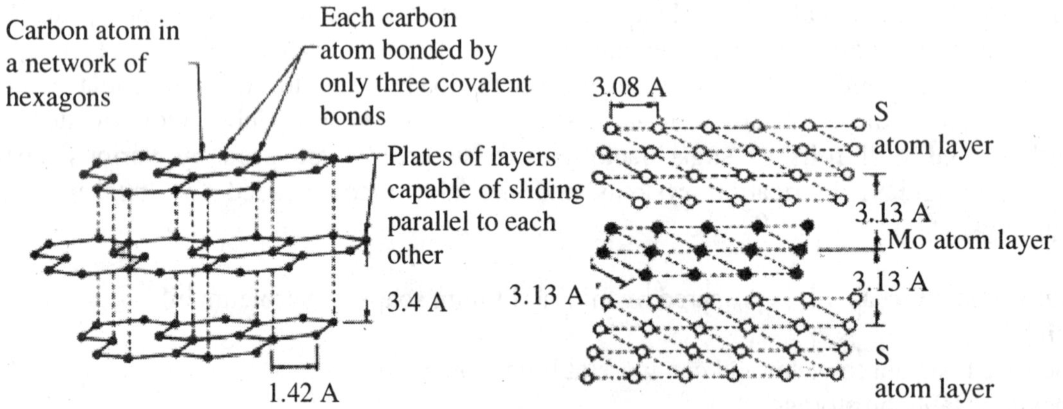

Fig. 3.4: (a) Layered structure of graphite **(b) Sandwitch- like structure of molybdenum disulphide**

(ii) **Mechanical Lubricants:** These lubricants include plastics and metals. They form a continuous adherent film on the rubbing surfaces and reduce the wear.

(iii) **Soaps**: They form compounds with metal surface by the fatty acids and metals. They also work as solid lubricants.

(iv) **Chemically Active Lubricants:** These include extreme pressure additives and other chemicals. They react with metal surface and form lubricating layer e.g. Phosphates, Chlorides, Oxidising agents.

(v) **Refractories, Ceramics and Glass:** Refractory materials work at higher temperature. They are mostly used in rocketry and defence programmes.

3.7 SYNTHETIC LUBRICANTS

They exhibit significant performance advantages over conventional oils, out performing them in all criterion and applications. The base stocks, designed through molecular engineering (organic synthesis), are enhanced with the finest additives available. The 'finished lubricants' reduce energy consumption, friction, heat, tear and wear, and extend maintenance intervals. These recyclable man-made lubes are synonymous with high performance.

Properties

1) Thermally stable at high operating temperature.
2) Chemically stable in corrosive environments.
3) Having high viscosity index.
4) Having high flash point and non- inflammable.
5) Having low freezing point.
6) Significant reduction in friction and wear.
7) Optimum performance at extended temperature extremes – cold and hot.
8) Rigorous and lengthy in-use operation without chemical breakdown.

Applications

1) Polymerized hydrocarbons like poly alkylene oxides, poly glycidyl ethers are used at high temp. in roller bearing of sheet glass machinery.
2) Di-2 ethyl sebacate (Diester) satisfactorily works at 50°C to 230°C temperatures. They are used for lubrication in turbo-jets.
3) Silicons are not oxidized below 200°C and possess high viscosity index. At high temperature (more than 200°C), they get oxidized and form gels. They are generally used in clocks timers and other electronic devices.
4) Fluorinated tubes/ Fluorocarbons are chemically and thermally stable but are less susceptible to oxidation and cracking. They are generally used in submarines.
5) Poly alkylene Glycols (PAGs) are thermally stable, free from corrosive action, stable even at high rates of mechanical shear. They are generally used in aircrafts turbines.

3.8 GAS LUBRICATION

Lubrication for extreme conditions and for special application: Gas lubrication bearings are resistant towards high speed and extreme temperature. Air, hydrogen, argon, helium, nitrogen, oxygen, carbon dioxide and uranium hexafluoride are used as gas lubrication bearings. When gases are used as lubricants at high speed, then wear can be reduced by using a wear resistant coating material like tungustun carbide, chromium oxide etc. Gas lubricated bearings have numerous advantages over liquid and solid lubricants for a wide range of applications. A gas bearing is virtually frictionless, silent and vibrationless. Gas bearing can be used for extremely large surface velocities. A gas bearing can eliminate risk of contaminating a process with lubricant.

Applications: In spindles, motor-driver or turbine driver, circulations, fans, gyroscopes, compressors, environmental stimulation tablets, turbo machinery etc.

Limitations

a) Due to low viscosity of gases, limited load of 15-30 K Pa is used.
b) Care should be required to minimize the entry of dust particles, moisture and wear debris.

Liquid Metal Lubricants: These are used where operating temperature goes beyond 250°C. Low melting point metals like Cs, Ga, Hg, K, Na, Rb and Na-K are used as liquid metal lubricants.

Cryogenic Bearing Lubrication: Such type of lubricants are corrosion-resistant. Liquid oxygen, liquid nitrogen and liquid hydrogen are used as cryogenic lubricants. They are used as fuels in liquid rocket-propulsion systems in pumps used to transfer large quantities of liquefied gases and for turbine expander in liquefaction and refrigeration.

Lubrication in nuclear reactor systems: They work as radiation resistant. They are required in control rod drives, compressors or coolant circulating pumps, motor operated valves and fuel handling valves of nuclear reactor systems. Polyphenyl ether oil and non soap thickners work satisfactorily in nuclear reactor systems.

Lubrication using Glass: They are thermally stable and work upto 1000 °C. They are used for extrusion and formation of Titanium and Zirconium alloys. Glass lubricants may be applied as fibre of powder to the die or hot work piece or as slurry with a polymeric bonding agent to the workpiece before heating. Fused silica, 96% silica soda lime, borosilicate and alumino silicates are used as glass lubricants.

Industrial oil can be classified into following types:

- Engine or machine oils.
- Spindle oils.
- Refrigeration oils.
- Circulation oils.
- Gear oils.
- Steam cylinder oils.

3.9 SELECTION OF LUBRICANTS

As the properties required for each class of lubricating oils are different, the selection of industrial lubricant requires the consideration of equipments used, available methods for handling, application of the lubricant itself and environmental conditions. It is better to use the lubricants recommended by the manufacturers of the equipment. In selecting a lubricant for a given application, it is essential to consider the various properties of the lubricant required in relation to the service conditions. Before using the lubricant, it is essential to know about the effect of load, temperature and speed at which the elements operate and also the contaminants which may affect the performance of the lubricants. Selections of a lubricant for few typical jobs are as follows:

1) **Lubricants for IC Engines:** In an internal combustion engine, the lubricant is exposed to high temperature, therefore lubricant should possess high viscosity index and high thermal stability. At high pressure it works as wear protection of piston rings and cylinder liners. It also provides a seal between piston ring and cylinder wall against high pressure combustion gases.

2) **Lubricants for cutting tools:** Cutting fluids are lubricants used in machining, cutting, furnishing and grinding of metal. In such operation, a metal is continuously exposed to tool used which increases friction and results in excessive power consumption and liberation of large amount of heat. Cutting fluids cool the tool and reduce wear to prevent distortion and dimensional inaccuracies.

3) **Lubricants for Gears:** Gears are under extreme pressure so the lubricants used should have high oiliness, resistance to oxidation and have high load carrying capacity. Extreme pressure additives like metallic soaps and chloride, sulphur compounds are employed.

4) **Lubricants for Transformers:** In transformers, lubricants are required to insulate the winding and to carry away the heat generated when the transformer is on load. Lubricants used in transformer possess high insulating property, optimum oxidation resistance and chemical stability.

5) **Lubricants for Textile Industry:** In textile industry, spindles are at high speed. Thin oil with oxidation and rust inhibitors are used in such industries.

6) **Lubricants for refrigeration system:** In refrigeration, temperature is near about -40^{0}F (maximum). In such conditions, lubricant should possess low pour point, low viscosity and low cloud point. Naphthalene based oils are generally used in refrigerators.

7) **Lubricants for delicate machines:** They are not exposed to high temperature, water or load. For this purpose thin vegetable or animal oil (like palm oil, neat oil etc) can be used.

3.10 PROPERTIES OF LUBRICATING OILS

Viscosity: Viscosity is a measure of the resistance of a fluid to deform under shear stress. It is commonly perceived as "thickness" or resistance to flow. Viscosity describes a fluid's internal resistance to flow and may be thought of as a measure of fluid friction. Thus, water is "thin", having a lower viscosity, while vegetable oil is "thick" having a higher viscosity. All real fluids (except superfluids) have some resistance to shear stress, but a fluid which has no resistance to shear stress is known as an ideal fluid or inviscid fluid.

When looking at a value for viscosity, the number that one most often sees is the coefficient of viscosity, simply put this as the ratio between the pressure exerted on the surface of a fluid in the lateral or horizontal direction, to the change in velocity of the fluid as you move down in the fluid (this is what is referred to as a velocity gradient). For example, at "room temperature", water has a nominal viscosity of 1.0 x 10^{-3} Pa·s and motor oil has a nominal apparent viscosity of 250 x 10^{-3} Pa·s. The word "viscosity" derives from the Latin word "viscum" for mistletoe. A viscous glue was made from mistletoe berries and used for lime-twigs to catch birds. If operating speed, temperature and pressure are same, viscosity of a liquid would depend on heat generation, friction loss, fluid film thickness, fluid flow, mechanical efficiency and wear etc.

The most important properties of lubricants which are of prime importance in lubrication are viscosity, viscosity temperature relation, viscosity index etc. In order to get efficient lubrication, there should be no change in these properties during lubrication, Moreover, there should be no effect of any chemical change such as decomposition, oxidation, reduction at higher temperature and emulsification during lubrication. The behavior of a lubricating oil or lubricant is determined by its viscosity. Viscosity is defined as the force in dynes necessary for the movement of 1 sq. cm layer of a fluid with a velocity of 1 cm/ sec, past another parallel layer 1 cm away. Absolute viscosity values are required for use in all bearing design calculations and other lubrication engineering technical design problems.

Newton's Theory: In general, in any flow, layers move at different velocities and the fluid's viscosity arises from the shear stress between the layers that ultimately oppose any applied force. Isaac Newton postulated that for straight, parallel and uniform flow, the shear stress, τ, between layers is proportional to the velocity gradient, $\partial u/\partial y$, in the direction perpendicular to the layers, in other words, the relative motion of the layers.

$$\tau = \eta \frac{\partial u}{\partial y}$$

Laminar shear of fluid between two plates: Friction between the fluid and the moving boundaries causes the fluid to shear. The force required for this action is a measure of the fluid's viscosity.

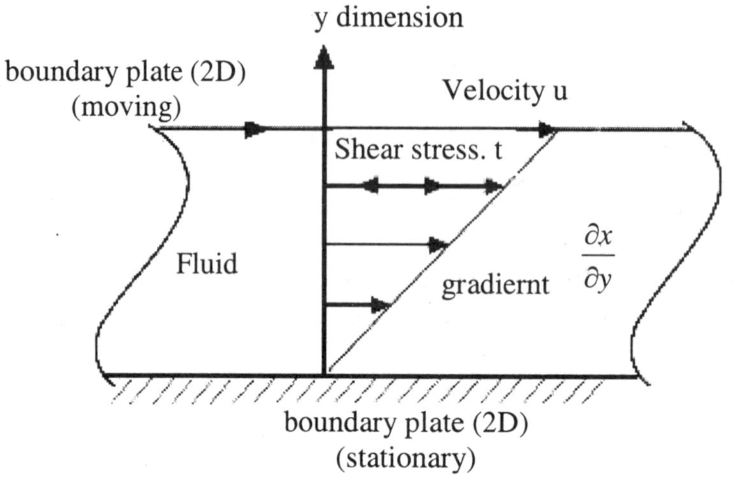

Fig.3.5: Shear Stress between two plates

Here, the constant η is known as the coefficient of viscosity, the viscosity, or the dynamic viscosity. Many fluids, such as water and most gases satisfy Newton's criterion and are known as Newtonian fluids. Non-Newtonian fluids exhibit a more complicated relationship between shear stress and gradient than simple linearity. Laminar shear, the non-linear gradient, is a result of the geometry the fluid is flowing through (e.g. a pipe).

The relationship between the shear stress and the velocity gradient can also be obtained by considering two plates closely spaced apart at a distance *y* and separated by a homogeneous substance. Assuming that the plates are very large, with a large area *A*, such that edge effects may be ignored, and that the lower plate is fixed, let a force *F* be applied to the upper plate. If this force causes the substance between the plates to undergo shear flow (as opposed to just shearing elastically until the shear stress in the substance balances the applied force), the substance is called a fluid. The applied force is proportional to the area and velocity of the plate and inversely proportional to the distance between the plates. Combining these three relations, we get

$$F = \eta(Au/y),$$

where η is the proportionality factor called the absolute viscosity with units Pa·s = kg/(m·s) or slugs/(ft·s). The absolute viscosity is also known as the dynamic viscosity and is often shortened to simply viscosity. The equation can be expressed in terms of shear stress;

$$\tau = F/A = \eta(u/y).$$

The rate of shear deformation is u / y and can be also written as a shear velocity, du/dy. Hence, through this method, the relation between the shear stress and the velocity gradient can be obtained. In many situations, we are concerned with the ratio of the viscous force to the inertial force, the latter characterised by the fluid density ρ. This ratio is characterised by the kinematic viscosity, defined as follows:

$$\nu = \frac{\eta}{\rho}$$

Unit of Viscosity (dynamic/absolute viscosity) η or μ: The IUPAC symbol for viscosity is the Greek symbol eta (η) and dynamic viscosity is also commonly referred to using the Greek symbol mu (μ). The SI physical unit of dynamic viscosity is the pascal-second (Pa·s), which is identical to 1 $kg \cdot m^{-1} \cdot s^{-1}$. If a fluid with a viscosity of one Pa·s is placed between two plates and one plate is pushed sideways with a shear stress of one pascal, it moves a distance equal to the thickness of the layer between the plates in one second. The name poiseuille (Pl) was proposed for this unit (after Jean Louis Marie Poiseuille who formulated Poiseuille's law of viscous flow) but not accepted internationally. Care must be taken in not confusing the poiseuille with the poise named after the same person.

The cgs physical unit for dynamic viscosity is the poise named after Jean Louis Marie Poiseuille. It is more commonly expressed, particularly in ASTM standards, as centipoise (cP). The centipoise is commonly used because water has a viscosity of 1.0020 cP (at 20 °C; the closeness to one is a convenient coincidence).

$$1\ P = 1\ g \cdot cm^{-1} \cdot s^{-1}$$

The relation between Poise and Pascal-second is:

$$10\ P = 1\ kg \cdot m^{-1} \cdot s^{-1} = 1\ Pa \cdot s$$

$$1\ cP = 0.001\ Pa \cdot s = 1\ mPa$$

Measurement: Absolute Viscosity can be measured by

1) Mac Michael Viscometer.
2) Brookfield Viscometer.
3) Stromer Viscometer.
4) Falling sphere Viscometer.

Absolute viscosity values are required for use in all bearing design calculations and other lubrication engineering technical design problems.

Kinematic viscosity ν: Kinematic viscosity (Greek symbol: ν) has SI units ($m^2 \cdot s^{-1}$). The cgs physical unit for kinematic viscosity is the stokes (abbreviated S or St), named after George Gabriel Stokes. It is sometimes expressed in terms of centistokes (cS or cSt). In U.S. usage, stoke is sometimes used as the singular form.

$$1\ \text{stokes} = 100\ \text{centistokes} = 1\ cm^2 \cdot s^{-1} = 0.0001\ m^2 \cdot s^{-1}$$

$$1\ \text{centistokes} = 1\ mm^2/s$$

Dynamic versus kinematic viscosity: Conversion between kinematic and dynamic viscosity is given by $\nu\rho = \eta$. Note that the parameters must be given in SI units, not in P, cP or St. For example, if $\nu = 1$ St ($=0.0001\ m^2 \cdot s^{-1}$) and $\rho = 1000\ kg\ m^{-3}$, then

$$\eta = \nu\rho = 0.1\ kg \cdot m^{-1} \cdot s^{-1} = 0.1\ Pa \cdot s$$

Significance of kinematic viscosity: Kinematic values are applied in oil blending procedures under extreme condition when additives are required.

Effect of temperature and pressure on viscosity

1) Viscosity is inversely proportional to temperature. This is due to the decrease in intermolecular attraction between the lubricating oil.

2) Viscosity is directly proportional to pressure. This is due to the increase in intermolecular attraction between the lubricating oil.

Viscosity Test: Four viscometers are used to measure the viscosity of fluids.
1) Redwood Viscometer 3) Saybolt Viscometer.
2) Engler Viscometer 4) Kinematic Viscometer

Redwood Viscometer: This was presented by Sir Boventon Redwood in year 1885. 50 ml of sample at a temperature of 38 ^{0}C is passed through a orifice of diameter 1.62 mm and 10 mm length, time recorded in seconds is stated as the 'seconds' Redwood. It is essential to maintain temperature, preventing spatter and gentle stirring.

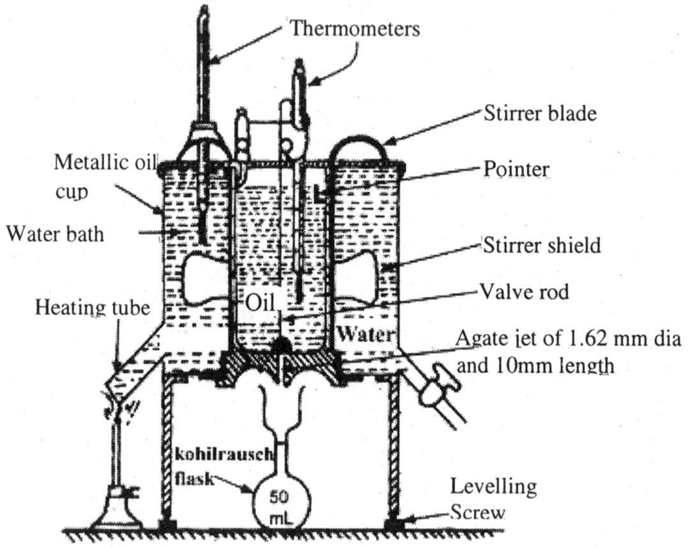

Fig. 3.6 Redwood Viscometer No.1

For more viscous fluid and to prevent some minor deficiencies, Redwood No. 2 model was introduced. The cylinder along with nozzle and the ball are made of silver plated brass. The essential difference between (a) Redwood Viscometer No.1 or universal and (b) Redwood viscometer No. 2 or Admiralty is:

Table 3.1: Difference between Redwood viscometer no.1 and 2

Characteristics	Redwood viscometer no.1	Redwood viscometer no.2
Dimensions of Orifice	Length 10 mm Diameter 1.62 mm	Length 50 mm Diameter 3.80 mm
Useful for	Low viscous oil	High viscous oil
Receiving flask	Smaller mouth	Larger mouth

Description of Apparatus: The Redwood Viscometer consists of a cylindrical brass oil cup (90 mm in the height and 46.5 mm in diameter) that holds the test sample of lubricating oil .The bottom of the oil cup is fitted with a polished agate discharge tube containing an orifice of the specified dimensions. The oil cup is surrounded by water bath for adjusting the temperature. A calibrated receiving flask (Kohlrausch flask) is provided for receiving the oil from polished agate discharge tube. When the sample reached test temperature, the time for 50 ml of the sample to flow through the orifice is measured. Results are reported in seconds stating the test temperature and viscometer type.

Engler Viscometer: This is used to compare the viscosity of oil with water. It is stated in Engler Degree ^{0}E.

Kinematic Viscometer: It is a U- type of glass apparatus having one and two bulbs at its two sides. At the bottom portion of two bulb side capillary tube is attached. It is used for the determination of kinematic viscosity. For a fixed volume of sample, time is measured for the sample to flow from capillary bulb (1) to (2) at a constant temperature. From the measured efflux time, the kinematic viscosity is measured.

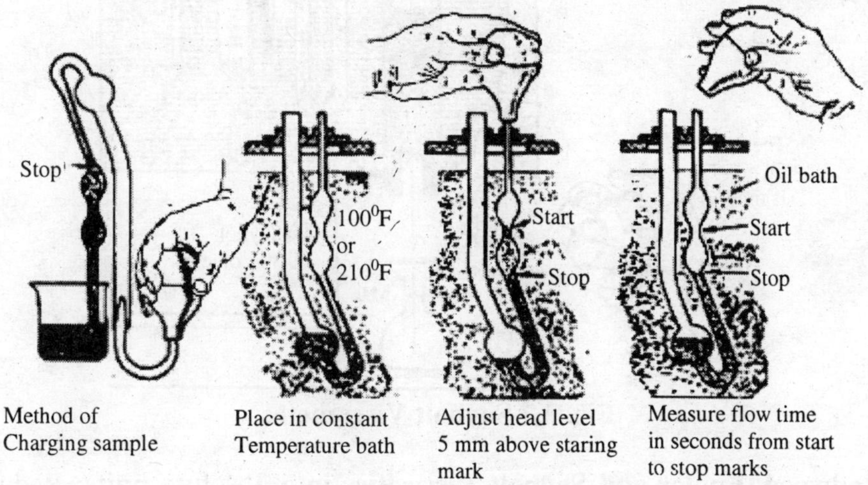

Fig. 3.6: The Kinematic Viscometer

Saybolt Viscometer: It consists of cylindrical brass cup in the bottom of which is an orifice. This cup is surrounded by a constant temperature oil bath. A desired bath temperature can be obtained by adjusting the temperature through regulator. When the sample of lubricating oil reaches test temperature, a 60 ml of test oil at temperature of 100 ^{0}F or 210 ^{0} F is allowed to run through orifice (nozzle) of 1.765 mm diameter and 12.25 mm length and the time reached in seconds is stated as Seconds SUS (Saybolt Universal Seconds). Proper care is taken to maintain temperature by gentle stirring and avoiding excess oil. The orifice is made up of hard, non corrodible metals like stainless steel. For high viscous oil, a viscometer with a larger nozzle diameter is used, which is termed as Saybolt Furol Viscometer. The time reached in seconds is stated as SFS (Saybolt Furol Seconds) . There is no maximum limit, but in general, for liquids having flow times over 1000 seconds, Saybolt Furol Viscometer is better.

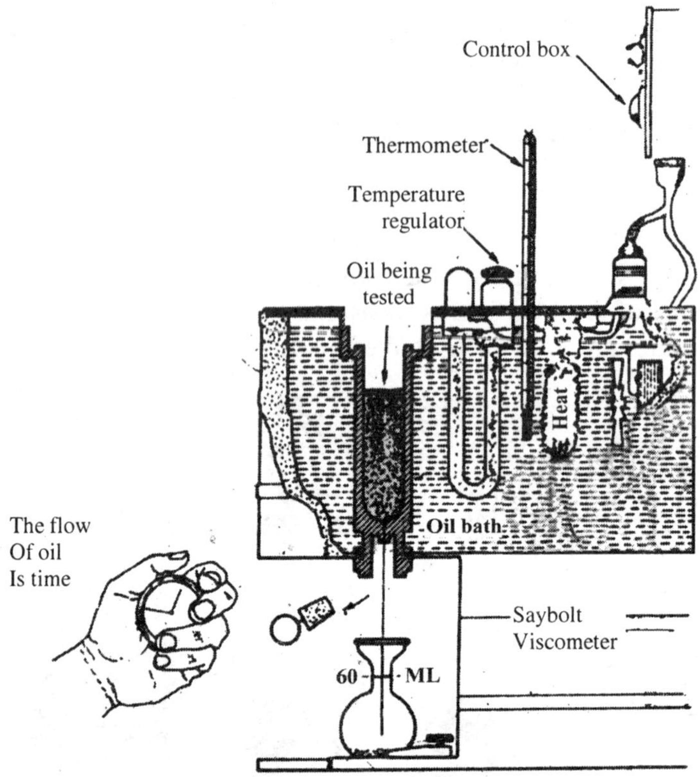

Fig. 3.7 Saybolt Viscometer

Conversion of Redwood, Engler and Saybolt Viscosities into absolute units: Redwood, Engler and Saybolt viscosities can be converted to absolute units (Centistokes).However since these instruments are not the ideal methods of determining the absolute viscosities, the conversion and that too only when taken at the same temperature can be converted into absolute units at say 40 ^{0} C, because, different fluids have different viscosity temperature relationships. The conversion of these relative viscosities to absolute is done with the help of the following equation.

$$v = ct - \beta/t$$

where v = kinematic viscosity in centistokes, t =time of flow in seconds and c and β are constants.

Table 3.2 Comparison of different viscometers

Instrument	Value of c	Value of β
Redwood No. 1	0.25	172
Redwood No. 2	2.72	1120
Saybolt Universal	0.22	180
Engler	0.147	374

Note: (1) t = (Degrees Engler) x 52, (2) Redwood Seconds No. 1 = 0.88 Saybolt universal seconds. (3) Degrees Engler = 0.0328 Redwood Seconds No. 1, (4) For accurate results, conversion constants should be determined experimentally at the temperature under consideration

Viscosity Index: Viscosity index is a petroleum industry term. It is a lubricating oil quality indicator, an arbitrary measure for the change of kinematic viscosity with temperature. The viscosity of liquids decreases as temperature increases. The viscosity of a lubricant is closely related to its ability to reduce friction. Generally, thinnest liquid oil is desired which forces the two moving surfaces apart. If the lubricant is too thick, it will require a lot of energy to move the surfaces (such as in honey); if it is too thin, the surfaces will rub and friction will increase.

As stated above, the Viscosity Index highlights how a lubricant's viscosity changes with variations in temperature. Many lubricant applications require the lubricant to perform across a wide range of conditions: for example, in an engine, automotive lubricants must reduce friction between engine components when it is started from cold (relative to engine operating temperatures) as well as when it is running (up to 200°C). The best oils (with the highest VI) will not vary much in viscosity over such a temperature range and therefore will perform well throughout. VI scale was set up by the Society of Automotive Engineers (SAE).

The temperatures chosen arbitrarily for reference are 100 °Fahrenheit (38 °C) and 210 °F (100 °C). The original scale only stretched between VI=0 (worst oil) and VI=100 (best oil) but since the conception of the scale, better oils have also been produced, leading to VIs greater than 100.VI improver additives and higher quality base oils are widely used now a days which increase the VIs attainable beyond the value of 100. The Viscosity Index of synthetic fluids ranges from 80 to over 400.

Determination of Viscosity Index: In 1929, Mr .E.W. Bean and Mr. G..H.B.Davis of U.S.A. derived viscosity index of test oil as follows. For this purpose they used two types of standard oils.

1) Paraffinic base Pennsylvanian oil (V.I.= 100) viscosity changing very low with temperature
2) Napthanic base Gulf oil (VI= 0) viscosity changing rapidly with temperature

$$V.I = \frac{L-U}{L-H} \times 100$$

where, L= viscosity in centistokes at 100 ^{0} F(38 ^{0} C) of an oil having zero VI and having the same viscosity at 210 ^{0} F (100 ^{0} C) as the test oil will have at 210 ^{0} F and H = Viscosity in centistokes at 100^0 F (38 ^{0} C) of an oil having 100 VI and having the same viscosity at 210 ^{0} F, U = Viscosity in centistokes at 100^0 F(38°C) of a test oil as that of the sample oil.The higher is the viscosity index, better are is the viscosity temperature characteristics.

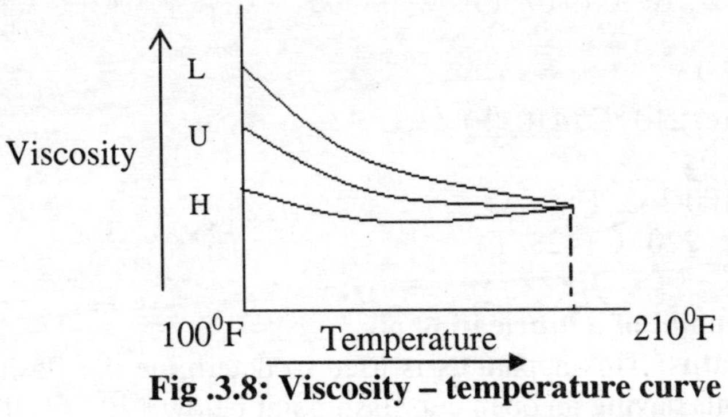

Fig .3.8: Viscosity – temperature curve

Table 3.3: Relation between viscosity index and oil

Viscosity Index	Oil
25-50	Low Viscosity Index (LV)
50-80	Medium Viscosity Index (MV)
More than 80	High Viscosity Index (HV)

Flash Point and Fire Point: The flash point of a flammable liquid is the lowest temperature at which it can form an ignitable mixture in air. At this temperature the vapor may cease to burn when the source of ignition is removed. A slightly higher temperature, the fire point, is defined as the temperature at which the vapor continues to burn after being ignited. Neither of these parameters is related to the temperatures of the ignition source or of the burning liquid, which are much higher. The flash point is often used as one descriptive characteristic of liquid fuel, but it is also used to describe liquids that are not used intentionally as fuel.

Significance:

1) Both flash and fire point are important parameters for petroleum products for safety reasons. Low flash point oils are more volatile oils and if used in applications involving high temperature operation, higher rates of oil consumption may occur.
2) For domestic purpose, flash point above 50^{0} C is not desirable.
3) A good lubricant should have flash point at least above the temperature at which it is to be used.

Examples of fuel flash points: Petrol (gasoline) is designed for use in an engine which is driven by a spark. The fuel should be premixed with air within its flammable limits and heated above its flash point, then ignited by the spark plug. The fuel should not pre-ignite in the hot engine. Therefore, gasoline is required to have a low flash point and a high auto ignition temperature.

Diesel is designed for use in a high-compression engine. Air is compressed until it has been heated above the auto ignition temperature of diesel; then the fuel is injected as a high-pressure spray, keeping the fuel-air mix within the flammable limits of diesel. There is no ignition source. Therefore, diesel is required to have a high flash point and a low auto ignition temperature.

Petrol

Flash point: > -43 °C (-45 °F [negative, below freezing point of water at +32° F])
Auto ignition temperature: 246 °C (475 °F)

Diesel

Flash point: >62 °C (143 °F)
Auto ignition temperature: 210 °C (410 °F)

Jet Fuel

Flash Point: >38 °C (100 °F)
Auto ignition Temperature: 210 °C (410 °F)

Kerosene:

Flash point: >38-72 °C (100-162 °F)
Auto ignition temperature: 220 °C (428 °F)

Measurement of flash and fire point of a lubricating oil

1) Cleveland open cup apparatus: This apparatus is used to determine the flash and fire point of all petroleum products except fuel oils having an open cup flash point below $120\ ^{0}$ C . The apparatus consists of cylindrical brass cup with a mark showing a level upto which the oil should be filled. The cup is supported by a metal plate made of brass or steel or cast iron which has a circular opening at the center,

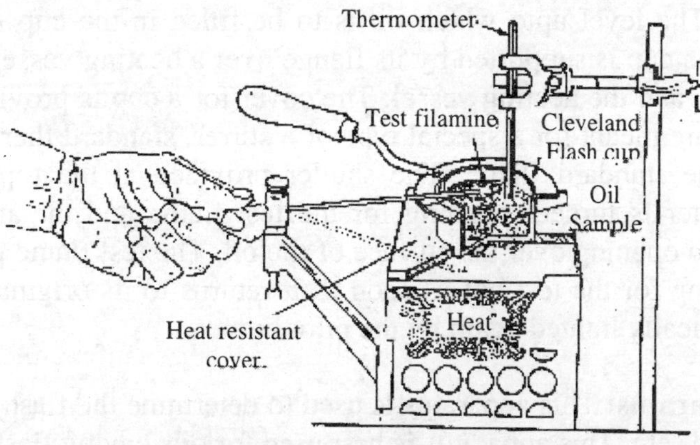

Fig. 3.9: Cleveland open cup apparatus

exactly enough to fit the cup in position. The plate is covered with a sheet of hard asbestos board with a circular hole at the centre in which the cup can be just fitted. An elaborate heating device is at the center, exactly enough to fit the cup in position. The plate is covered with a sheet of hard asbestos board with a circular hole at the centre in which the cup can be just fitted. An elaborate heating device is provided in such a way that the cup can be uniformly heated without any local super heating. A clamp is provided to hold the standard thermometer (0- 400 ^{0} C) supplied with the apparatus.

Procedure: Oil tested is filled in cup to the specified filling mark. The thermometer is dipped in the sample and then oil is heated at a rate of 9° to 11^{0} F per minute. At every 2^{0} C rise in temperature, a small flame is passed over the oil surface. If flame appeared at any point on the surface of oil, the temperature shall be recorded as the flash point. Oil is heated continuously at the same rate. The test flame is applied again for 2^{0}C every rise in temperature until oil ignites and burns continuously at least for 5 sec, that point is fire point. Fire point should be 5 to 40 ^{0}C higher than flash point. The flash point of lubricating oil should be greater than120^{0} C and this is only limitation.

2) The Pensky Martin closed cup apparatus: It is used to determine the flash point of lubricating oils, combustible oils, solvents, solvent containing materials and suspension of solids, except cut- back asphalt.

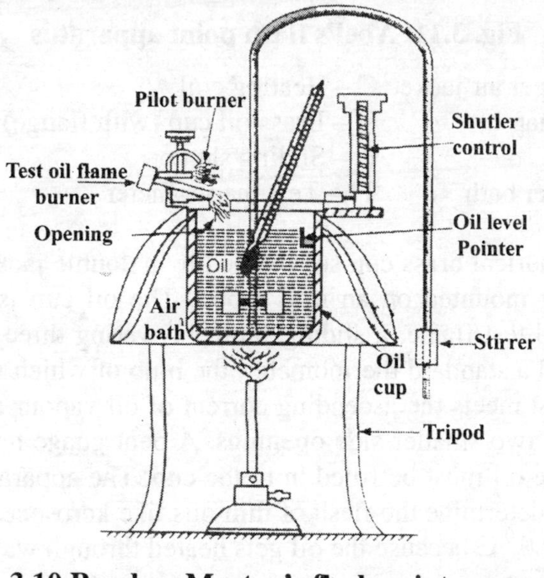

Fig. 3.10 Penskey-Marten's flash point apparatus

It consists of brass cup which is 5.5 cm deep and 5 cm in diameter. The cup is provided with four openings of standard size. The level upto which oil is to be filled in the cup is marked to about 1 cm below the top of the cup. The cup is supported by its flange over a heating vessel in such a way that there is clearance between the cup and the heating vessel. The cover for a cup is provided with four opening of standard dimension, which are meant for a special type of a stirrer, standard thermometer, an air inlet and a device for introducing the standard flame. The shutter provided at the top of the cup has a lever mechanism. When the shutter is turned, opening for the test flame and air are opened and the flame exposure device dips into the opening over the surface of the oil. The test flame gets extinguished when it is introduced into the opening for the test but as soon as it returns to its original position on closing the shutter, the flame is automatically lighted again by the pilot burner.

3) Abel's Closed Cup Apparatus: This apparatus is used to determine the flash point of fuel oil, organic solvents, valuable compounds etc. This apparatus is best used for oils having flash point below 80^0 C.

Procedure: The sample is placed in the oil cup and heated at the rate of $2\ ^0$ C per min. The heating vessel is filled to overflowing with warm water. A small test flame is directed into the cup at regular intervals and the lowest temperature at which application of the test flame causes the vapour above the sample to ignite with a distinct flame inside the cup, is recorded as Abel's flash point.

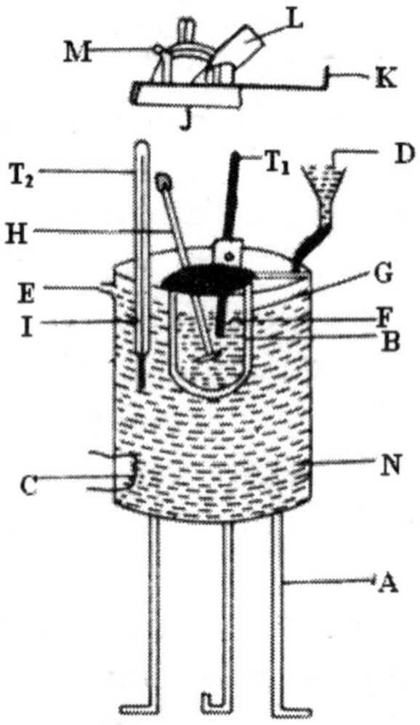

Fig. 3.11: Abel's flash point apparatus

A – Tripod stand	B – Copper air jacket	C – Heating coil	D – Water inlet
E – Water outlet	F – Air gap	G – Brass oil cup (with flange)	H – Stirrer
I – Pointer	J – Lid	K – Sliding shutter	L – Test flame
M – White bead	N – Water bath	T_1 – Test thermometer	

Apparatus: It consists of cylindrical brass cup surrounded by a double jacketed copper water bath which is enclosed in a copper casing mounted on an iron tripod. The oil cup is provided with a brass cover having arrangement for a small test flame, a sliding shutter covering three small openings in the lid and opening for a paddle stirrer and a standard thermometer, the bulb of which should be immersed in the oil. When the shutter is opened, test meets the ascending current of oil vapour and air while at the same time atmospheric air passes into the two smaller side openings. A bent guage terminating with a point ending indicates the depth to which the oil must be filled in to the cup. The apparatus is provided with electrical heating device. This is used to determine the flash of thin oils like kerosene, diesel, organic solvent etc. It can be used satisfactorily upto $80\ ^0$ C because the oil gets heated through water bath.

Cloud and Pour Points: The temperature at which paraffin wax starts to crystallize to separate out from the oil when cooled under specified condition is known as cloud point. The pour point of petroleum oil is the temperature at which the oil ceases to flow. At the cloud point, oil becomes cloudy or hazy in appearance. Cloud and pour points indicate the suitability of lubricants in cold conditions.

Significance: It is useful in measuring the relative amount of wax in oil.

Test: In a test jar, the oil is cooled at least 25 °F above the cloud point. The cooling bath should be maintained between 15 and 30 °F below the cloud point of the oil. At different time intervals, the test jar is taken from the brine bath without disturbance to the oil. A distinct cloudiness or haziness at the bottom of the test jar appears, this temperature is recorded as the cloud point.

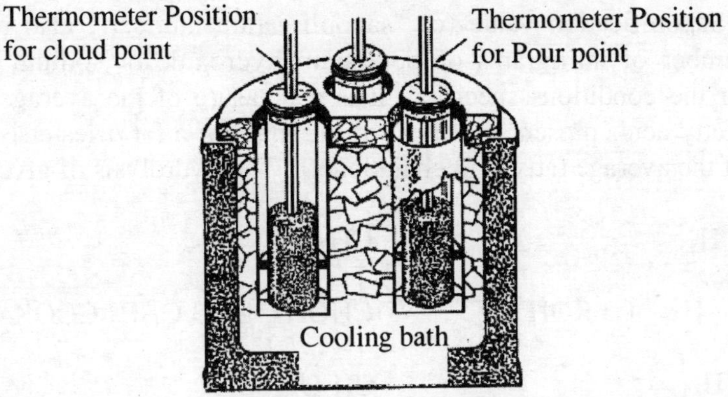

Fig. 3.12: Apparatus for cloud and pour points determination

Pour Point

Test: It is carried out in the same way as cloud point measurement. First of all the wax is dissolved at 115°F and cooled to 90 °F before the test. The bath should be held 15 to 30 °F below estimated pour point. At regular interval of 5 °F, the test jar is taken out from the bath and tilted to make sure if the oil will flow or move. It shows no movement when the jar is held horizontal for 5 sec., it is treated as solid point. Above 5 °F, this solid point is known as pour point.

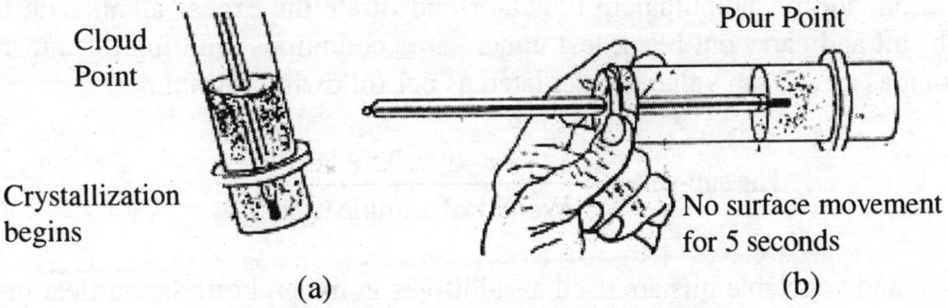

Fig. 3.13: Cloud and Pour points

Significance: Pour point values of petroleum and non petroleum lubricants are significant, as many operations must function in sub freezing conditions. Generally pour point of the oils is lower than minimum ambient temperature at the place of application, so that the oil will readily flow at all time in the engine oil pumps or in the system.

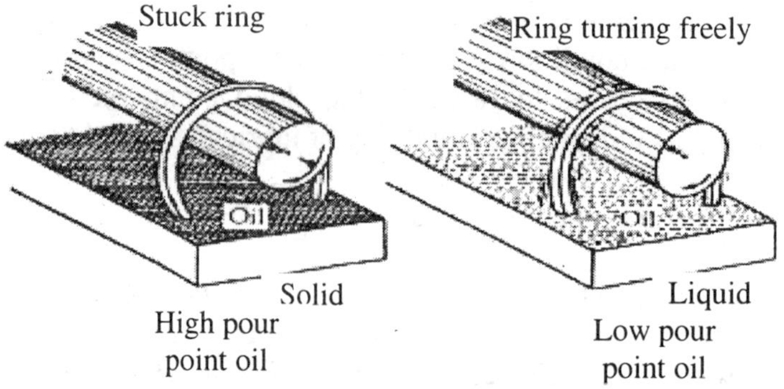

Fig. 3.14: Pour point (Temperature at which the oil will cease to flow)

Saponification Value: Saponification value (or "saponification number", also referred to as "sap" in short) represents the number of milligrams of potassium hydroxide or sodium hydroxide required to saponify 1g of fat under the conditions specified. It is a measure of the average molecular weight (or chain length) of all the fatty acids present. As most of the mass of a fat /triester is in the 3 fatty acids, it allows for comparison of the average fatty acid chain length. The hydrolysis of glyceride is:

$$\begin{array}{l} CH_2\text{-}O\text{-}CO\ C_{17}H_{35} \\ | \\ CH-O-CO\text{-}C_{17}H_{35} \\ | \\ CH_2-O\ CO\text{-}C_{17}H_{35} \end{array} + 3\,KOH \longrightarrow \begin{array}{l} CH_2OH \\ | \\ CHOH \\ | \\ CH_2OH \end{array} + 3\,C_{17}H_{35}COOK$$

Stearic acid | Pot. Hydroxide | Glycerol | Potassium stearate

Procedure: 0.5 N solution of potassium hydroxide is prepared by dissolving 30 g potassium hydroxide in 20 ml of water making the final volume 1 litre by 95 % ethanol. Leave the solution to stand for 24 hrs. Weigh approximately 2 g of oil sample into a 250 ml conical flask with glass joint and add 25 ml of the potassium hydroxide solution Attach a reflux condenser and heat the flask for 1 hour with frequent shaking. In hot solution, add phenolphthalein indicator and titrate the excess alkali with the 0.5 N HCl. Note this reading 'b' ml and carry out blank test under same conditions omitting the substance. Note the volume in ml of titrant as a. The sap value is calculated as per following formula:

$$\text{The sap value} = \frac{(a - b) \times 0.5 \times 56.1}{\text{Weight of sample used (g)}}$$

Significance: Animal and vegetable oils are used as additives in mineral oil. Saponification number gives an indication of the amount of animal and vegetable oils added to mineral oils to improve oiliness. Most of the animal and vegetable oils possess their own characteristic sap values. Any deviation from this value gives the extent of adulteration. This test gives the information whether the oil under study is animal / vegetable or mineral / compounded oil.

Neutralization Number: It is a number derived from a standard test indicating the acid or base composition of lubricating oils; it in no way indicates the corrosive attack of the used oil in service. It is also known as corrosion number. Acid value (or "neutralization number" or "acid number" or "acidity") is the mass of potassium hydroxide (KOH) in milligrams that is required to neutralize one gram of oil sample. The acid number is a measure of the amount of carboxylic acid groups in a chemical compound such as a fatty acid. In a typical procedure, a known amount of sample dissolved in organic solvent is titrated with a solution of potassium hydroxide with known concentration and with phenolphthalein as a color indicator.

Acidity and Alkalinity of lubricating oil are determined by neutralization number. It represents either the Total Acid Number or Total Base Number. It is the number of milligrams of KOH needed to neutralize any acid in one gram of oil. This is known as Total Acid Number. Total Base Number is defined as the number of milligrams of HCl needed to neutralize any base in one gram of oil.

Procedure

1) Take weighed amount of the sample (20 gm sample for light coloured oil or 2 gm sample for dark coloured oil).
2) Add 100 ml of titration solvent (made by mixing 500 ml of toluene and 5 ml of distilled water with 495 ml of iso propyl alcohol) and 30 drops of indicator (para napthylo benzene) solution to the flask, then add mixture until the sample is completely dissolved.
3) Acidic solution turns yellow- orange or deep orange in colour and basic solution becomes green or blue colour, then titrate it with alc. HCl.
4) Add alc. KOH solution slowly from the burette until the green or green blue colour appears which persists for at least 15 sec.
5) Note the reading from the burette

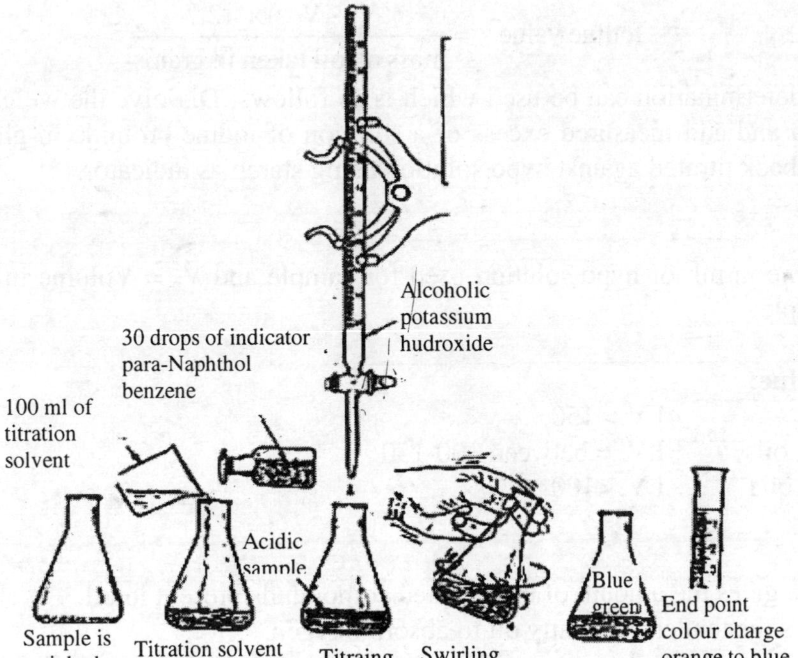

Fig. 3.15 Determination of Total acids numbers (TAN)

$$\text{Neutralization no.} = \frac{\text{Total ml of titrating solution}}{\text{Weight of sample used}} \times 5.61$$

Significance:

1) Neutralization number gives the value of relative change in an oil due to oxidation.
2) TAN and TBN when compared with new oil will indicate the formation of harmful products or the depletion of additives.
3) Higher acid number indicates the oxidation of oil which leads to corrosion along with gummy compound and sludge formation.

Iodine Value: The iodine value (or "iodine adsorption value" or "iodine number") in chemistry is the mass of iodine in grams that is consumed by 100 grams of a chemical substance. An iodine solution is yellow/brown in color and any chemical group in the substance that reacts with iodine will make the color disappear at a precise concentration. The amount of iodine solution thus required to keep the solution yellow/brown is a measure of the amount of iodine sensitive reactive groups.

Determination: 0.2 grams of the fat is mixed with 20 cm^3 Wij's solution and 10 cm^3 1,1,1-trichloroethane. It is then left in the dark for 30 mins. Next, 15cm^3 of 10% potassium iodide solution and 10 cm^3 of deionised water are added. This is then titrated against 0.1M sodium thiosulphate (VI) solution.

$$1cm^3 \text{ of } 0.1M \text{ sodium thiosulphate solution} = 0.01269g \text{ of iodine.}$$

The difference between a control titration and the titration with the fat present multiplied by this factor gives the mass of iodine absorbed by the oil.

$$\text{Iodine value} = \frac{(V_b - V_s) \times 12.7}{\text{mass of oil taken in grams}}$$

Other method for determination can be used which is as follows: Dissolve the weighed quantity of oil in CCl_4 or acetic acid and add measured excess of a solution of iodine bromide in glacial acetic acid. The unused IBr is then back titrated against hypo solution using starch as indicator.

where, Vs = Volume in ml .of hypo solution used for sample and V_b = Volume in ml. of hypo solution used for blank sample

Limit of iodine value:

For drying oils	I.V.> 150,
For semidrying oils	I.V. = between 100-150
For non drying oils	I.V. <100

Significance

1) Iodine value gives the amount of unsaturated compounds present in oil.
2) It also shows the tendency of fatty oil to absorb oxygen.
3) When the oil is exposed to air and heat, it combines with oxygen and forms certain chemical compounds which are unsuitable for use as lubricants.
4) Acids and Gummy sludge are the products of oxidation.

Steam Emulsion Number: When water enters in an oil system, turbulence is caused by high volume flow resulting in the formation of emulsion. Some oil forms emulsion with water more easily than others. Due to the formation of emulsion, abrasion and wearing out of the lubricated parts of the machinery occur. Hence, it is essential that the lubricating oil should form such an emulsion with water which breaks off readily. SEN or demulsification number is defined as the time in seconds in which oil and water emulsion separate out in distinct layers. The quicker the oil separates out from the emulsion, the lower is the steam emulsion number and better is the lubricating oil.

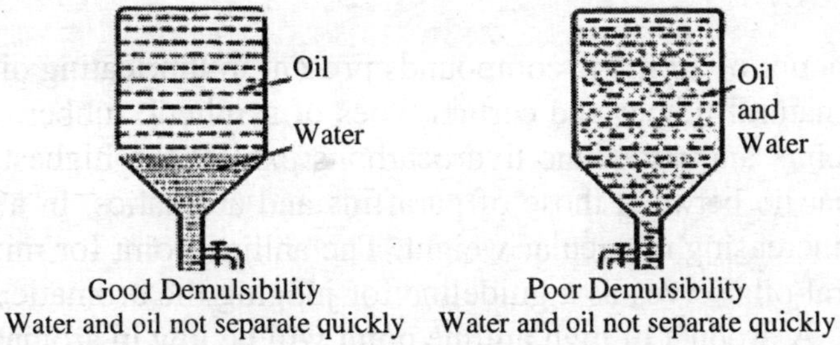

Fig. 3.16: Demulsibility

Determination: Steam at 100 °C is bubbled through a test tube containing 20 ml of oil sample till the volume becomes 40 ml, temperature increases to 90 °C and the time is noted when the oil and water separate out in distinct layers.

Significance: To avoid corrosion of polished steel surfaces, it is important to check the speed of water and oil separation.

Aniline Point: Aniline point is used to characterize pure hydrocarbons and to indicate the aromatic content of hydrocarbon mixtures. Equal volumes of aniline and sample or sample plus n-heptane are stirred together while being heated at a controlled rate. After the two phases become miscible, the mixture is cooled at a controlled rate and the temperature at which the two phases separate is known as the aniline point or mixed aniline point of the sample. It is defined as the minimum equilibrium solution temperature for equal volume of aniline and oil sample.

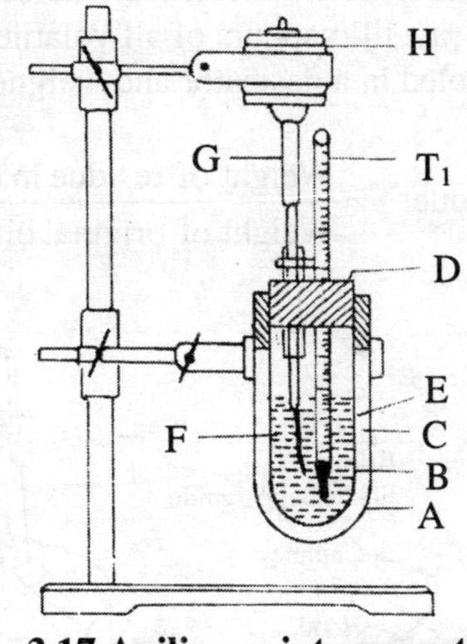

Fig.3.17 Aniline point apparatus

A – Outer air jacket	B – Test apparatus
C – Air gap	D – Corks
E – Equal volumes of oil and aniline	F – Glass stirrer with auger tip
G – Rubber tubing	H – Variable speed motor
T_1– Aniline point thermometer	

Determination: Equal volumes of oil and aniline are thoroughly mixed in a test tube and heat the mixture to obtain a homogenous solution. Then the tube is allowed to cool at a controlled rate. The temperature at which the oil and aniline separate out is known as aniline point.

Significance: It gives the amount of aromatic compounds present in lubricating oil. Aromatic compounds have a tendency to dissolve natural rubber and certain types of synthetic rubber. Aromatic hydrocarbons exhibit the lowest aniline points and paraffinic hydrocarbons exhibit the highest values. Cycloparaffins and olefins exhibit values that lie between those of paraffins and aromatics. In a homologous series, the aniline point increases with increasing molecular weight. The aniline point for mixtures of hydrocarbons, such as diesel oils and mineral oils serves as a guideline for judging the aromatic hydrocarbon content of an oil and for comparing oils. A product of high aniline point will be low in aromatics and naphthenes and therefore, high in paraffins. Aniline point is often specified for spray oils, cleaning solvents and thinners, where effectiveness depends upon aromatic content. The aniline point may be used to calculate the net heat of combustion for aviation fuels.

Carbon Residue: This test method covers the determination of the amount of carbon residue left after evaporation and pyrolysis of an oil and it is intended to provide some indication of relative coke-forming propensity. This test method is generally applicable to relatively nonvolatile petroleum products which partially decompose on distillation at atmospheric pressure.

When the oil is subjected to high temperature, the carbon present in oil gets decomposed and forms a carbonaceous deposit. Two apparatus are used to measure the amount of carbon residue.
1) Conradson's apparatus
2) Ramsbottom apparatus

1. Conradson's Apparatus:
Procedure: Weighed amount of sample is taken in a silica crucible which is covered with an iron hood. Heat the crucible at certain prescribed rate till vapours of all volatile matter are burnt completely. After 30 minutes, silica crucible is removed, cooled in a desicator and weighed.

$$\% \text{ carbon residue} = \frac{\text{Weight of residue in crucible}}{\text{Weight of original oil sample}} \times 100$$

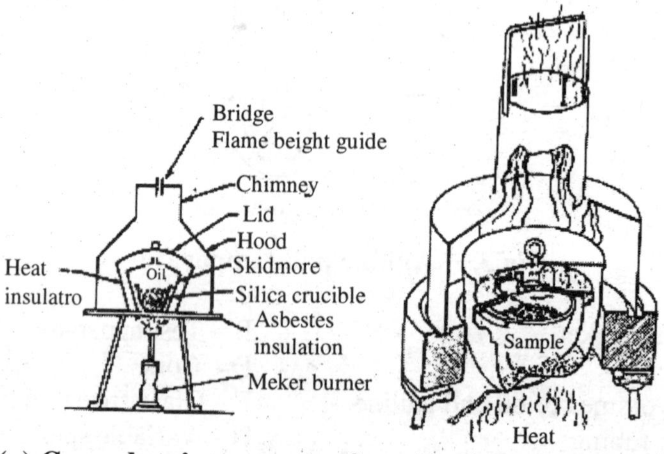

Fig. 3.18: (a) Conradson's apparatus for Carbon residue estimation (b) Cutaway view of Conradson's apparatus

2. Ramsbottom Apparatus: This method is used with more fluid products.

Procedure: A weighed sample is placed in a special bulb through the capillary inlet by means of a syringe. This glass bulb containing sample is inserted in one of the hole of an electrically heated small furnace (Ramsbottom Apparatus) maintained at approx. 550° C. At this temperature, all the volatile matter escapes through the bulb capillary leaving a residue that undergoes cracking and possible coke formation. After heating, bulb is taken out and cooled in a dessicator and weighed.

$$\%\ \text{carbon residue} = \frac{\text{Weight of residue in bulb}}{\text{Weight of original oil sample}} \times 100$$

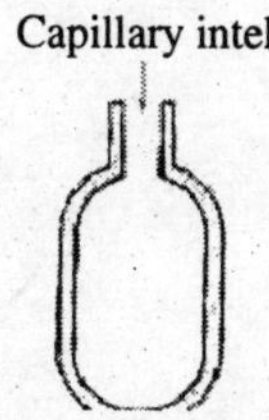

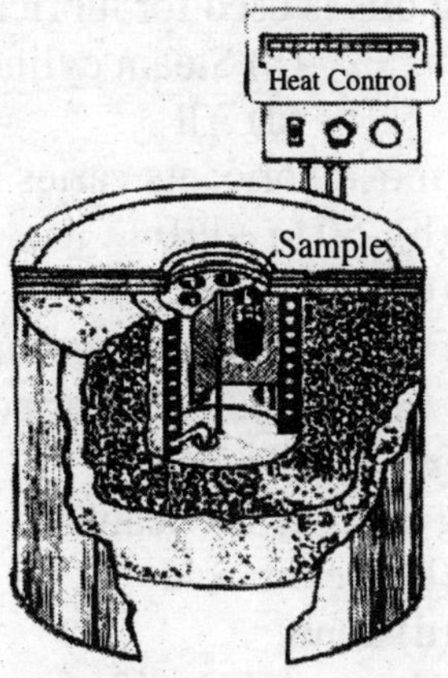

Fig. 3.19 (a) Glass bulb with a capillary opening **(b) Cutaway view of Ramsbottom apparatus**

Significance of carbon residue

1) In diesel fuel, the presence of alkyl nitrates such as amyl nitrate, hexyl nitrate, or octyl nitrate, causes a higher carbon residue value than observed in untreated fuel, which can lead to erroneous conclusions as to the coke-forming propensity of the fuel. The presence of alkyl nitrate in the fuel can be detected.

2) The value of carbon residue test is used in the evaluation of crude base and feed stocks in lubricants and fuels which are used in extreme temperature service.

OBJECTIVE QUESTIONS

1. A suitable lubricant for watches is:
   (a) Graphite (b) Palm oil
   (c) Grease (d) Hazel nut oil
2. Better Lubricants are those which have:
   (a) Low coke number (b) High coke number
   (c) Hydrolytic properties under lubricating conditions (d) none
3. Greases are not used to lubricate.
   (a) Gears (b) Rail axle boxes
   (c) Bearing working at high temperature (d) Delicate instruments
4. Which of the following oils is used for lubricants.
   (a) Spindle oil (b) Steam cylinder oil
   (c) Red and pale oil (d) All
5. The viscosity index of most lubricants varies from?
   (a) +50 to 110 (b) -50 to +110
   (c) -20 to 50 (d) -50 to 300
6. Important properties of boundary lubricants are.
   (a) Good oiliness (b) Low pour point
   (c) High viscosity index (d) All
7. Which of the following is better lubricant?
   (a) Oleic acid (b) Stearic acid
   (c) Acetic acid (d) none
8. Which of the following is vegetable oil?
   (a) Olive oil (b) Palm oil
   (c) Castor oil (d) Rapeseed oil.
   (f) All
9. Oiliness is excellent in:
   (a) Mineral oils (b) Castor oil
   (c) Olive oil (c) Greases
10. Oiliness is minimum in: –
    (a) Mineral oils (b) Castor oil
    (c) Olive oil (d) Palm oil
11. Which of the following is used as antioxidant to prevent the oxidation of lubricant?
    (a) Phenol (b) Amines
    (c) Organic phosphides (d) All
12. Which of the following is added to increase the oiliness and film strength of lubricant?
    (a) Dibenzyl disulphide (b) Amyl phenyl phosphate
    (c) Methyl dichloro phosphate(d) Tri cresyl phosphate
    (e) All
13. Which of the following is used as galling agent?
    (a) Fatty acids (b) Na-soap
    (c) Ca-soap (d) Al-soap
    (e) All
14. Which of the following fatty acids is used as galling agent?
    (a) Oleic acid (b) Palmitic acid
    (c) Stearic acid (d) All

15. Which of the following is used as solid lubricant?
(a) Graphite (b) Molybdenum disulphite
(c) Mice (d) Soap stone
(e) Talc (f) All
16. In the presence of additives, the neutralization number of lubricating oil is?
(a) Less than 0.10 (b) More than 1.0
(c) More than 0.1 (d) Less than 1.0
17. A high aniline point for lubricant indicates that.
(a) It contains higher percentage of paraffinic hydrocarbons.
(b) It contains lower percentage of paraffinic hydrocarbons.
(c) It contains lower percentage of aromatic hydrocarbons.
(d) It contains higher percentage of aromatic hydro carbons.
18. Fire point has been found to be ……to…… ^{0}C higher than the flash point.
(a) 4-40^{0}C (b) 10-50^{0}C
(c) 25-75^{0}C (d) 4-10^{0}C
19 Which of the following are extreme pressure additives?
(a) Fatty acids (b) Ketones
(c) Esters (d) Chlorinated wax
(e) Sulphurized fats and olefins (f) All
20. Galling agents give which property to grease?
(a) Oiliness (b) Stiffness
(c) Resistance to temperature (d) All
21. Anti foaming additive is:
(a) Sodium salt of sulphonic acid (b) Silicon polymer
(c) Aryl phosphate (d) Poly acrylate polymer
22. Machines operating under high temperatures and loads are best lubricated by:
(a) Mineral oil (b) Solid lubricants
(c) Greases (d) Animal oils
23. Viscosity index is zero for:
(a) Paraffin base Gulf oil (b) Paraffin base Pennsylvanian oil
(c) Napthanic base Gulf oil (d) Napthanic base Pennsylvanian oil
24. Which of the following possess low pour point?
(a) Poly glycidal ether (b) Organic amines
(c) Organic amide (d) Organic imines
(e) All
25. Greases are made by saponification of:
(a) Fats (b) Protein
(c) Carbohydrates (d) None
26. The order of coefficient of kinetic friction μ_k , sliding friction μ_s rolling friction μ_r is:
(a) $\mu_s > \mu_r > \mu_k$ (b) $\mu_s > \mu_k > \mu_r$
(c) $\mu_s > \mu_r > \mu_k$ (d) $\mu_s > \mu_k > \mu_r$
27. Which of the following lubricating oil can be used in air craft at 50^{0}C to 250^{0}C?
(a) Animal oil (b) Synthetic oil
(c) Mineral oil (c) None
28. Amount of lime in calcium based grease is:
(a) 10-30% (b) 50-70%
(c) 80-90% (d) 1-3%

29. Which is added to remove asphaltic impurity from oil?
(a) HNO_3 (b) H_2SO_4
(c) BF_3 (d) HCl
30. Insulating property can be measured by:
(a) Aniline point (b) Electric conductivity
(c) Dielectric strength (d) None
31. The wax present in oil raises the:
(a) Drop point (b) Aniline point
(c) Pour point (d) Fire point
32. Which of the following grease is water proof ?
(a) Calcium based (b) Sodium based
(c) Lithium based (d) Both a and c
33. Molybdenum disulphide is stable upto:
(a) 200^0C (b) 300^0C
(c) 400^0C (d) 600^0C
34. Dimensions of kinematics viscosity are:
(a) LT^{-1} (b) $L^{-1}T^{-1}$
(c) L^2T^{-1} (d) LT
35. Redwood viscometer -2 is used for oils having flowing time:
(a) More than 1000 sec
(b) More than 2000 sec.
(c) Less than 2000 sec
(d) More than 200 sec.
36. Say bolt furl viscometer is used for:
(a) Thin oil (b) Thick oil
(c) Blended oil (d) Vegetable oil
37. Abels closed cup can be used upto temperature:
(a) 250^0C (b) 120^0C
(c) 80^0C (d) 50^0C
38. Addition of alcohol decreases cloud point because:
(a) Wax precipitates (b) Wax dissolves
(c) Wax remains suspended (d) None
39. When paraffin is added to oil, then cloud point:
(a) Decreases (b) Increases
(c) Remains same (d) Increases but pour point decreases
40. Which lubricant is used on the surface of moon?
(a) Graphite (b) Mineral oil
(c) Vegetable oil (d) Axle grease
41. Aromatic compounds present in oil:
(a) Make oil viscous (b) Give fragrance
(c) Degrade rubber (d) None
42. Conrad son method is used in determination of:
(a) Cloud point (b) Fire point
(c) Carbon residue (d) Aniline point
43. Dimensions of absolute viscosity are.
(a) $ML^{-1}T^{-1}$ (b) MLT^{-2}
(c) MLT^{-1} (d) LT^{-1}

44. Which type of grease is formed by resin?
(a) Cup grease (b) Soda based grease
(c) Both a and b (d) Axle grease
45. When the temperature is very low, which grease is suitable for use?
(a) Na-based (b) Li-based
(c) Cup grease (d) None of these
46. Viscosity index improvers are having:
(a) High molecular weight (b) Low molecular weight
(c) Moderate molecular weight (d) None
47. Corrosion preventers are the organic compounds of:
(a) Phosphorous (b) Sulphur
(c) Nitrogen (d) None
48. In light cutting the most effective lubricants are:
(a) Oil-water emulsions (b) Water-oil emulsions
(c) Greases (d) Oil emulsions
49. Which one is the open- cup apparatus for determination of flash and fire point of lubricatry oil?
(a) Abel's apparatus (b) Cleaveland's apparatus
(c) Pens key – Marten's apparatus (d) None of the above

Answer Key

(1)d	(2)a	(3)d	(4)d	(5)b	(6)e	(7)a	(8)f	(9)b	(10)a	(11)d	(12)e	(13)e	(14)d
(15)f	(16)c	(17)a,c	(18)a	(19)f	(20)b	(21)b	(22)d	(23)c	(24)e	(25)a	(26)b	(27)b	(28)a
(29)b	(30)c	(31)c	(32)d	(33)c	(34)c	(35)b	(36)b	(37)c	(38)b	(39)b	(40)a	(41)c	(42)c
(43)a	(44)d	(45)b	(46)a	(47)a	(48)d	(49)b							

SOLVED NUMERICAL PROBLEMS

Problem 1

An oil sample under test has a saybolt universal viscosity of 64 seconds at 210° F and 564 seconds at 100° F. The low viscosity standard (Gulf oil) possesses a saybolt viscosity of 64 seconds at 210° F and 774 Seconds at 100° F. The high viscosity standard gave the saybolt viscosity values of 64 seconds at 210° F and 414° seconds at 100° F. Calculate the viscosity index of the oil sample under test. **[RGPV 01]**

Solution

Here L = 774 s , H = 414 s and U = 564 s

$$V.I = \frac{L-U}{L-H} \times 100$$

$$= \frac{774-564}{774-414} \times 100 = 58.33$$

Problem 2

An oil sample under test has a saybolt universal viscosity of 64 S at 210° F and 600 S at 100° F. The high viscosity standard (Pennsylvanian oil) gave the saybolt universal viscosity of 64 S at 210°F and 400 S at 100° F. The low viscosity standard (Gulf oil) possesses a saybolt viscosity of 64 S at 210° F and 700 S at 100° F. Calculate the viscosity index of the oil sample under test. **[RGPV 06]**

Solution

Here L = 700 s H = 400 s U = 600 s

$$V.I = \frac{700-600}{700-400} \times 100 = 33.33$$

Problem 3

An oil sample under test has Sabolt universal viscosity same as that of standard gulf oil (low viscosity standard) and pennsylvanian oil (high viscosity standard) at 210 F . The saybolt universal viscosity at 100 F are 50, 750, 450 respectively. Calculate the V.I. of the sample oil. **[RGPV 06]**

Solution

Here L = 750 s, H = 450 s, U= 50 s

$$V.I = \frac{L-U}{L-H} \times 100$$

$$= \frac{750-50}{750-450} \times 100 = 233.33$$

Problem 4

A lubricating oil has a S.U.V of 58 seconds at 210 ^{0} F and of 600 seconds at 100 ^{0} F. The high viscosity index standard of Pennsylvanian oil has S.U.V of 58 seconds at 210 ^{0} F and 400 seconds at 100 ^{0} F. The low viscosity index standard of Gulf Oil has a S.U.V of 58 seconds at 210 ^{0} F and 800 seconds at 100 ^{0} F. Calculate the viscosity index of the oil. **[RGPV 07]**

Solution

$$V.I = \frac{L-U}{L-H} \times 100$$

$$= \frac{800-600}{800-400} \times 100 = \frac{200}{400} X100 = 50$$

Problem 5

An oil sample under test has a Saybolt Universal Viscosity same as that of Standard Gulf Oil (low viscosity standard) and Pennsylvanian oil (high viscosity standard) at 210 ^{0} F. Their Saybolt Universal viscosities at 100 ^{0} F are 600, 800 and 500 respectively. Calculate viscosity – index of the oil sample. **[RGPV 07]**

Solution

$$V.I = \frac{L-U}{L-H} \times 100$$

$$= \frac{800-600}{800-500} \times 100 = \frac{200}{300} \times 100 = 66.67$$

Problem 6

A lubricating oil has Saybolt universal viscosity of 58 seconds at 210°F and 564 seconds at 100°F. The low V.I. standard Gulf oil has Saybolt universal viscosity of 58 seconds at 210°F and 758 seconds at 100°F. The high value is 58 seconds at 210°F and 420 seconds at 100° F. Calculate V.I. of the lubricating oil. **[RGPV 07]**

Solution

$$V.I = \frac{L-U}{L-H} \times 100$$

$$= \frac{758-564}{758-420} \times 100 = \frac{194}{338} \times 100 = 57.69$$

Problem 7

An oil sample under test has a saybolt universal viscosity same as that of standard gulf oil (low viscosity index standard) and Pennsylvanian oil (high viscosity index standard) at 210^0F. Their saybolt universal viscosities at 100^0 F are 60, 760 and 425 seconds respectively, calculate viscosity index of the oil sample. **[RGPV 09]**

$$V.I = \frac{L-U}{L-H} \times 100$$

$$= \frac{760-60}{760-425} \times 100 = \frac{700}{338} \times 100 = 207.10$$

THEORETICAL QUESTIONS

1. Match the following:

A	Graphite	Ca – based greases
B	Anti wear additives	Exanol
C	Cup greases	Tricresyl phosphates
D	Polymeric thickners	Solid lubricants

[RGPV 01]

2. a) How are lubricants classified ? What are the different mechanisms of lubrication? Discuss boundary film lubrication.
   b) What are greases? Mention their some specific uses. **[RGPV 01]**
3. Define lubricants. Mention their important functions. Explain and discuss the significance of any two properties of lubricants. **[RGPV 02,08,09]**
4. Discuss in brief lubrication, its mechanism and significance. Explain Viscosity Index of lubricating oil. **[RGPV 02]**
5. Define lubricants. How are they classified? Mention their important functions and describe any two of their important properties. **[RGPV 03,10]**
6. Define the term lubrication. Explain hydrodynamic and extreme pressure lubrication. Discuss the important functions of lubricants. Describe any two properties of lubricants. **[RGPV 04]**
7. a) Write informative notes on **[RGPV 05,07,10]**
   1 Graphite
   2 Extreme Pressure lubricants
   3 Solid lubricants
   4. Fluid film lubricant
   b) Comment on:
   i) Flash point determination by closed cup apparatus gives lower values than that determined by an open cup apparatus.
   ii) Determination of a pour point has a greater significance. **[RGPV 04]**
8. Define lubrication. **[RGPV 05]**
9. Define lubricants and mention the chief functions of lubricants. Explain flash and fire points.
10. What is a lubricant? Discuss the classification with examples. **[RGPV 05]**
11. Write short notes on : **[RGPV 06,08]**
    I Greases
    II Synthetic lubricants
12. a. What is boundary lubrication? **[RGPV 06,08]**
    b. Describe Aniline point , Cloud point and Pour point with its significance.

13. a. What are extreme pressure lubricants? **[RGPV 08]**
    b. What are solid lubricants?
    c. Discuss their structure, properties and uses.
    d. How can you determine flash and fire point by Pensky Martin apparatus? **[RGPV.06]**
14. Write note on consistency of greases. **[RGPV 07, 06,08]**
15. Discuss hydrodynamic lubrication with its mechanism. **[RGPV 06,08]**
16. Describe the determination of flash point by Pensky Martin method. **[RGPV 06,08,09,10]**
17. a. Discuss the important function of lubricants. **[RGPV 08]**
    b. Describe any three properties of lubricants.
    c. Discuss mechanism of hydrodynamic lubrication.
    d. Define greases. Under what situation are used as lubricants? **[RGPV 06, 07]**
18. Write informative note on synthetic lubricants. **[RGPV 01, 07]**
19. a. How lubricants are classified? **[RGPV 08]**
    b. What are different mechanisms of lubricants?
    c. Discuss boundary film lubrication.
    d. A good lubricant has:
    (i) Low freezing point.
    (ii) Low vapour pressure.
    (iii) High melting point.
    (iv) All the above. **[RGPV 07]**
20. a. Write a short note on cloud point and pour point.
    b. How viscosity of an oil sample is determined with the help of Redwood viscometer?
    c. What are Greases? Mention their specific uses. **[RGPV 07,09]**
21. Write short note on Flash point and Fire point of lubricating oils. **[RGPV 07]**
22. How can you determine carbon residue in any lubricating oil? **[RGPV 07,08]**
23. How can you determine Viscosity and Viscosity –index of thin lubricating oil? Explain with neat labeled diagram. **[RGPV 07]**
24. Define Steam Emulsion number (SEN) and Aniline Point with its significance. **[RGPV 07]**
25. Describe the mechanism of Hydrodynamic lubrication. **[RGPV 07,08]**
26. Write the factors to be considered for selecting the lubricants. **[RGPV 07]**
27. What is Lubrication? Describe with their significance of the following: **[RGPV 07,09,10]**
    i.) Aniline point
    ii.) Cloud point and Pour point
    iii) SEN
    iv) Viscosity Index
    v) Carbon residue
28. Write a note on solid lubricants. **[RGPV 07]**
29. How would you determine the viscosity index of lubricating oil using Redwood viscometer? **[RGPV 07, 09]**
30. Explain hydrodynamic lubrication and extreme pressure lubrication mechanism. **[RGPV 07]**
31. Comment on the following: **[RGPV 08]**
    i) Oils having high viscosity need not necessarily have high viscosity index.
    ii) An ideal lubricant should have low aniline point.
    iii) Closed cup apparatus gives a more reliable flash point than that given by the open cup apparatus.
32. Discuss the method of flash point determination by Abel's apparatus. **[RGPV 08]**
33. How the selection of a lubricant can be made for the following: **[RGPV 08]**
    i) Cutting tool

ii) Internal combustion engines.

34. Define and write the significance of following: **[RGPV 09]**
 (i) Oiliness (ii) Pour point
35. Discuss mechanism of lubrication by explaining fluid film lubrication. **[RGPV 09]**
36. Explain why:
 (i) Graphite act as a good lubricant on the surface of moon.
 (ii) A lubricant should have a high aniline point. **[RGPV 09]**

........✷........

Unit – IV

Polymers

4.1 INTRODUCTION

There is no product so widely used in the every sphere of life like polymeric materials, designated as resins, plastics and elastomers. Right from morning to our toothbrush to night to our bed, everyone lives in Polymers and common man just wonders the Polymer as gift of God. Nature was the first synthesizer of polymers with the production of protein and DNA from the elements and started life on this planet. Before year 1920, chemists doubted the existence of molecules having molecular weights greater than a few thousand. This view was challenged by Hermann Staudinger, a German chemist. In contrast to the prevailing rationalization of these substances as aggregates of small molecules, Staudinger proposed they were made up of macromolecules composed of 10,000 or more molecules. He formulated a polymeric structure for rubber, based on a repeating isoprene unit (referred to as a monomer). For his contributions to chemistry, Staudinger received the 1953 Nobel Prize.

The terms polymer and monomer were derived from the Greek roots -poly (many), mono (one) and meros (part). Polymers are complex and giant molecules known as macromolecules. Polymers are substances whose molecules have high molar masses and are composed of a large number of repeating units .Thus a polymer can be defined as a substance composed of molecules with large molecular mass composed of repeating structural units, or monomers, connected by covalent chemical bonds. Polymeric macromolecules make up many important natural materials and their synthetic analogs were prepared having a variety of properties. Indeed, applications of these materials as fibers, flexible films, adhesives, resistant paints and tough but light solids have transformed modern society. Current applications extend from adhesives, coatings, foams and packaging materials to textile and industrial fibers, composites, electronic devices, biomedical devices, optical devices and precursors for many newly developed high-tech ceramics.

Degree of Polymerisation: Number of repeating units n in a polymer chain is known as degree of polymerization

$$\left[CH_2\text{-}CH_2 \right]_n$$

The molecular weight of a particular polymer molecule is a product of the degree of polymerization and the molecular weight of the repeating unit. For instance a particular polyethylene molecule with DP = 1000 will have a molecular weight of 28,000. Because polymeric materials do not consist of strictly identical molecules, but a mixture of many species having different values of DP, the DP of the material only is an average value, $\overline{DP}$. Hence, measured polymer molecular weights are only average values.

Average Molecular Weight: Unless they have been purified, synthetic polymers have a distribution of molecular weights. Different methods of measuring the molecular weight yield different types of averages. Two most important methods are the number-average and the weight-average molecular weights.

Suppose that we have a set of values $\{x_1, x_2. \ldots x_n\}$ for which we calculate an average value. If the probability of each value occurring is given by $\{P_1, P_2. \ldots P_n\}$, then the average is given by the sum below.

$$\sum_{i=0}^{\infty} P_i X_i$$

The type of average depends on the formula used for the probability P_i.

Number-Average Molecular Weight: Suppose that we have a mixture of polymer molecules with different molecular weights in which the number of molecules having a particular molecular weight, M_i, is given by N_i. The "number-average" probability of a given mass being present is

$$P_i = \frac{N_i}{\sum_{j=0}^{\infty} N_j}$$

and the number-average molecular weight is given by the formula

$$\bar{M}_n = \sum_{i=0}^{\infty}\left(\frac{N_i}{\sum_{j=0}^{\infty} N_j}\right) mi = \frac{\sum_{i=0}^{\infty} N_i M_i}{\sum_{j=0}^{\infty} N_j}$$

The number average is the simple arithmetic mean, representing the total weight of the molecules present divided by the total number of molecules. Most thermodynamic measurements are based on the number of molecules present and hence depend on the number-average molecular weight: examples are the colligative properties, osmotic pressure and freezing point depression. End-group analysis also produces a value for $\overline{M}_n$.

Weight-Average Molecular Weight: The probability factor in a weight-average emphasizes the mass of the molecules so that the heavier molecules are more important.

$$P_i = \frac{N_i M_i}{\sum_{j=0}^{\infty} N_j M_j}$$

The weight-average formula then is the following.

$$\bar{M}_w = \sum_{i=0}^{\infty}\left(\frac{N_i M_i}{\sum_{j=0}^{\infty} N_j M_j}\right) M_i = \frac{\sum_{i=0}^{\infty} N_i M_i}{\sum_{j=0}^{\infty} N_j M_j}$$

Molecular weight measurements that depend on the contributions of molecules according to their sizes give weight-average molecular weights. Light scattering and ultracentrifuge methods are examples of this type of technique. The weight-average molecular weight is larger than or equal to the number-average molecular weight.

The ratio of the weight-average and number-average molecular weights, M_w/M_n, is a measure of the polydispersity of a polymer mixture which is widely distributed in the range of molecular weights. A ratio that is around 1.0 indicates that the range of molecular weights in the mixture is narrow; a high ratio indicates that the range is wide. With rare exceptions, all synthetic polymers are polydisperse.

4.2 CLASSIFICATION OF POLYMERS

The structural properties of a polymer relate to the physical arrangement of monomers along the backbone of the chain. Structure has a strong influence on the other properties of a polymer. For example, a linear chain polymer may be soluble or insoluble in water depending on whether it is composed of polar monomers (such as ethylene oxide) or non polar monomers (such as styrene). On the other hand, two samples of natural rubber may exhibit different durability even though their molecules comprise of the same monomers. Polymer scientists have developed terminology to precisely describe both the nature of the monomers as well as their relative arrangement. The most common way of classifying polymers is to separate them into three groups - thermoplastics, thermosets and elastomers. The thermoplastics can be divided into two types - those that are crystalline and those that are amorphous.

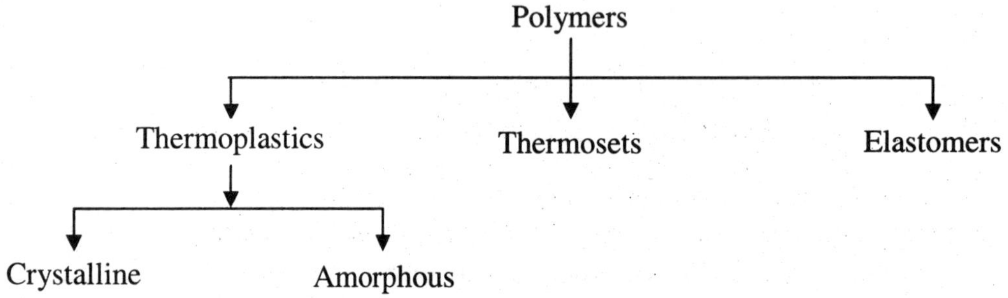

Polymers are also classified on the basis of structure as follows:

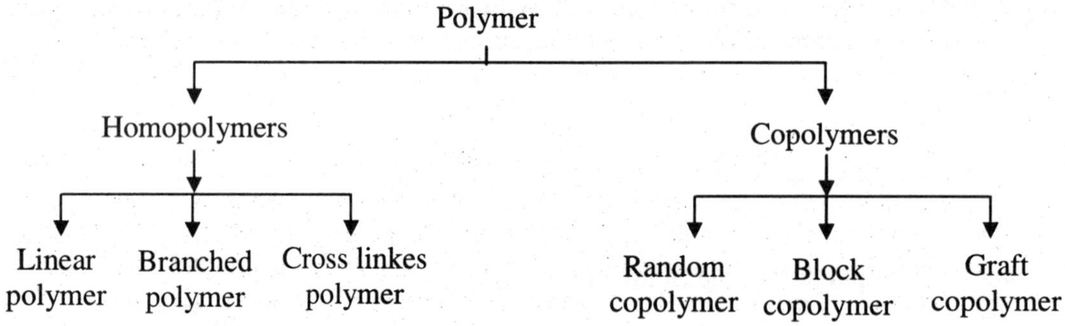

Polymers can be classified in many ways:

1) On basis of origin:

i) Natural Polymer: The polymers are obtained from nature (plants and animals) e.g. starch, cellulose and natural rubber.

ii) Synthetic Polymer: The polymers are prepared in the laboratories. These are man made polymers e.g. polyethylene, nylon, Teflon etc.

2) **On basis of chemical structure of their backbones**:

i) Homopolymer: Polymer consists of identical monomer.

-A-A-A-A-

ii) Co-Polymer: The synthesis of macromolecules composed of more than one monomeric repeating unit has been explored as a means of controlling the properties of the resulting material. In this respect, it is useful to distinguish several ways in which different monomeric units might be incorporated in a polymeric molecule. The following examples refer to a two component system, in which one monomer is designated A and the other B.

Table 4.1: Types of Co-polymers

Statistical Copolymers	Also called random copolymers. Here the monomeric units are distributed randomly and sometimes unevenly, in the polymer chain: ~ABBAAABAABBBABAABA~.
Alternating Copolymers	Here the monomeric units are distributed in a regular alternating fashion, with nearly equimolar amounts of each in the chain: ~ABABABABABABABAB~.
Block Copolymers	Instead of a mixed distribution of monomeric units, a long sequence or block of one monomer is joined to a block of the second monomer: ~AAAAA-BBBBBBB~AAAAAAA~BBB~.
Graft Copolymers	As the name suggests, side chains of a given monomer are attached to the main chain of the second monomer: ~AAAAAAA(BBBBBBB~)AAAAAAA(BBBB~)AAA~.

3) On basis of their polymeric structure:

i) Linear Chain Polymer: These are polymers in which monomeric units are linked together. These linear polymers are well packed and therefore have high densities; high tensile strength and high melting point e.g. polyethylene and polyesters.

A – A – A – A – A
Linear Homopolymer

A – B – A – B –A
Linear Copolymer

ii) Branched Chain Polymer: In this, monomer units are joined to form long chain with side chain or branches of different length irregularly packed, therefore they have lower tensile strength and melting point than linear polymers e.g. glycogen, starch etc.

```
A – A – A – A – A
        |
        A
        |
        A
```
Branched Chain Homopolymer

```
A- B –A – B –A –B – A
        |
        B
        |
        A
```
Branched Chain Co- polymer

iii) Cross- Linked Polymer: In this, monomer units are cross linked together to form a three dimensional network. These polymers are hard, rigid and brittle because of network structure, e.g. Bakelite, Melamine formaldehyde resin.

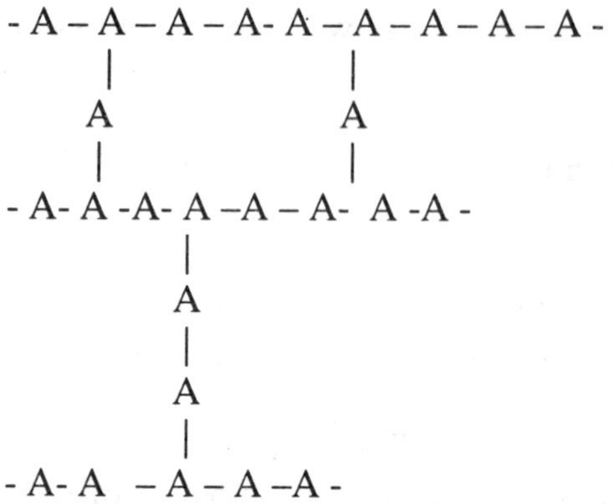

Cross linked homopolymer

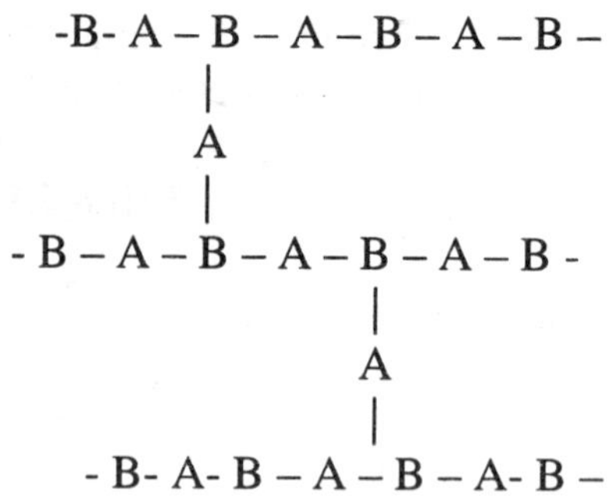

Cross –linked Copolymer

4. On basis of mode of synthesis:

a) Addition Polymerization: Addition of same monomers or different monomers without elimination of any molecule is known as addition polymerization. Because of addition of large number of monomers we get macromolecules known as polymers. Polymer synthesized by addition polymerization has the same empirical formula as that of monomer. Mostly direct copolymerization of equimolar mixtures of different monomers gives statistical copolymers.

The copolymerization of styrene with methyl methacrylate, for example, proceeds differently depending on the mechanism. Radical polymerization gives a statistical copolymer. However, the product of cationic polymerization is largely polystyrene and anionic polymerization favors formation of poly methyl methacrylate. In cases where the relative reactivities are different, the copolymer composition can sometimes be controlled by continuous introduction of a biased mixture of monomers into the reaction.

Formation of alternating copolymers is favored when the monomers have different polar substituents (e.g. one electron withdrawing and the other electron donating) and both have similar reactivities toward radicals. For example, styrene and acrylonitrile copolymerize in a largely alternating fashion.

b) Condensation Polymerization: A large number of important and useful polymeric materials are not formed by chain-growth processes involving reactive species such as radicals, but proceed instead by conventional functional group transformations of polyfunctional reactants. These polymerizations often (but not always) occur with formulation of a by-product, such as water and generally (but not always) combine two different components in an alternating structure.

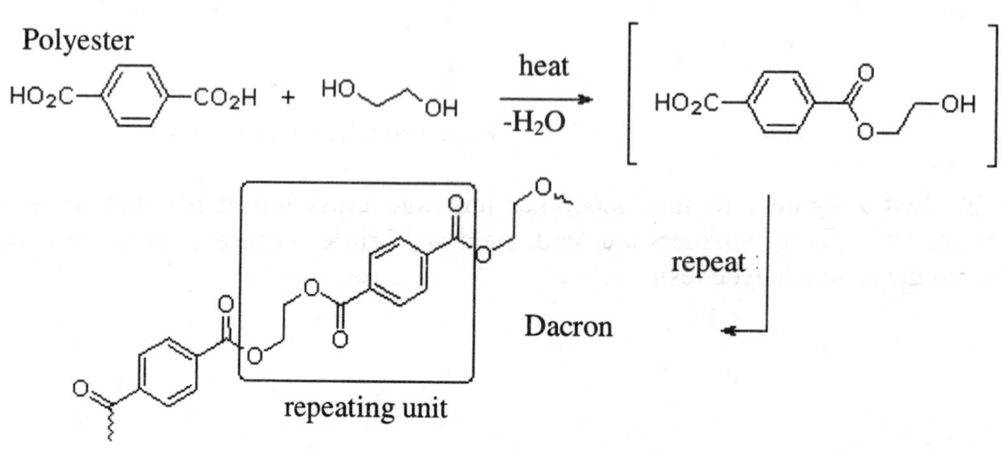

Polyamide

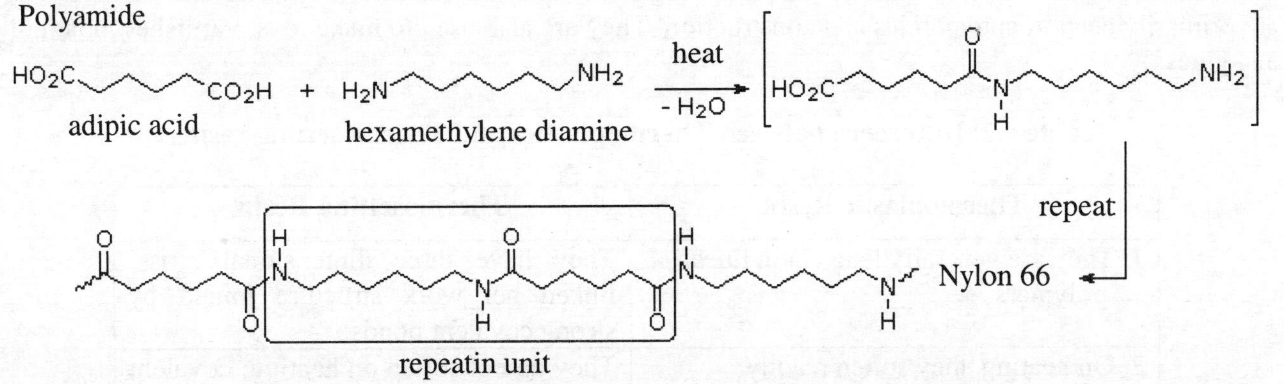

Examples of Condensation Polymers

The polyester Dacron and the polyamide Nylon 6:6, shown here, are two examples of synthetic condensation polymers, also known as step-growth polymers. In contrast to chain-growth polymers, most of which grow by carbon-carbon bond formation, step-growth polymers generally grow by carbon-heteroatom bond formation (C-O & C-N in Dacron & Nylon respectively). Although polymers of this kind might be considered to be alternating copolymers, the repeating monomeric unit is usually defined as a combined moiety. Examples of naturally occurring condensation polymers are cellulose, the polypeptide chains of proteins and poly β-hydroxybutyric acid, polyesters synthesized in large quantity by certain soil and water bacteria.

5. On basis of orientation of monomer units(Tacticity): If the polymer chain is drawn in a zigzag fashion, each of the substituent groups (Z) will necessarily be located above or below the plane defined by the carbon chain. Consequently we can identify three configurational isomers of such polymers. If all the substituents lie on one side of the chain, the configuration is called isotactic. If the substituents alternate from one side to another in a regular manner, the configuration is termed syndiotactic. Finally, a random arrangement of substituent groups is referred to as atactic. Examples of these configurations are shown here:

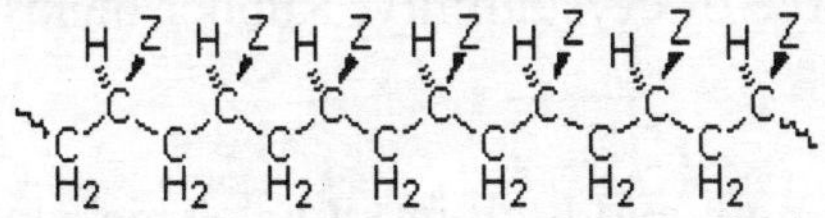

isotactic

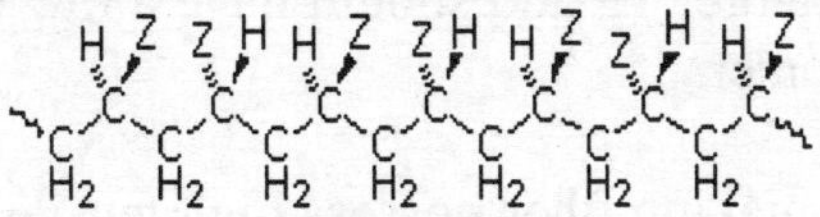

syndiotactic

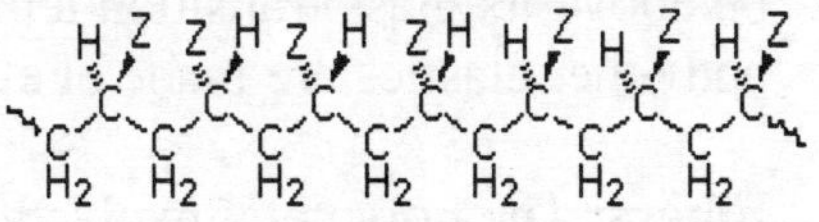

atactic

6. On basis of intermolecular forces:

Thermoplastics: Molecules in a thermoplastic are held together by relatively weak intermolecular forces so that the material softens when exposed to heat and then returns to its original condition when cooled. Thermoplastic polymers can be repeatedly softened by heating and then solidified by cooling - a process similar to the repeated melting and cooling of metals. Most linear and slightly branched polymers are thermoplastic. All the major thermoplastics are produced by chain polymerization. Thermoplastics have a wide range of applications because they can be formed and reformed in so many shapes. Some examples are food packaging, insulation, automobile, bumper and credit cards.

Thermosets: A thermosetting plastic, or thermoset, solidifies or "sets" irreversibly when heated. Thermosets cannot be reshaped by heating. Thermosets usually are three-dimensional networked polymers in which there is a high degree of cross-linking between polymer chains. The cross-linking restricts the motion of the chains and leads to a rigid material. Thermosets are strong and durable. They are primarily used in automobiles and construction. They are also used to make toys, varnishes, boat hulls and glues.

Table 4.2: Difference between Thermoplastics and Thermosetting resins

Thermoplastic Resin	Thermosetting Resin
1. They are generally long chain linear polymers.	They have three dimensional cross-linked net work structure joined by strong covalent bonds.
2. On heating, they soften readily because secondary forces between the chain can be easily broken.	They do not soften on heating; covalent bonds retain their strength on heating. They can, however, be charred on strong heating.
3. They can be softened, reshaped and even reused by reheating to a suitable temperature.	They can not be reshaped and reused because they do not soften on heating and retain their shape and structure.
4. They are generally weak, soft and less brittle.	They are usually hard, strong and more brittle.
5. They can be reclaimed from waste.	They can not be reclaimed from waste.
6. They can dissolve in some organic solvents.	They are insoluble almost in all organic solvents because of the presence of cross-linking and strong covalent bonds.

Elastomers: They are rubbery polymers that can be stretched easily to several times their unstretched length and which rapidly return to their original dimensions when the applied stress is released. Elastomers are cross-linked, but have a low cross-link density. The polymer chains still have some freedom to move, but are prevented from permanently moving relative to each other by the cross-links. To stretch, the polymer chains must not be part of a rigid solid - either a glass or a crystal. An elastomer must be above its glass transition temperature, Tg and should have a low degree of crystallinity. Rubber bands and other elastics are made of elastomer.

Fibers: The polymers involved for making fiber possess high tensile strength and high modulus. This can be attributed to strong intermolecular force like hydrogen bonding which for example exists in polyamides (Nylon 66). These strong forces also lead to close packing of chains. These polymers show sharp melting point.

Classification of polymers on the basic of growth of polymer chain

(a) Chain growth polymers: In this case chain growth takes place due to successive addition of monomer unit to the growing chain. The monomer unit gets converted to some active intermediate species which reacts with another monomer unit to form polymer

Example

Initiator → $\dot{A}$
(Free radical)

$\dot{A} + CH_2 = CH_2$ → $A\text{-}CH_2\text{-}\dot{C}H_2$
Monomer (Intermediate Species)

$A\text{-}CH_2\text{-}\dot{C}H_2 + CH_2 = CH_2 \rightarrow A\text{-}(CH_2\text{-}CH_2\text{-}CH_2\text{-}CH_2\text{-})_n$
Polymer

(b) Step Growth Polymers: The growth of chain takes place in a step wise manner through a series of intermediate reactions. Here condensation takes place between two different monomeric units with loss of by-products like H_2O, HCl.

(i)
$$A+B \xrightarrow{Step\ I} A\text{-}B$$
$$A\text{-}B+A \xrightarrow{Step\ II} A\text{-}B\text{-}A$$
$$A\text{-}B\text{-}A+B \xrightarrow{Step\ III} A\text{-}B\text{-}A\text{-}B$$

(ii)
$$A+B \xrightarrow{Step\ I} A\text{-}B$$
$$A\text{-}B \xrightarrow[Step\ II]{A-B} A\text{-}B\text{-}A\text{-}B$$
$$A\text{-}B\text{-}A\text{-}B \xrightarrow[Step\ III]{n(A-B)} (A\text{-}B)_n$$

4.3 MECHANISM OF POLYMERIZATION

All the monomers, from which addition polymers are made, are alkenes or functionally substituted alkenes. The most common and thermodynamically favored chemical transformations of alkenes are addition reactions. Many of these addition reactions are known to proceed in a stepwise fashion by way of reactive intermediates and this is the mechanism followed by most of the polymerizations. A general diagram illustrating this assembly of linear macromolecules, which supports the chain growth polymers, is presented here. Since a pi-bond in the monomer is converted to a sigma-bond in the polymer, the polymerization reaction is usually exothermic by 8 to 20 kcal/mol.

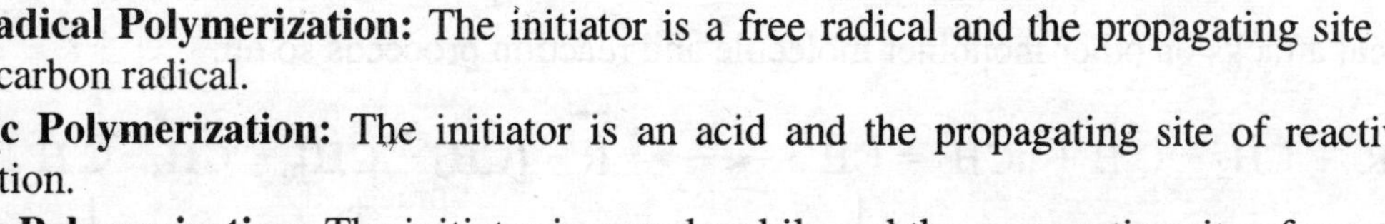

Z* is an initiating species * may be a radical, a cation or an anion

It is useful to distinguish four polymerization procedures fitting this general description.

- **Free Radical Polymerization:** The initiator is a free radical and the propagating site of reactivity (*) is a carbon radical.
- **Cationic Polymerization:** The initiator is an acid and the propagating site of reactivity (*) is a carbocation.
- **Anionic Polymerization:** The initiator is a nucleophile and the propagating site of reactivity (*) is a carbanion.
- **Coordination Catalytic Polymerization:** The initiator is a transition metal complex and the propagating site of reactivity (*) is a terminal catalytic complex.

Free radical mechanism: Virtually all the monomers are subject to free radical polymerization. Since this can be initiated by traces of oxygen or other minor impurities, pure samples of these compounds are often "stabilized" by small amounts of radical inhibitors to avoid unwanted reaction. Free radicals are formed when bond break homolytically that is each atom acquire one of bonding electron.

a) **Chain Initiation**: Here organic peroxide undergoes homolytic fission and gives free radical.

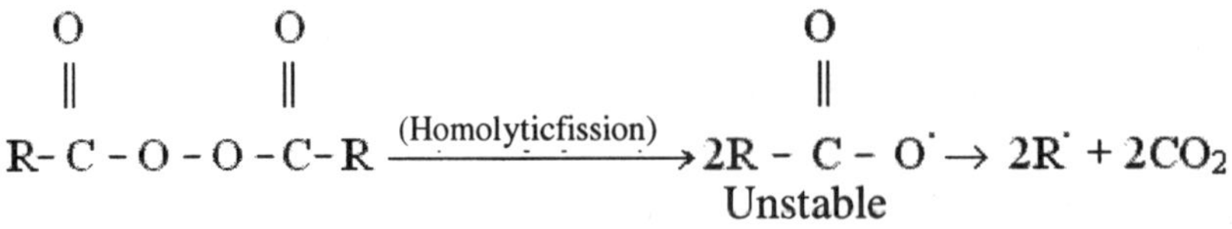

When radical polymerization is desired, it must be started by using a radical initiator, such as peroxide or certain azo compounds. The formulas of some common initiators and equations showing the formation of free radical species from these initiators are presented below:

Some Radical Initiators Subsequent Reactions

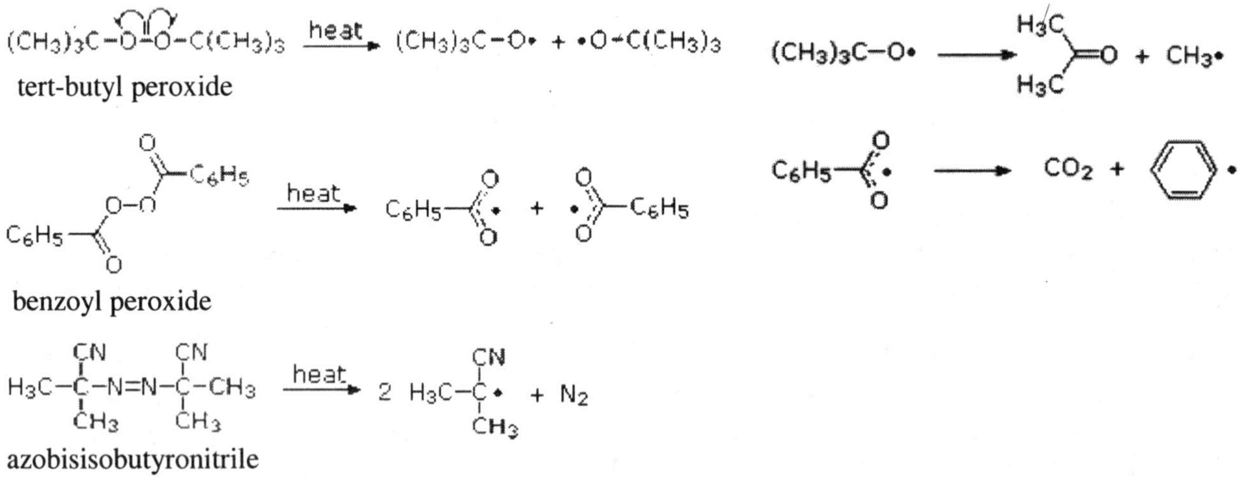

b) **Chain Propogation:** The free radical formed in above step is very reactive and attacks on π electron pair and forms σ bond from one electron and other one is shifted to end of the molecule.

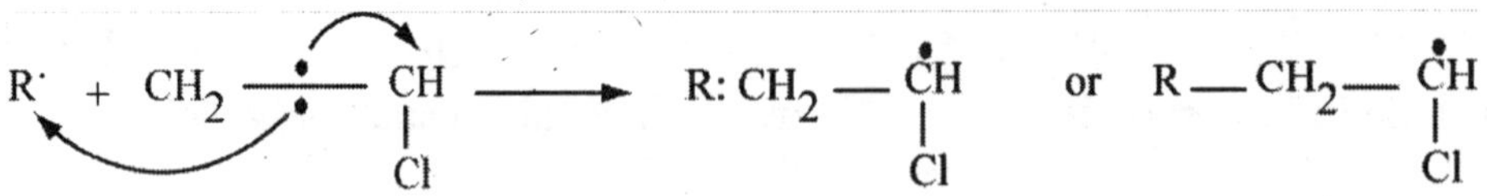

The free radical attacks on other monomer molecule and reaction proceeds so on.

In principle, once started, a free radical polymerization might be expected to continue unchecked, producing a few extremely long chain polymers. Larger numbers of moderately sized chains are formed, indicating that chain-terminating reactions must be taking place.

c) **Chain termination**: The most common termination processes are radical combination and disproportionation. In both types of termination, two reactive radical sites are removed by simultaneous conversion to stable product. Since the concentration of radical species in a polymerization reaction is small relative to other reactants (e.g. monomers, solvents and terminated chains), the rate at which these radical-radical termination reactions occurs, is very small and most growing chains achieve moderate length before termination

(i) **By combination or coupling**

$$2R-[CH_2-\underset{Cl}{\underset{|}{CH}}]-CH_2-\underset{Cl}{\underset{|}{\dot{C}H}} \rightarrow R-[CH_2-\underset{Cl}{\underset{|}{CH}}]-CH_2-\underset{Cl}{\underset{|}{CH}}-\underset{Cl}{\underset{|}{CH}}-CH_2-[\underset{Cl}{\underset{|}{CH}}-CH_2]_n-R$$

(ii) **By disproportionation**

$$R-[CH_2-\underset{Cl}{\underset{|}{CH}}]-CH_2-\underset{Cl}{\underset{|}{\dot{C}H}}+\underset{Cl}{\underset{|}{\dot{C}H}}-CH_2-[\underset{Cl}{\underset{|}{CH}}-CH_2]_n-R$$

$$R-[CH_2-\underset{Cl}{\underset{|}{CH}}]-CH_2-\underset{Cl}{\underset{|}{CH_2}}+\underset{Cl}{\underset{|}{C}}=CH_2-[\underset{Cl}{\underset{|}{CH}}-CH_2]_n-R$$

The relative importance of these terminations varies with the nature of the monomer undergoing polymerization. For example, acrylonitrile and styrene combination are the major process. However, methyl methacrylate and vinyl acetate are terminated chiefly by disproportionation.

Another reaction that diverts radical chain-growth polymerizations from producing linear macromolecules is called chain transfer. As the name implies, this reaction moves a carbon radical from one location to another by an intermolecular or intramolecular hydrogen atom transfer. These possibilities are demonstrated by the following equations:

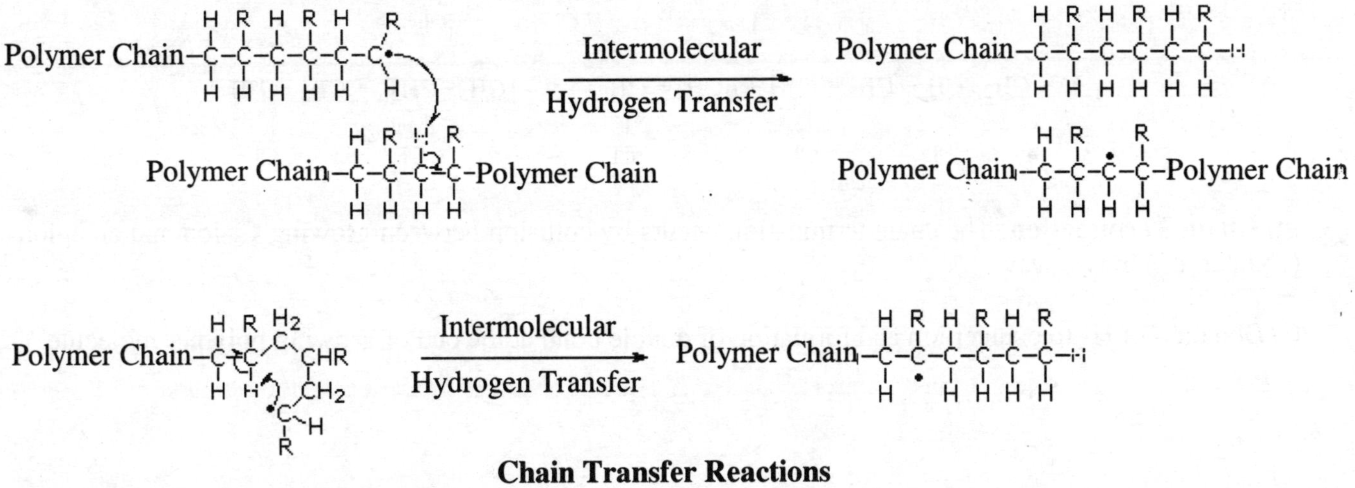

Chain Transfer Reactions

Chain transfer reactions are prevalent in the high pressure radical polymerization of ethylene, which is the method used to make LDPE (low density polyethylene). The 1° radical at the end of a growing chain is converted to a more stable 2°-radical by hydrogen atom transfer. Further polymerization at the new radical site generates a side chain radical and this may in turn lead to creation of other side chains by chain transfer reactions. As a result, the morphology of LDPE is an amorphous network of highly branched macromolecules.

Cationic Mechanism: It is a type of ionic polymerization. The active species which initiates the addition polymerization is a cation such as proton. The initiators used for this purpose are BF_3, $AlCl_3$, $SnCl_4$, $TiCl_4$, H_2SO_4, HF and Lewis acid etc. For example isobutylene styrene, methyl styrene and many vinyl ethers follow cationic mechanism to form polymers.

The initiator or proton attacks on π-electron pair of the monomers, in this bond breaks heterotically i.e. the atom acquires negative charge and carbonium ion is formed. In it positive charge of the proton is transferred to the further end of the monomer molecule. In it σ bond is formed between the proton and monomer unit and polymer growth is initiated.

Cationic catalysts are generally electrophilic reagents which acquire a shaired pair of π- electron from double bond. There are 3 steps in mechanism

(a) **Chain initiation**: It involves the addition of positive ion to monomer.

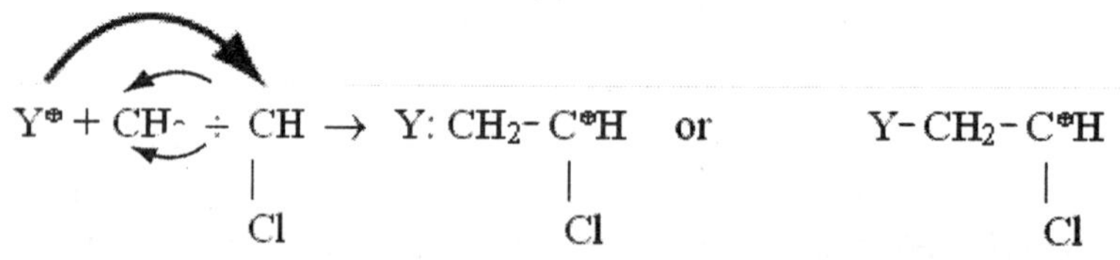

Acid Cation Carbonium ion

(b) **Chain propogation:** It involves attack of carbonium ion so formed in 1st step to the monomer.

$$Y - CH_2 - \overset{\oplus}{C}H(Cl) + CH_2 = CH(Cl) \rightarrow Y - CH_2 - CH(Cl) - CH_2 - \overset{\oplus}{C}H(Cl)$$

$$Y - CH_2 - CH(Cl) - CH_2 - \overset{\oplus}{C}H(Cl) + nCH_2 = CH(Cl) \rightarrow y - [CH_2 - CH(Cl)]_n - CH_2 - \overset{\oplus}{C}H(Cl)$$

(c) **Chain Termination:** The chain termination occurs by collision between growing C^+ ion and an anion (counter ion) in two ways:

(i) Donation of H^+ to counter ion and formation of double bond at the end of growing polymer molecule.

$$\underset{\text{Growing polymer Chain}}{Y\text{-}[CH_2\text{-}\underset{|}{\overset{}{CH}}(Cl)]_n\text{-}CH_2\text{-}C^{\oplus}H(Cl)} \xrightarrow{[F3BOH^{-}]} \underset{\text{Dead polymer molecule}}{Y\text{-}[CH_2\text{-}CH(Cl)]_n - CH{=}C(Cl)H} + [F_3BOH^{\oplus}]H^{\oplus}$$

It is called as "ion-pair precipitation"

(ii) Formation of covalent bond between carbonium ion and the counter ion, termination occurs by simple "Coupling"

$$Y - [CH_2 - CH(Cl)]_n - CH_2 - C^{\oplus}H(Cl) \xrightarrow[\text{anion}]{+x^-} Y - [CH_2 - CH(Cl)]_n - CH_2 - CH(Cl) - X$$

For successful polymerization by the cationic process, electron releasing group should be attached to carbon with double bond to stabilize the developing carbocation.

Polymerization of isobutylene (2-methylpropene) by traces of strong acids is an example of cationic polymerization. The polyisobutylene product is a soft rubbery solid, $T_g = {}^-70°$ C, which is used for inner tubes. This process is similar to radical polymerization, as demonstrated by the following equations. Chain growth ceases when the terminal carbocation combines with a nucleophile or loses a proton, giving a terminal alkene (as shown here).

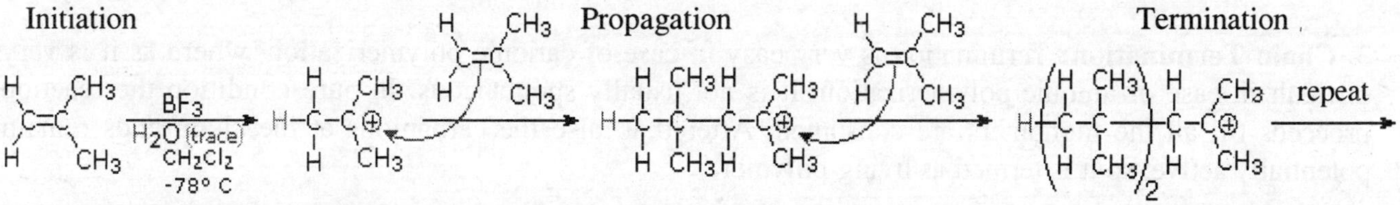

Polymer Chain 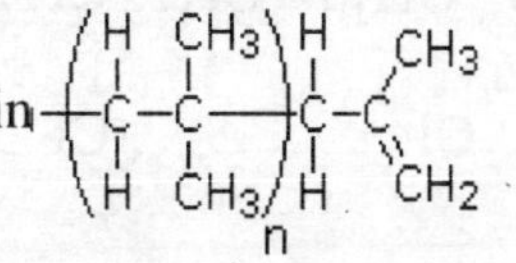

Polyisobutylene (Butyl Rubber)
[one possible terminating group is shown]

Monomers bearing cation stabilizing groups, such as alkyl, phenyl or vinyl can be polymerized by cationic processes. These are normally initiated at low temperature in methylene chloride solution. Strong acids, such as $HClO_4$, or Lewis acids containing traces of water (as shown above) serve as initiating reagents. At low temperatures, chain transfer reactions are rare in such polymerizations, so the resulting polymers are cleanly linear (unbranched).

Anionic Mechanism: The initiating species in this case is an anion such as NH_2^-. It was known for many years. The production of buna type synthetic rubber by polymerization of butadiene with Na or K as catalyst was known (Germany – Russia).

Anionic polymerization proceeds through formation of carbanion ion. It is initiated by stronger donor like Z^-: commonly it is base or anion. It has extra electrons and resultant negative charge, which attacks on π-electron pair and pushes it at the end of the molecule and σ bond is formed with monomer molecule.

Just as in cationic polymerization, it acquires electron releasing group like that anionic polymerization requires electron attracting group like CN^-, $RCOO^-$, Cl^- etc. The mechanism is just similar to that of cationic mechanism except in termination reaction.

The mechanism involves following 3 steps:

1. **Chain initiation:** It involves the addition of negative ion to monomer.

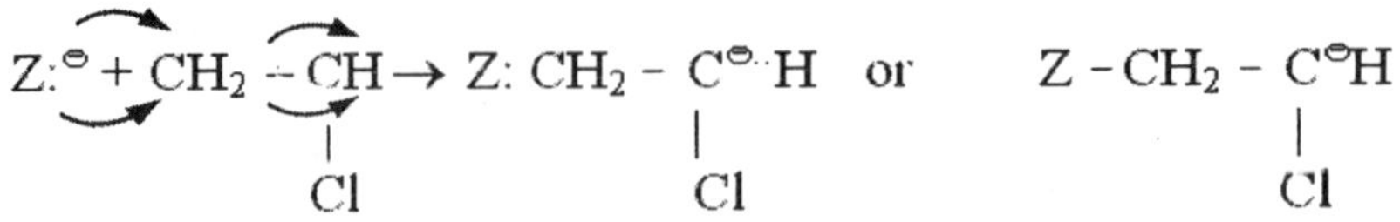

2. **Chain Propagation:** The carbanion ion formed will participate in the reaction.

$$Z-CH_2-\underset{\underset{Cl}{|}}{C^{\ominus}H}+CH_2=\underset{\underset{Cl}{|}}{CH} \rightarrow Z-CH_2-\underset{\underset{Cl}{|}}{CH}-CH_2-\underset{\underset{Cl}{|}}{C^{\ominus}H}$$

$$Z-CH_2-\underset{\underset{Cl}{|}}{CH}-CH_2-\underset{\underset{Cl}{|}}{C^{\ominus}H}+nCH_2=\underset{\underset{Cl}{|}}{CH} \rightarrow Z-[CH_2-\underset{\underset{Cl}{|}}{CH}]_n-CH_2-\underset{\underset{Cl}{|}}{C^{\ominus}H}$$

3. **Chain Termination:** Termination is very easy in case of cationic polymerization, where as it is very difficult in case of anionic polymerization. It is not usually spontaneous. In pure condition the reaction proceeds till all the monomers are consumed. After that, also the carbanions at the chain ends remain potentially active, so it is termed as living-polymer.

$$Z-[CH_2-\underset{\underset{Cl}{|}}{CH}]_n-CH_2-\underset{\underset{Cl}{|}}{C^{\ominus}H} \xrightarrow{+H^{\oplus}} \rightarrow Z-[CH_2-\underset{\underset{Cl}{|}}{CH}]n-CH_2-\underset{\underset{Cl}{|}}{CH_2}$$

There are a lot of different initiators used in anionic vinyl polymerization, but the most often used is an unassuming little molecule called butyl lithium. Now a little bit of the butyl lithium will always fall apart. It falls apart to form a positive lithium cation and a negative butyl anion. We call an anion like this where the negative charge is on a carbon atom, a carbanion

A pair of electrons from the butyl anion will be donated to one of the double bond carbon atoms of the monomer. Now this carbon atom already has eight electrons in its outer shell which it shares with the atoms to which it is bonded, so one pair of these electrons, specifically a pair in the carbon-carbon double bond, will leave the carbon atom and settle on the other carbon atom of the carbon-carbon double bond. This forms a new carbanion, with the negative charge resting on that carbon. The process in which the butyl lithium falls apart and the butyl anion reacts with a monomer molecule is called initiation.

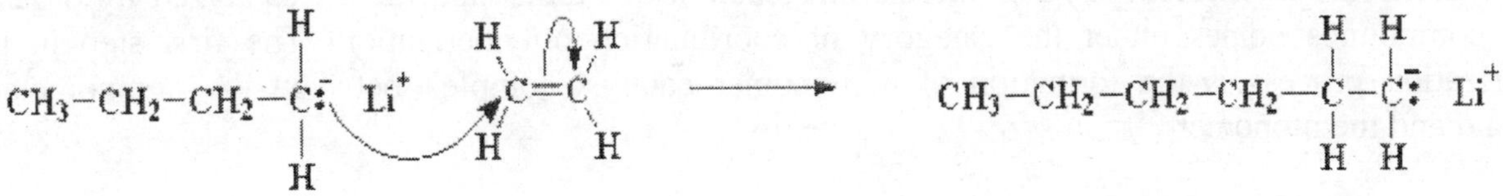

The carbanion now reacts with another monomer molecule in just the same manner as the initiator reacted with the first monomer molecule; another carbanion is generated. This keeps happening and each time another monomer is added to the growing chain, a new anion is generated allowing another monomer to be added. In this way the polymer chain grows. This adding of monomer after monomer is called propagation.

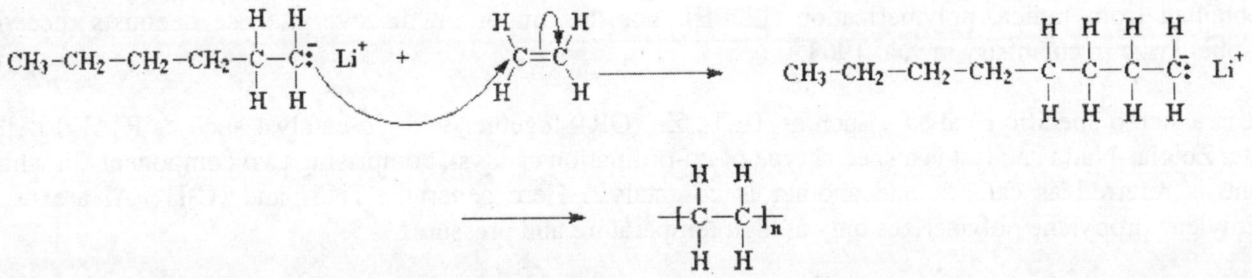

Now one may get this feeling that this can not go on forever, that something has to put a stop to this convenient process. Funny thing, though: it doesn't stop! In many cases, the only thing that stops monomers from adding to the growing chain is that eventually there are no more monomer molecules in the beaker left to add! And even then, if someone came along some time later and dumped more monomer into the beaker, they would add to the chain and the chain would grow some more. Some chains of polystyrene have been known to stay active like this for years. In order to stop them, something like water, which reacts with the carbanions, has to be added to the polymer. Systems like this are called living anionic polymerizations.

Species that have been used to initiate anionic polymerization include alkali metals, alkali amides, alkyl lithiums and various electron sources. A practical application of anionic polymerization occurs in the use of superglue. This material is methyl 2-cyanoacrylate, $CH_2{=}C(CN)CO_2CH_3$. When exposed to water, amines or other nucleophiles, a rapid polymerization of this monomer takes place.

Table 4.3: Difference between cationic and anionic mechanism

Cationic mechanism	Anionic mechanism
1. Proceed through the formation of cabonium $-\overset{|}{\underset{|}{C}}\oplus$	Proceed through the formation of carbonion $-\overset{|}{\underset{|}{C}}^{-}$
2. Initiation occurs by formation of carbocation.	Indication occurs by the formation of carbanion.
3. Initiated by protonic acid, carbonium salt, Lewis acid.	Initiated by compound which release anion that is by Lewis base.
4. Propagation occurs by addition of monomer to carbonation.	Propagation occurs by addition of monomer to carbanion.
5. The polymer which is formed has long range of molecular weight distribution.	The polymers which are formed have narrow range of molecular weight distribution.

4. Co-ordination Polymerization: Polymerization reaction of olefins and dienes catalyzed by organo-metalic compounds comes under the category of coordination polymerization. The first step in the polymerization process is the formation of a monomer catalyst complex between the organometalic compound and the monomer.

An efficient and stereo specific catalytic polymerization procedure was developed by Karl Ziegler (Germany) and Giulio Natta (Italy) in the 1950's. Their findings permitted for the first time, the synthesis of unbranched, high molecular weight polyethylene (HDPE), a laboratory synthesis of natural rubber from isoprene and configurational control of polymers from terminal alkenes like propene (e.g. pure isotactic and syndiotactic polymers). In the case of ethylene, rapid polymerization occurred at atmospheric pressure at moderate to low temperature, giving a stronger (more crystalline) product (HDPE) than that obtained from radical polymerization (LDPE). For this important discovery, these chemists received Nobel Prize in chemistry in year 1963.

It is a stereo specific catalyst – such as $TiCl_4$, Zn $(OR)_4$ together with co-catalyst such as R_3Al, $LiAlH_4$ etc. Zeiglar-Natta catalyst is a special type of co-ordination catalyst, comprising two components in which one is referred as catalyst and another is co-catalyst. Here generally $TiCl_4$ and $(C_2H_5)_3Al$ are used. Ethylene propylene polymerizes only at high temperature and pressure.

Ziegler-Natta catalysts are prepared by reacting certain transition metal halides with organometallic reagents such as alkyl aluminum, lithium and zinc reagents. The catalyst formed by reaction of triethyl aluminium with titanium tetrachloride has been widely studied, but other metals (e.g. V & Zr) have also proved effective. Many structures have been proposed for this complex as follows-

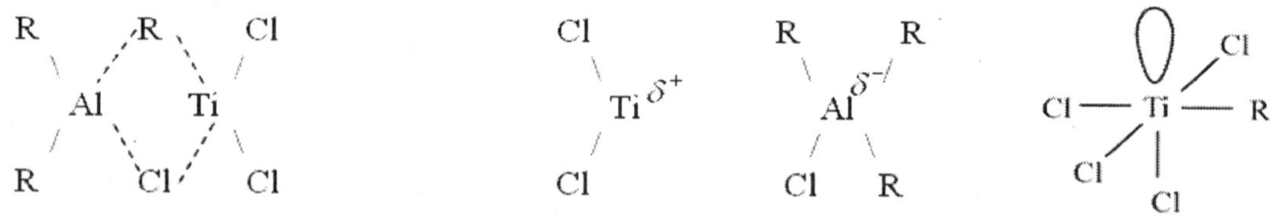

(a) (b) (c)

Polypropylene

The poly propylene is prepared as follows:

$$2n\,CH_3-CH=CH_2 \xrightarrow[\text{270°K, inert solvent (hexane)}]{TiCl_4,(C_2H_5)_3Al,\ 10\ \text{Atm.pre}} -[\underset{\displaystyle CH_3}{\underset{|}{CH}}-CH_2-\underset{\displaystyle CH_3}{\underset{|}{CH}}-CH_2]_n$$

Mechanism of polypropylene: Here aluminium alkyls act as electron acceptor and electron donor is titanium halides and the combination therefore readily forms coordination complexes, which are insoluble in solvents and are heterogeneous in nature.

Here stereo – regular polymers are formed because monomer is complexed with the metal ion of the active centre before its insertion into the growing chain. In this complex, monomer is attracted to wards the Ti-C bond (carbon from the alkyl group) in the active centre, where it forms a pi – complex with titanium ion.

Then the bond between R and Ti opens up and forms electrons deficient Ti and carbanion at R. The titanium ion then attracts the pi- electrons pair of monomer and forms a sigma bond while the counter ion attacks the electron deficient centre of monomer. In this way, monomer 'inserts' into a transition state ring structure.

This transition state now gives rise to the chain growth at the metal carbon bond, regenerating the active centre as follows:

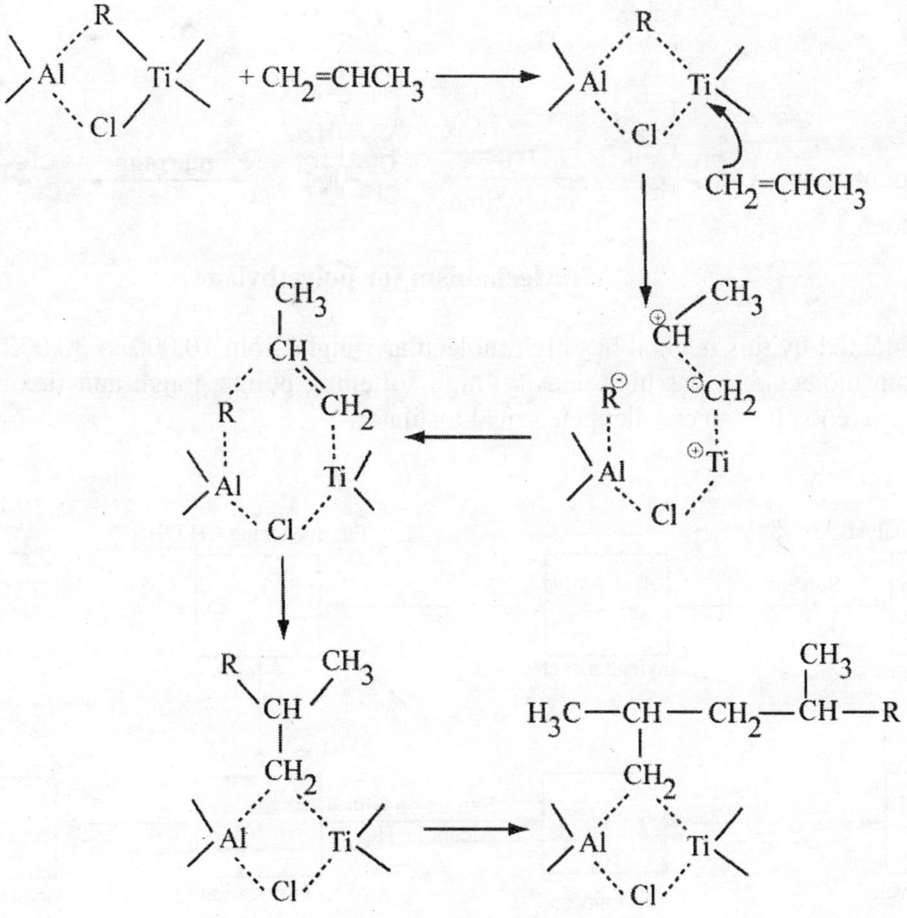

Mechamism of poly propylene

The monomer insertion is repeated in this manner, the orientation of the substituents group of the monomer is always taken from the metal ion resulting in stereo-regulated polymer. Polypropylene prepared by this mechanism is a stronger and lighter and has higher softening point. It is used for making wrapping films and ropes.

Polythylene

Mechanism of polyethene: Polyethylene is formed as powder or granules which are insoluble in the reaction mixture. After the addition of H_2O, CH_3OH or ethanol, finally the polymer is centrifuged, dried, extracted and granulated (high density polyethylene). The mechanism is as follows:

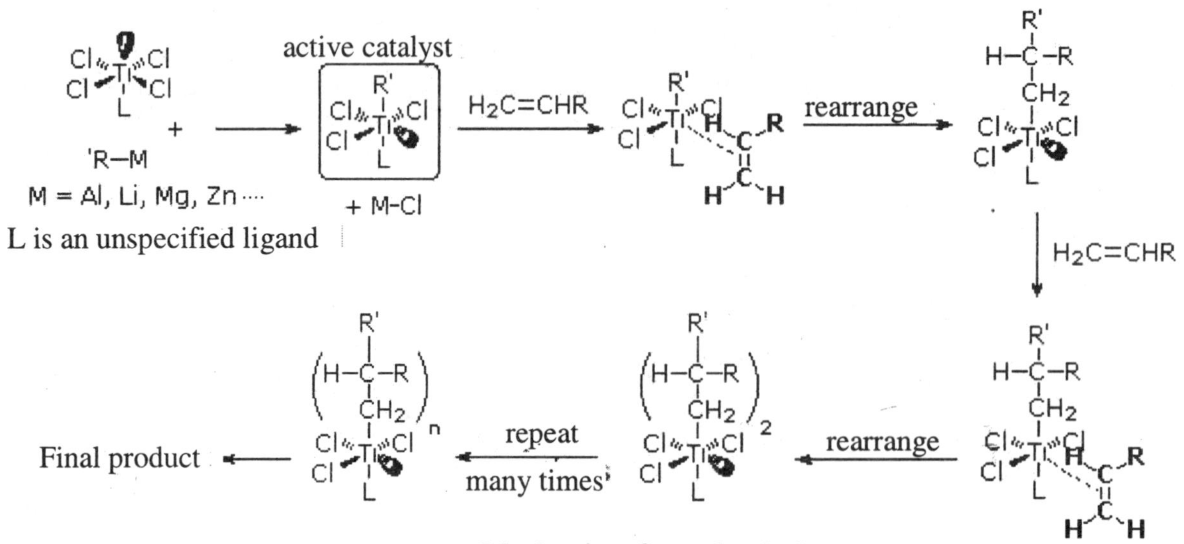

Mechanism for polyethylene

Polyethylene obtained by this method has high molecular weight from 10,000 to 30,000,00 and contains unbranched chain molecule. It has high density, high softening points, tough and flexible. It is inert to acid, alkali and solvents. It is an excellent electrical insulator.

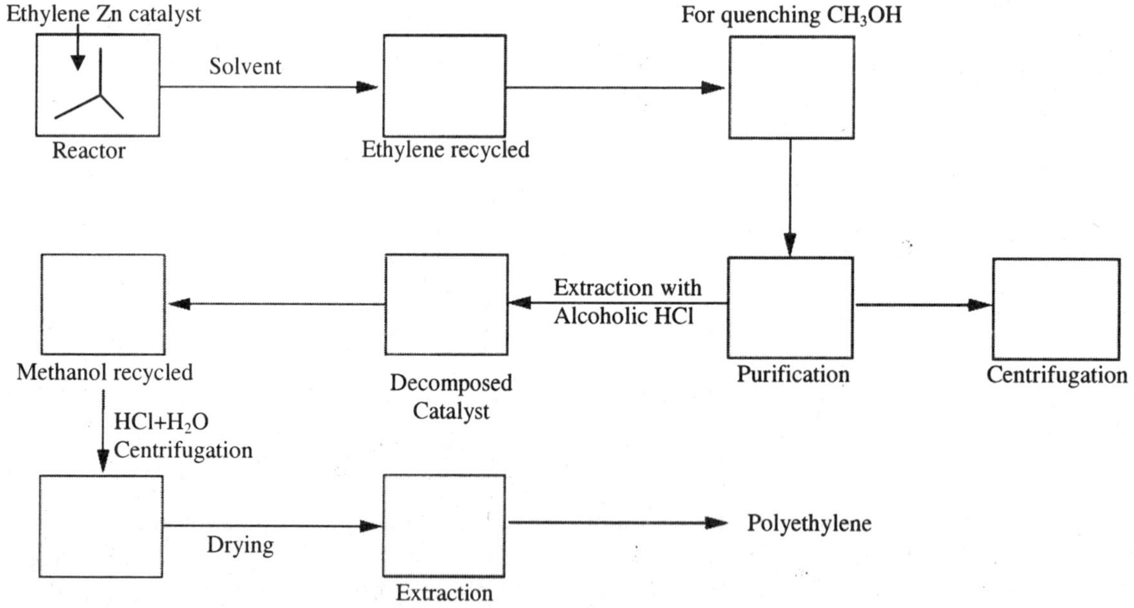

Flow sheet of Preparation of polyethylene (Zieglar-Natta mechanism)

Table 4.4: Some Useful Copolymers

Monomer A	Monomer B	Copolymer	Uses
$H_2C=CHCl$	$H_2C=CCl_2$	Saran	films & fibers
$H_2C=CHC_6H_5$	$H_2C=CH-CH=CH_2$	SBR styrene butadiene rubber	tyres
$H_2C=CHCN$	$H_2C=CH-CH=CH_2$	Nitrile Rubber	Adhesives, hoses
$H_2C=C(CH_3)_2$	$H_2C=CH-CH=CH_2$	Butyl Rubber	inner tubes
$F_2C=CF(CF_3)$	$H_2C=CHF$	Viton	gaskets

Table 4.5: Some Addition Polymers

Name(s)	Formula	Monomer	Properties	Uses
Polyethylene low density (LDPE)	$–(CH_2-CH_2)_n–$	ethylene $CH_2=CH_2$	soft, waxy solid	film wrap, plastic bags
Polyethylene high density (HDPE)	$–(CH_2-CH_2)_n–$	ethylene $CH_2=CH_2$	rigid, translucent solid	electrical insulation, bottles, toys
Polypropylene (PP) different grades	$–[CH_2-CH(CH_3)]_n–$	propylene $CH_2=CHCH_3$	atactic: soft, elastic solid isotactic: hard, strong solid	similar to LDPE carpet, upholstery
Poly(vinyl chloride) (PVC)	$–(CH_2-CHCl)_n–$	vinyl chloride $CH_2=CHCl$	strong rigid solid	pipes, siding, flooring
Poly(vinylidene chloride) (Saran A)	$–(CH_2-CCl_2)_n–$	vinylidene chloride $CH_2=CCl_2$	dense, high-melting solid	seat covers, films
Polystyrene (PS)	$–[CH_2-CH(C_6H_5)]_n–$	styrene $CH_2=CHC_6H_5$	hard, rigid, clear solid soluble in organic solvents	toys, cabinets packaging (foamed)
Polyacrylonitrile (PAN, Orlon, Acrilan)	$–(CH_2-CHCN)_n–$	acrylonitrile $CH_2=CHCN$	high-melting solid soluble in organic solvents	rugs, blankets clothing
Polytetrafluoro ethylene (PTFE, Teflon)	$–(CF_2-CF_2)_n–$	tetrafluoroethylene $CF_2=CF_2$	resistant, smooth solid	non-stick surfa-ces, electrical insulation
Poly(methyl methacrylate)(PMMA Lucite, Plexiglas)	$–[CH_2-C(CH_3)CO_2CH_3]_n–$	methyl methacrylate$CH_2=C(CH_3)CO_2CH_3$	hard, transparent solid	lighting covers, signs, skylights
Poly(vinyl acetate) (PVAc)	$–(CH_2-CHOCOCH_3)_n–$	vinyl acetate $CH_2=CHOCOCH_3$	soft, sticky solid	latex paints, adhesives
cis-Polyisoprene natural rubber	$–[CH_2-CH=C(CH_3)-CH_2]_n–$	isoprene $CH_2=CH-C(CH_3)=CH_2$	soft, sticky solid	requires vulcanization for practical use
Polychloroprene (cis + trans) (Neoprene)	$–[CH_2-CH=CCl-CH_2]_n–$	chloroprene $CH_2=CH-CCl=CH_2$	tough, rubbery solid	

4.4 PLASTICS

Polythene: Polyethylene is probably the polymer seen most in daily life. Polyethylene is the most popular plastic in the world. This is the polymer that makes grocery bags, shampoo bottles, children toys and even bullet proof vests. For such a versatile material, it has a very simple structure, the simplest of all commercial polymers. A molecule of polyethylene is nothing more than a long chain of carbon atoms, with two hydrogen atoms attached to each carbon atom. Chain of carbon atoms consists of many thousands of atoms and is very long.

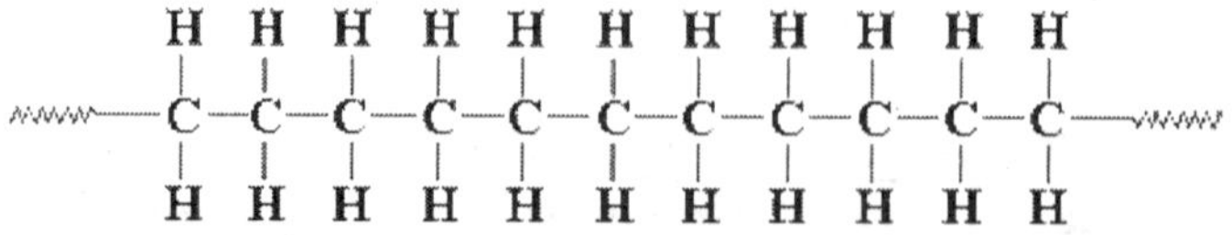

Novel

Sometimes it is a little more complicated. Sometimes some of the carbons, instead of having hydrogen attached to them, will have long chains of polyethylene attached to them. This is called branched, or low-density polyethylene, or LDPE. When there is no branching, it is called linear polyethylene, or HDPE. Linear polyethylene is much stronger than branched polyethylene, but branched polyethylene is cheaper and easier to make.

There are two types of polythene.

1. Low density polyethylene (LDPE)
2. High density polyethylene (HDPE)

1. LDPE: It is prepared by heating ethylene at about 473 k under high pressure (1500-2000 atm) in presence of a very small amount of oxygen.

$$\underset{\text{Ethylene}}{nCH_2=CH_2} \xrightarrow[473k, 1500\text{-}2000\,atm]{O_2} \underset{\text{Polythene}}{-[CH_2-CH_2]_n-}$$

A molecule of branched polyethylene, or LDPE

Linear polyethylene is normally produced with molecular weights in the range of 200,000 to 500,000, but it can be made even higher. Polyethylene with molecular weights of three to six million is referred to as ultra-high molecular weight polyethylene, or UHMWPE. UHMWPE can be used to make fibers which are so strong that they replaced Kevlar for use in bullet proof vests. Large sheets of it can be used instead of ice for ice skating rinks

Properties
1. It is branched structure.
2. It is flexible.
3. It is transparent polymer.
4. It is a poor conductor of electricity.
5. It is tough with moderate tensile strength.
6. It has low density and low melting point.

Uses
1. It is used for packing and wrapping frozen food, textile products etc.
2. In manufacturing of pipes and bottles etc.
3. It is used as insulators for electric wires and cables.

Reason of low density and low melting points: Due to branched chain structure, they are not packed properly. Therefore, they have low density and low melting points.

2. HDPE: It is prepared by heating ethylene at 330-470 K and 6-7 atm. Pressure in presence of catalyst (Ziegler-Natta)

$$nCH_2{=}CH_2 \xrightarrow[Al(C_2H_5)_3 + TiCl_4]{330-470k,\,6-7\,atm} -[CH_2-CH_2]_n-$$

Ethylene (Ziegler- Natta Catalyst) Polythene

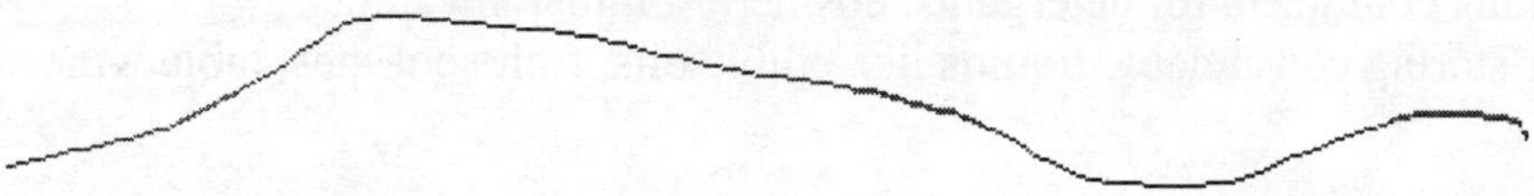

A molecule of linear polyethylene or HDPE

Properties
1. It is linear chain structure.
2. It is chemically inert.
3. It is translucent polymer.
4. Its hardness, toughness and tensile strengths are greater than low density polymer.
5. Due to liner structure, close packing is found in this polymer.

Uses
1. It is used in the manufacturing of buckets, tubes etc.
2. HDPE is used in the manufacture of toys, crates closures, caps, buckets etc.
3. HDPE is also used in the manufacture of overhead tanks for water storage.

Reason of high density and high melting points: Due to linear chain structure, polymers are properly packed. Therefore, it has high density and high melting points.

Poly vinyl chloride: It is the plastic known at the hardware store as PVC. This is the PVC from which pipes are made. The" vinyl" siding used on houses is made of poly vinyl chloride. Inside the house, PVC is used to make linoleum for the floor. In the seventies, PVC was often used to make vinyl car tops. PVC is useful because it resists two things that hate each other: fire and water. Because of its water resistance it is used to make raincoats and shower curtains and of course, water pipes. It has flame resistance, too, because it contains chlorine. When PVC is burnt, chlorine atoms are released and chlorine atoms inhibit combustion.

Structurally, PVC is a polymer. It is similar to polyethylene, but on every other carbon in the backbone chain, one of the hydrogen atoms is replaced with a chlorine atom. It is produced by the free radical polymerization of vinyl chloride.

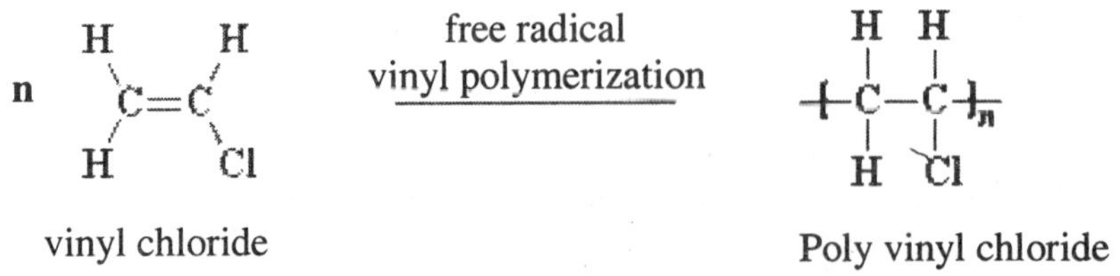

Properties

1. It is colourless, odourless, non inflammable and chemically inert powder.
2. PVC is thermally not very stable and degrades above 200^0C with the evolution of HCl.
3. It is resistant to atmospheric oxygen, inorganic acids and alkalies.
4. It is water proof and washable.
5. It is less brittle and lighter when compared to glass.

Use (Rigid PVC)

1. It is used for making window frames.
2. It is used for making containers for detergents, cosmetics, mineral water.
3. It is also used for storing consumable liquids like edible oils, fruit squashes, table wine etc.

(Plasticized PVC)

1. It is used as insulating material, ladies hand bags, bathroom curtains, kitchen upholstery.
2. In the film form it is used in membrane separation technology.
3. It is also used as thermal insulating foam in buildings, cinemas and in crafts.

Polymethyl Methyacrylate or Lucite or Plexiglass: It is prepared by free radical polymerization of methyl methacrylate in the presence of benzoyl peroxide or hydrogen peroxide. It is an acrylic polymer.

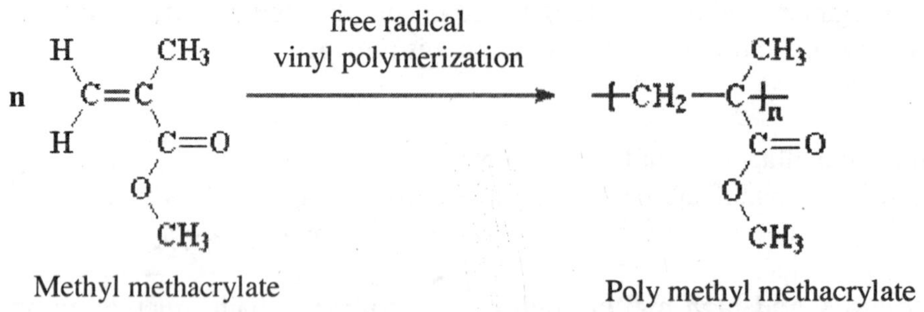

Properties

1. It is a colourless transparent plastic.
2. It is amorphous in nature due to presence of bulky side groups.
3. It become like rubber at above 65°C.
4. It has low chemical resistance to hot acids and alkalis.
5. It has poor scratch resistance.

Uses

1. PMMA is the nearest alternative to glass as it does not shatter and can be moulded into any shape. Its sheets known as Plexiglas or Lucite are used as an alternative to glass.
2. It is used for making lenses, aircraft, light fixtures, bomber noses, gun, turrets, cockpits, canopies.
3. PMMA is also found in paints.
4. The barrier at the ice rink which keeps hockey pucks from flying in the faces of fans is made of PMMA.
5. Lucite is used to make the surfaces of hot tubs, sinks and the ever popular one piece bath tub and shower units.

Poly Methyl Acrylate (PMA): The polymer of methyl acrylate, PMA or poly methyl acrylate, is similar to poly methyl methacrylate, except for the lack of methyl groups on the backbone carbon chain. PMA is a soft white rubbery material which is softer than PMMA because its long polymer chains are thinner and smoother and can slide more easily past each other.

TEFLON or Poly Tetra Fluro Ethylene (PTFE): PTFE is either synthesized by the emulsion polymerization of tetrafluoroethylene monomer under pressure, using free-radical catalysts or it may be produced by the direct substitution of hydrogen atoms on polyethylene with fluorine, using polyethylene and flourine gas at 20 °C.

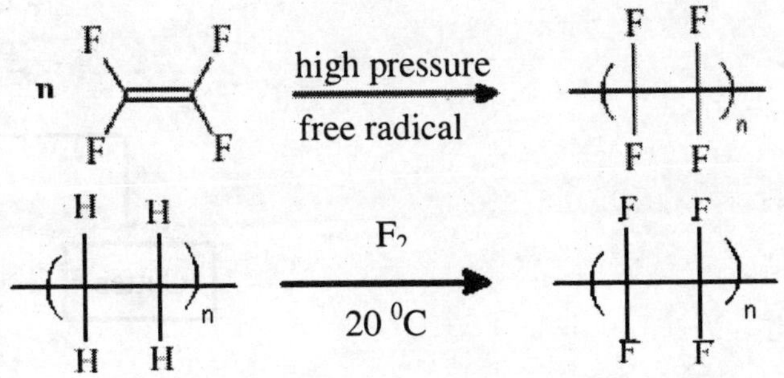

Properties

1. PTFE is a white solid at room temperature, with a density of about 2.2 g/cm^3. According to DuPont, its melting point is 327 °C (620.6 °F), but its properties degrade above 260 °C (500 °F).
2. The coefficient of friction of plastics is usually measured against polished steel. Teflon's coefficient of friction is 0.1 or less, which is the lowest of any known solid material.
3. PTFE has excellent dielectric properties. This is especially true at high radio frequencies.
4. It is chemical inert. PTFE can not be cross-linked like an elastomer.

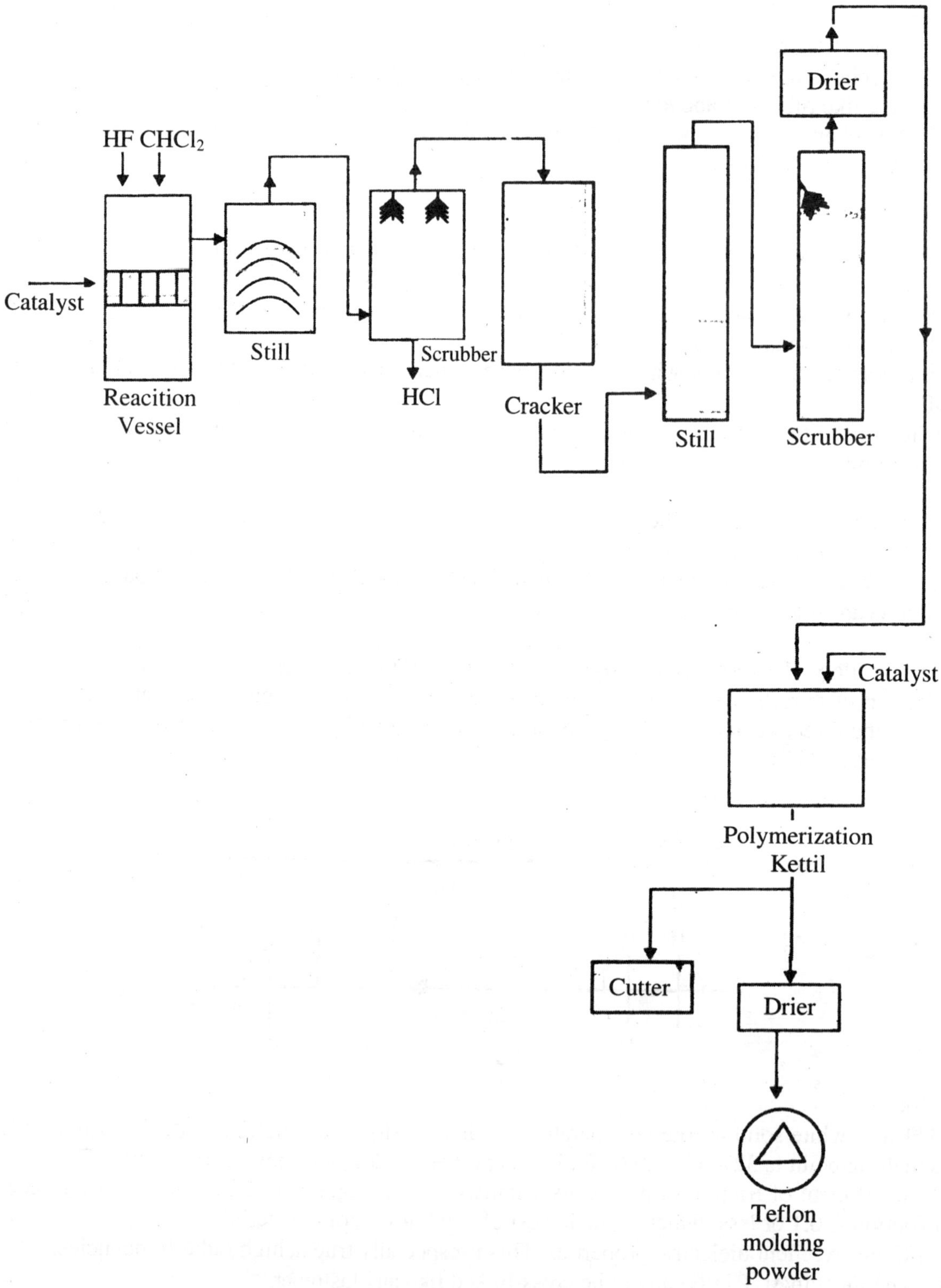

Flow-sheet for producing polytetrafluoroethylene (Teflon)

Applications

1. Its extremely high bulk resistivity makes it an ideal material for fabricating long life electric, useful devices that are the electrostatic analogues of magnets.
2. PTFE is often used to coat non-stick frying pans as it has very low friction and high heat resistance.
3. Gore-Tex is a material incorporating fluoropolymer membrane with micropores. The roof of the Hubert H. Humphrey Metrodome in Minneapolis is one of the largest applications of Teflon PTFE coatings on Earth, using 20 acres (about 8 hectares) of the material in a double-layered, white dome, made with PTFE-coated fiberglass, that gives the stadium its distinctive appearance. The Millennium Dome in London is also substantially made of PTFE.
4. Powdered PTFE is used in pyrotechnic compositions as oxidizer together with powdered metals such as aluminium and magnesium.
5. PTFE is also used in body piercing such as a sub-clavicle piercing, due to its flexibility and bio-compatibility.

Polyacrylonitrile: Polyacrylonitrile is a vinyl polymer and a derivative of the acryl ate family of polymers. It is made from the monomer acrylonitrile by free radical vinyl polymerization.

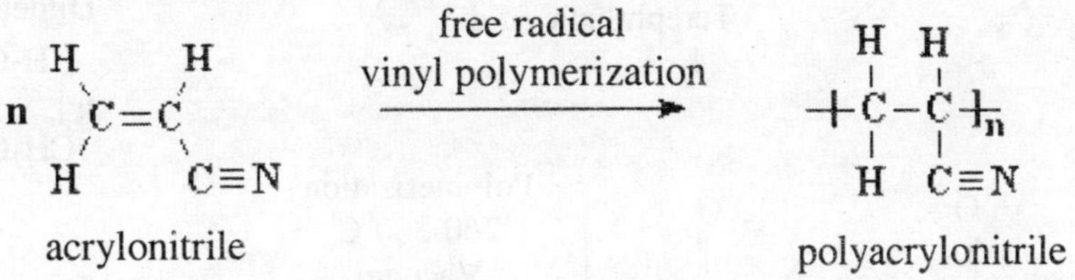

Properties: It is hard, horny and high melting substance also known as acrilon or Orlon.

Uses:

1. It is used for making blankets, sweaters, bathing suits etc.
2. It is also used for making synthetic carpets.

Polyvinyl acetate (PVA): It is prepared by heating vinyl acetate in the presence of small amount of benzoyl peroxide.

$$nCH_2 = CH - COOCH_3 \rightarrow -[CH_2 - \underset{\substack{|\\COOCH_3}}{\overset{\substack{H\\|}}{C}} -]\,n$$

Properties:

1. PVA is a colourless, transparent material having no taste or odour.
2. It is resistant to water, atmospheric oxygen and chemicals.
3. It is a fairly soluble in inorganic acid and organic solvent.
4. It is resistant to heat, but slightly yellowing takes place after prolonged storage above 120^0 C.
5. It is harmless if taken orally.

Uses

1. PVA is used as a basic material for chewing gums and surgical dressings.
2. It is used in the preparation of lacquers, paints and adhesives.
3. It is also used for finishing of textile fabrics.

4. On co-polymerization with polyvinyl chloride, it is converted into a polymer having varying degree of softeners. For example, Vinylite which is a copolymer of polyvinyl acetate and polyvinyl chloride, is especially useful as a surface coating material for metals.
5. It is used as an adhesive for porous materials, particularly wood, paper and clothes. It is the most commonly used wood glue, both as "white glue" and the yellow "carpenter's glue."
6. PVA is widely used in bookbinding and book arts due to its flexibility and it is non-acidic, unlike many other polymers. Elmer's Glue is a popular brand of white PVA glue sold in the United States.
7. PVA is also commonly recommended for use in making paper machine.

Dacron or Terylene : Dacron or terylene is produced by the condensation of two different bi or poly functional monomers having functional groups which have affinity for each other. It can be prepared from terephthalic acid and ethylene glycol either by direct estrification or by catalyzed ester interchange.

Chemical Reaction:

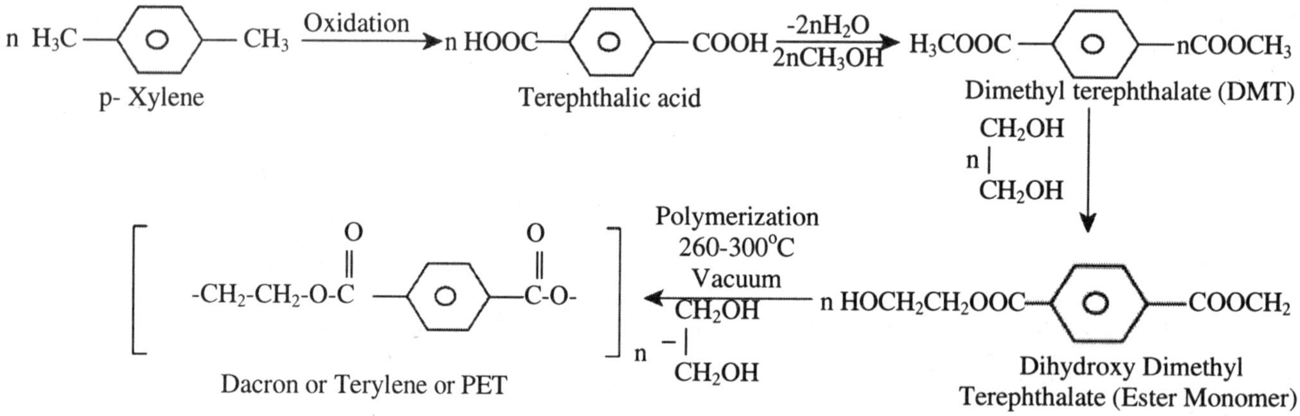

Flow chart of manufacturing of Dacron:

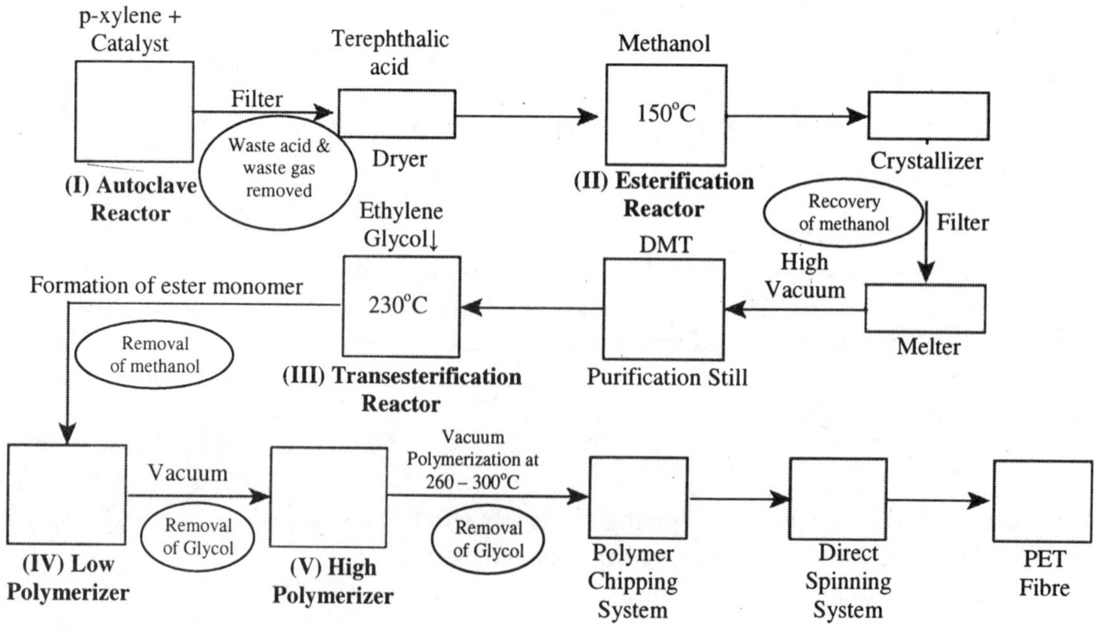

Dacron or PET is prepared from terephalic acid obtained by the oxidation of p-xylene in autoclave reactor(1). Terephthalic acid obtained is further treated with methyl alcohol at 150°C in esterification reactor(2) using sulphuric acid as catalyst.

The product dimethyl terephthalete (DMT) is purified by crystallization and distillation. Then this purified DMT is reacted at 230°C with ethylene Glycol in Transesterification Reactor (3) so as to get dihydroxy dimethyl terephthalate (ester monomer).

The Dacron formation from this ester monomer proceeds in two steps. First step is done in low polymerizer (4), low molecular weight polyester is formed along with glycol. Then temperature is slightly raised and pressure is lowered to remove Glycol. The reaction conditions in high polymerizer (5) are adjusted so as to bring about effective condensation. At 260-300°, under vacuum, terylence is formed in high polymerizer. Simultaneously ethylene glycol is distilled out. Terylene is then extruded and from direct spinning system, PET fibre is obtained.

Properties

1. It is resistant to heat and moisture.
2. It is resistant to both weak acids and bases at room temperature but readily attacked by strong acids and bases.
3. Because of its relatively symmetrical structure and presence of numerous polar groups, the polyesters are a good fiber forming material and are converted into commercial fibers.
4. It is resistant to almost all kinds of insects attacks.
5. It is highly crease and wrinkle resistant.
6. It is also resistant towards abrasion and oxidation.
7. PET has too low glass transition temperature that is the temperature at which the PET becomes soft.

Uses

1. It is generally used in making synthetic fibers like Terylene, Dacron etc.
2. It is also used for making films and transparency because of its high strength, durability and transparency.
3. It is also used for electric insulation.
4. Glass reinforced PET is used for the manufacture of housing for coffee machines, car heaters, toasters etc.
5. It is used to make magnetic recording tapes.
6. The continuous filament yarn is used in curtains, dress fabrics, high-pressure fire hoses, menis shirts and thread.
7. The staple fiber is ideal for mixing with wool in men and women suits, as well as in dress fabrics, knitted wear and washable woven sportswear.

Table 4.6: Some Condensation Polymers

Formula	Type	Components	T_g °C	T_m °C
~[CO(CH$_2$)$_4$CO-OCH$_2$CH$_2$O]$_n$~	**polyester**	HO$_2$C-(CH$_2$)$_4$-CO$_2$H, HO-CH$_2$CH$_2$-OH	< 0	50
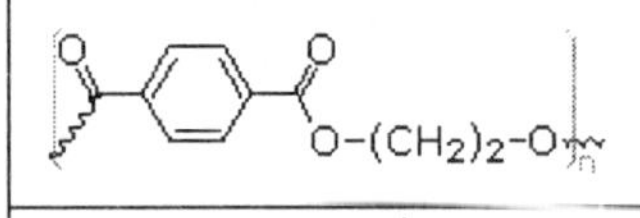	**polyester** Dacron Mylar	para HO$_2$C-C$_6$H$_4$-CO$_2$H, HO-CH$_2$CH$_2$-OH	70	265
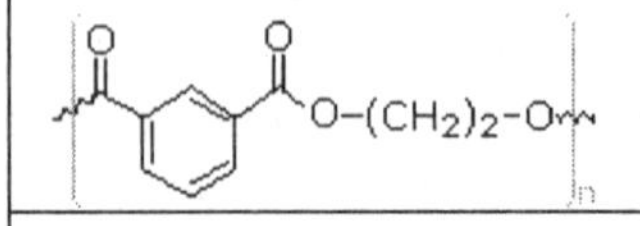	**polyester**	meta HO$_2$C-C$_6$H$_4$-CO$_2$H, HO-CH$_2$CH$_2$-OH	50	240
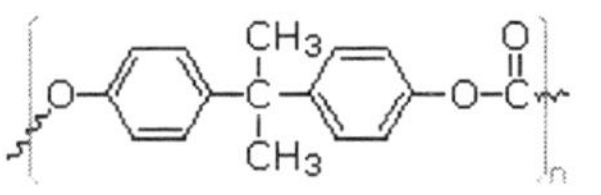	**polycarbonate** Lexan	(HO-C$_6$H$_4$-OH)$_2$ C(CH$_3$)$_2$ (Bisphenol A), X$_2$C=O (X = OCH$_3$ or Cl)	150	267
~[CO(CH$_2$)$_4$CO-NH(CH$_2$)$_6$NH]$_n$~	**polyamide** Nylon 66	HO$_2$C-(CH$_2$)$_4$-CO$_2$H, H$_2$N-(CH$_2$)$_6$-NH$_2$	45	265
~[CO(CH$_2$)$_5$NH]$_n$~	**polyamide** Nylon 6 Perlon	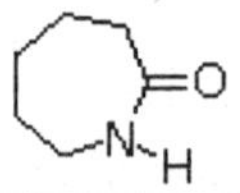	53	223
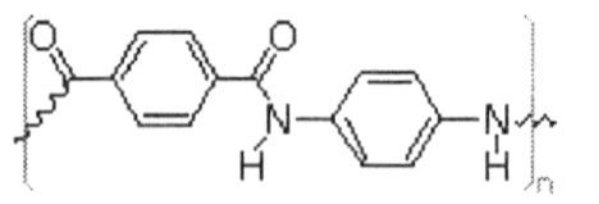	**polyamide** Kevlar	para HO$_2$C-C$_6$H$_4$-CO$_2$H, para H$_2$N-C$_6$H$_4$-NH$_2$	---	500
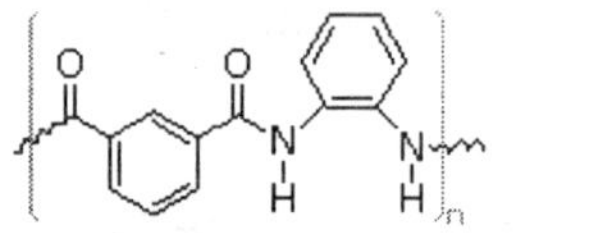	**polyamide** Nomex	meta HO$_2$C-C$_6$H$_4$-CO$_2$H, meta H$_2$N-C$_6$H$_4$-NH$_2$	273	390
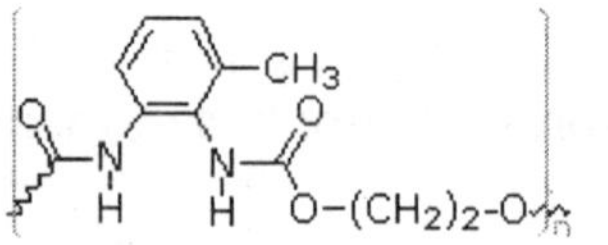	**polyurethane** Spandex	HOCH$_2$CH$_2$OH, 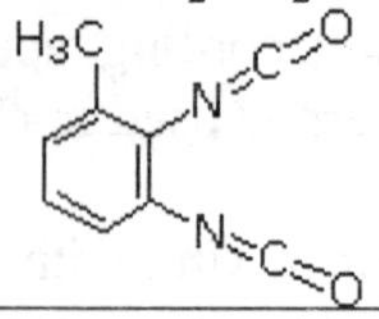	52	---

4.5 NYLONS

Nylon is a type of polymer in category of polyamides having linkage (--) in the chain. Nylon is the first man-made synthetic fiber. It was first produced in 1935. Scientists in United States were successful in producing a material after synthesizing polyamide synthetic fibers. They named it nylon and acronym for New York (NY) and London (Lon).

Nylons are condensation copolymers formed by reacting equal parts of a diamine and a dicarboxylic acid, so that peptide bonds form at both ends of each monomer in a process analogous to polypeptide biopolymers. The numerical suffix specifies the numbers of carbons donated by the monomers; the diamine first and the diacid second. The most common variant is nylon 6-6 which refers to the fact that the diamine (hexamethylene diamine) and the diacid (adipic acid) each donate 6 carbons to the polymer chain.

The general reaction is-

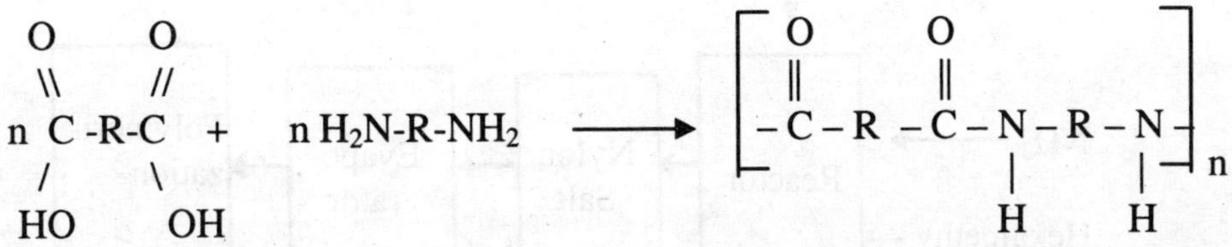

A molecule of water is given off and the nylon is formed. Its properties are determined by the R and R' groups in the monomers. In nylon 6,6, R' = 6C and R = 4C alkanes, but one also has to include the two carboxyl carbons in the diacid to get the number it donates to the chain. In Kevlar, both R and R' are benzene rings.Nylon 6-6, Nylon 6,10 and Nylon 6 are the commercially important polyamides.

Nylon 6:6: It is obtained by condensing hexamethylene diamine with adipic acid. The elimination of water molecules takes place. The chain length of the polymer depends upon the temperature and the time for which the process is carried out.

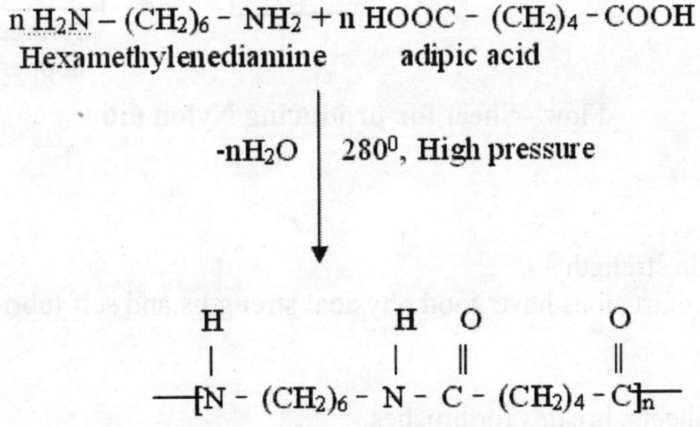

Nylon 6:6

The name of nylon – 66 is given because its monomers (hexamethylene diamine and adipic acid) have six carbon each.

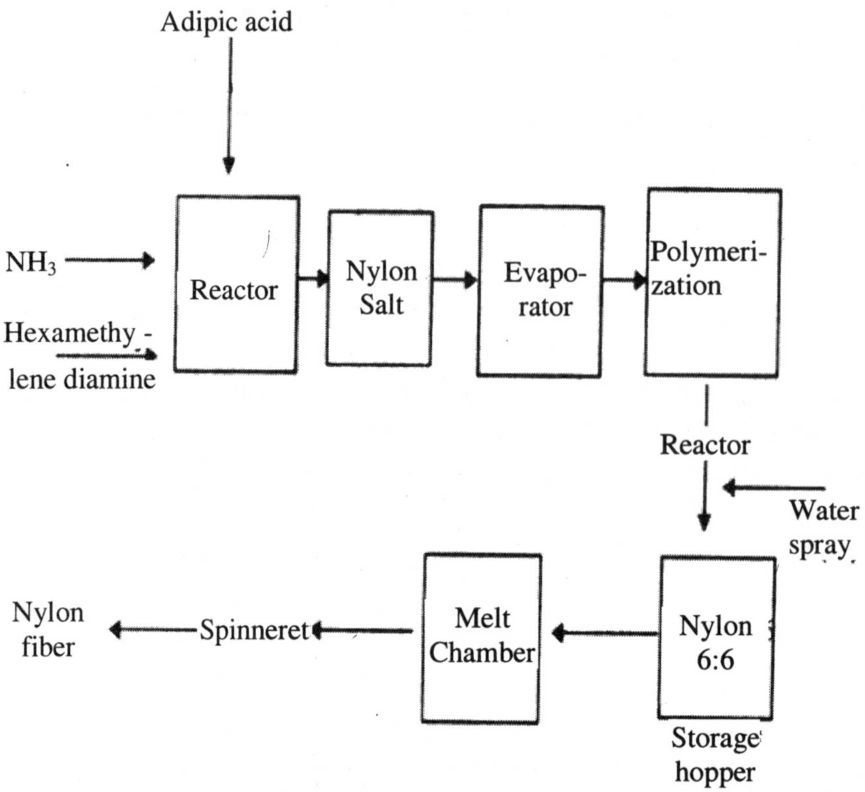

Flow –Sheet for producing Nylon 6:6

Properties

1. It is a linear polymer
2. It has very high tensile strength
3. Their mouldings and extrusions have good physical strengths and self lubricating properties.

Uses

1. It is used in making sheets, bristles for brushes.
2. In textile industry, crinkled nylon fibers are useful for making elastic hosiery (sports wear, socks, stockings, nightwear etc.)
3. Nylon 6:6 is a tough plastic and it is used as a substitute for metals in gears and bearing etc.

Nylon-6: It is also called perlon-L. Nylon-6 is obtained from the monomer caprolactum which in turn is prepared from cyclohexane which is petro chemical product.

Preparation of Caprolactum:

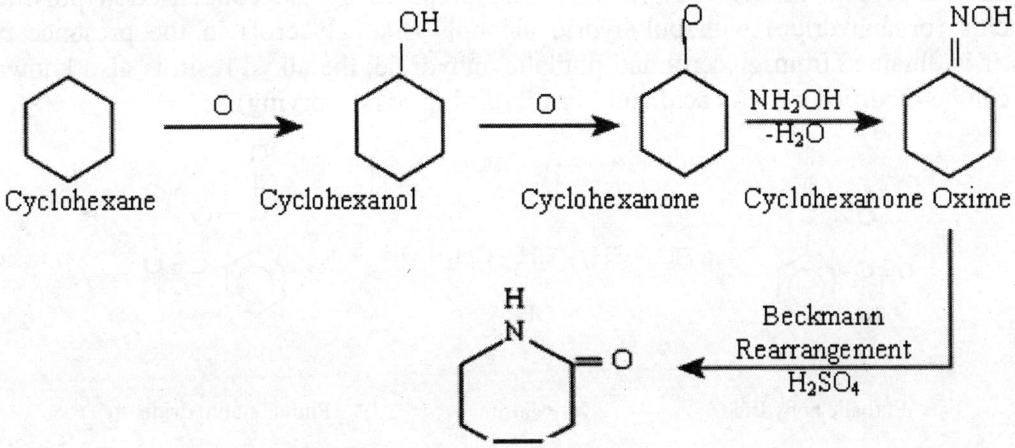

Caprolactam is heated with traces of water gives aminocaproic acid which is monocarboxylic acid having six atoms which on polymerization gives nylon-6.

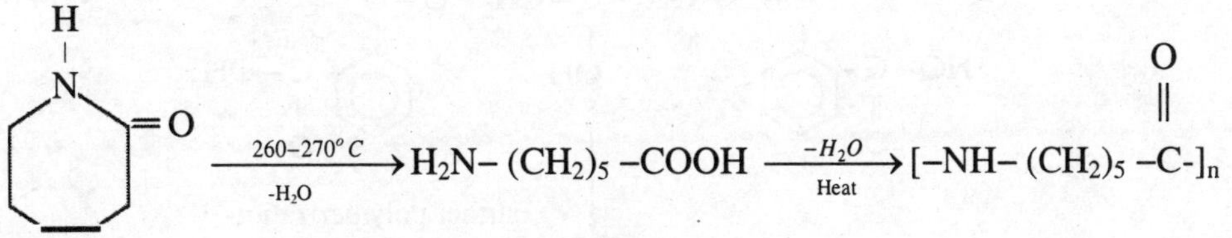

Caprolactam amino caproic acid nylon-6

Properties

1. Nylon 6 fibres are tough, possessing high tensile C 'ength.
2. They are wrinkle proof. H_2
3. It has the potential to be used as a technical nutri‹
4. They are very flexible and retain their original shape after use.

Uses

1. For making tyres, cords, ropes etc.
2. Due to its good barrier properties, nylon-6 film is used for packaging some oxygen sensitive food

General applications of Nylon

Bristles for toothbrushes, sutures for surgery etc.

- Manufacture of hosiery, knitted garments etc.
- Manufacture of a large variety of threads, ropes, filaments, nets, tyre cords etc. having high tenacity and good elasticity.
- It is also used in making rollers, slides and door latches.
- Nylon 6, 10 is used to manufacture article like brushes and bristles.
- Due to its high tenacity, it is used for parachute fabric.
- It is also used in making transmission belting, ribbons for electric typewriters and spindle bands on textile spinning machines etc.
- Nylon is also used for making insect screens.

Alkyd Resins (or glyptal resins): Alkyd resins are prepared by the condensation polymerization of polybasic acids (or anhydride) with polyhydric alcohols (like glycerol) in the presence of heat and catalyst. As it is obtained from glycerol and phthalic anhydride, the alkyd resin is also known as glyptal resin. They can be modified by fatty acid and / or oil (drying or non-drying).

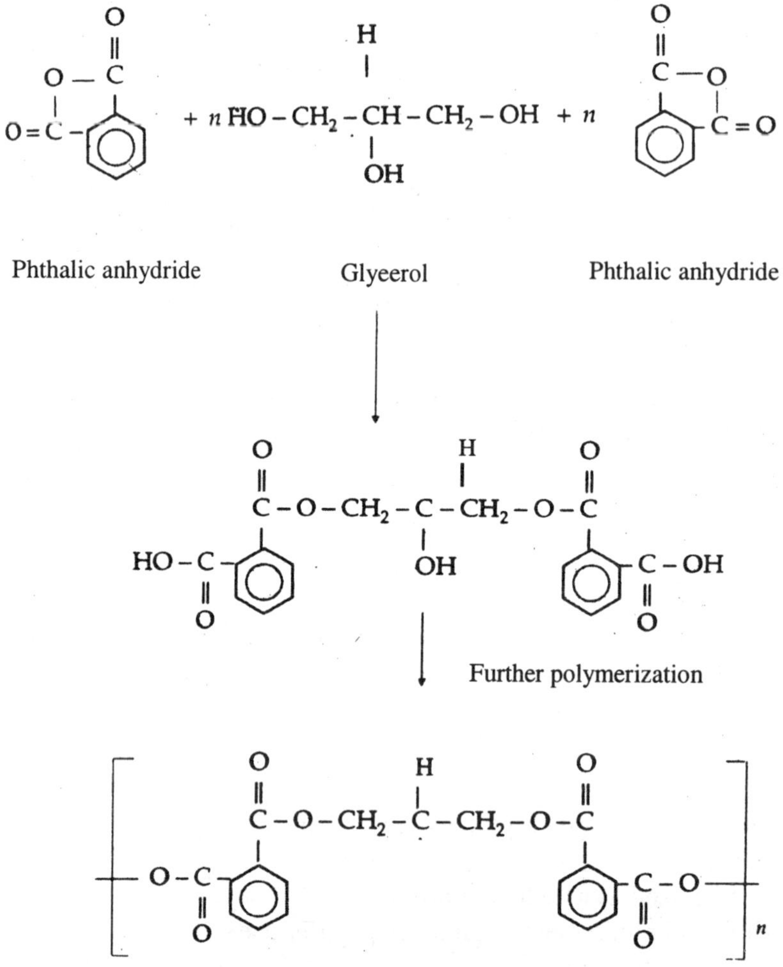

Alkylated resin (polyester)

Properties

(a) Hard.
(b) Resistant towards atmospheric corrosion and acids.
(c) Insoluble and infusible.
(d) Dimensionally stable.

Applications: The alkyd resins are used to make

(a) Paints, enamels and varnishes.
(b) Car Panels and bodies.
(c) Binding material for cements, asbestos etc.
(d) Circuit-break insulations and
(e) Switches and gears.

Phenol Formaldehyde Resin: It is manufactured by the reaction between phenol and formaldehyde in the presence of either acid or base as a catalyst.

1. **Novolac formation**: Depending upon the ratio of phenol formaldehyde, different resins are obtained. Example – Navolac and resol resins. The novolac with linear structure is obtained when P/F ratio is greater than unity.
2. **Resole Formation:** Resole with linear structure is obtained in the presence of alkaline catalyst when P/F ratio is less than 1. The resoles are soluble in the reaction mixture and have excess of methylol groups capable of further reaction during continued heating. Resols therefore have limited shelf life. However the reaction may be stopped at the desired step by cooling.
3. **Resite Formation:** On further heating, resole is transformed into a three dimensional polymer, called resite due to the presence of active groups.

(I) **Novolak:** formaldehyde is heated with some excess phenol in presence of acid catalyst ortho and para hydroxy benzyl alcohols are formed. The molecules of O-hydroxy benzyl alcohol condense to give a linear polymer which is called novolak.

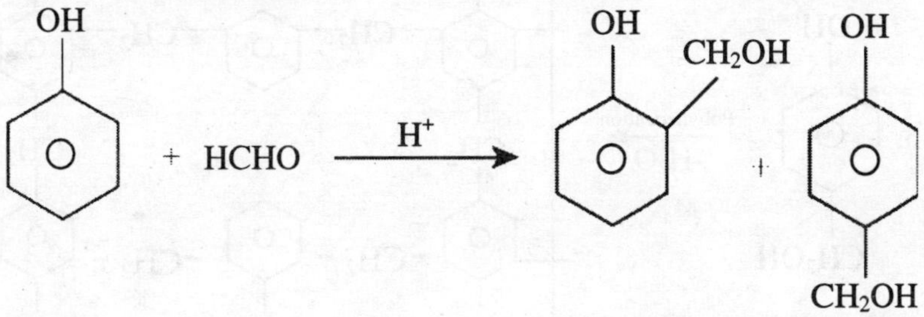

Phenol Formaldehyde o- hydroxyl benzyl alcohol p-hydroxy benzyl alcohol

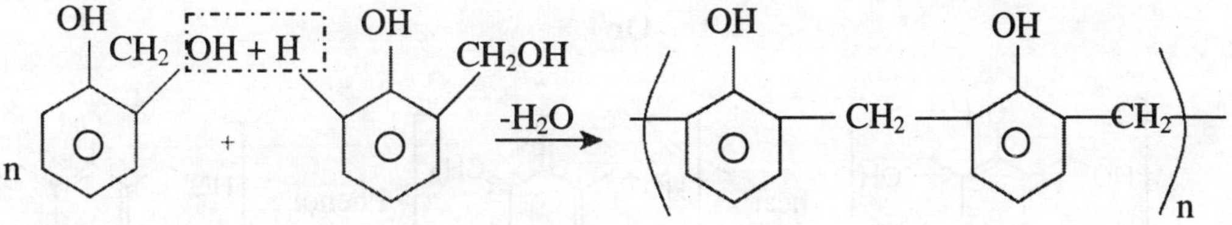

orthohydroxy benzyl alcohol orthohydroxy benzyl alcohol Linear Polymer Novolak

(ii) **Bakelite:** When excess of formaldehyde is heated with phenol in presence of an alkali (catalyst), a three-dimensional (or cross linked) polymer or resin is formed. It is known as bakelite in the name of the scientist L.H. Bakeland who prepared it for the first time in 1910.

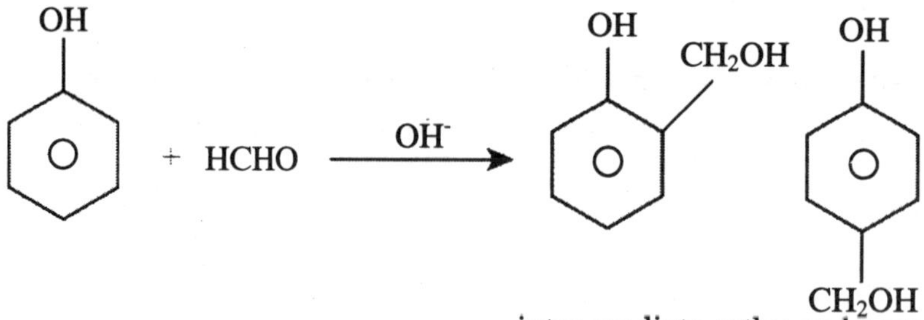

inter mediate ortho and para hydroxy benzyl alcohol

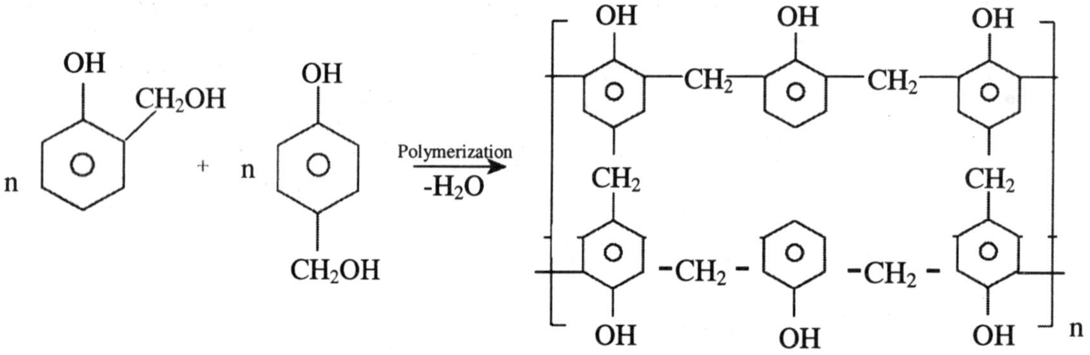

Cross linked Polymer Bakelite

Or

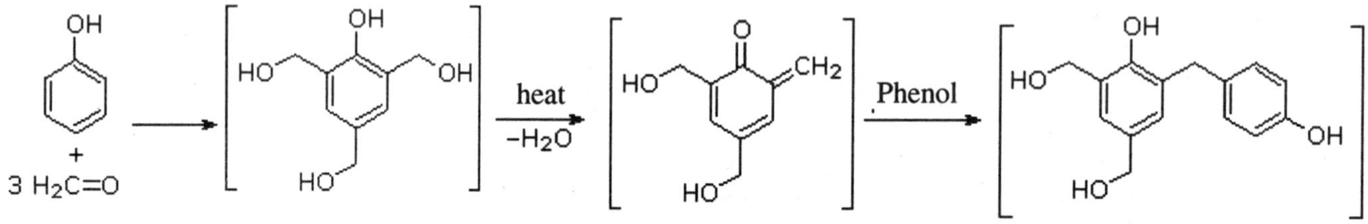

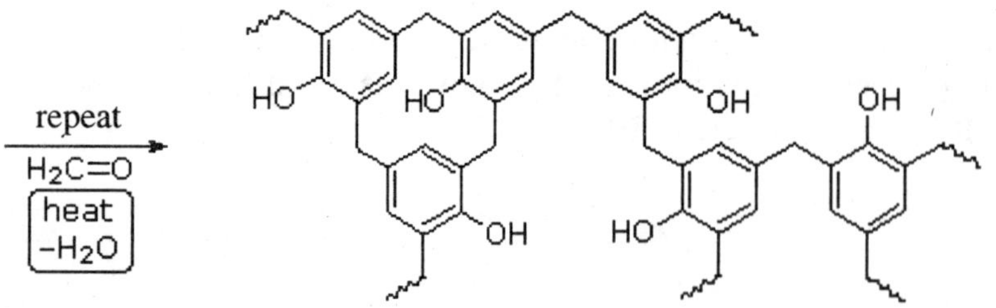

Bakelite (a cross-linked solid)

Cross-linked bakelite is a thermo setting type of polymer. Soft Bakelite formed by low degree of polymerization is used as binding glue for laminated wooden products and in varnishes and lacquers. Once it is set to a particular shape, it is not softened when heated further. It can not be reused.

Properties

1. Phenolic resins (bakelite) set to rigid hard, scratch resistant, infusible water resistant, insoluble solids which are resistant to non-oxidizing acids, salts and many organic solvents.
2. They are attacked by alkalies.
3. They are electrically insulated.

4. They are usually dark coloured- pinkish brown.
5. These resins have excellent heat resistance.

Uses

1. It is used for making electric insulated parts like switches, plugs, switches, electric boards etc.
2. Handles for cooker and sauce pans.
3. Distributor heads of cars.
4. High degree polymerization produces hard bakelite which is used for making combs, fountain pens, phonographs, records, electrical goods, laminated table tops etc.
5. Sulphonated Bakelite's are useful as Ion exchange resins.

Urea Formaldehyde Resin: Urea-formaldehyde, also known as urea-methanal, is transparent thermosetting resin or plastic, made from urea and formaldehyde (also known as methanal) heated in the presence of a mild base such as ammonia or pyridine. Polymerization can take place from mono or dimethylol urea or possibly through both with the formation of long chains. Thermosetting of the resin takes place during the moulding process. For moulding, the methylol derivatives are compounded with fillers, plasticizers, pigments etc. and then are subjected to heat and pressure, resulting into a hard, infusible product. To prepare urea formaldehyde plastic, urea is dissolved in formaldehyde at temperature below 280 k. and then condensation process is carried at 400 k. A fully cross linked urea-formaldehyde resin can be represented as

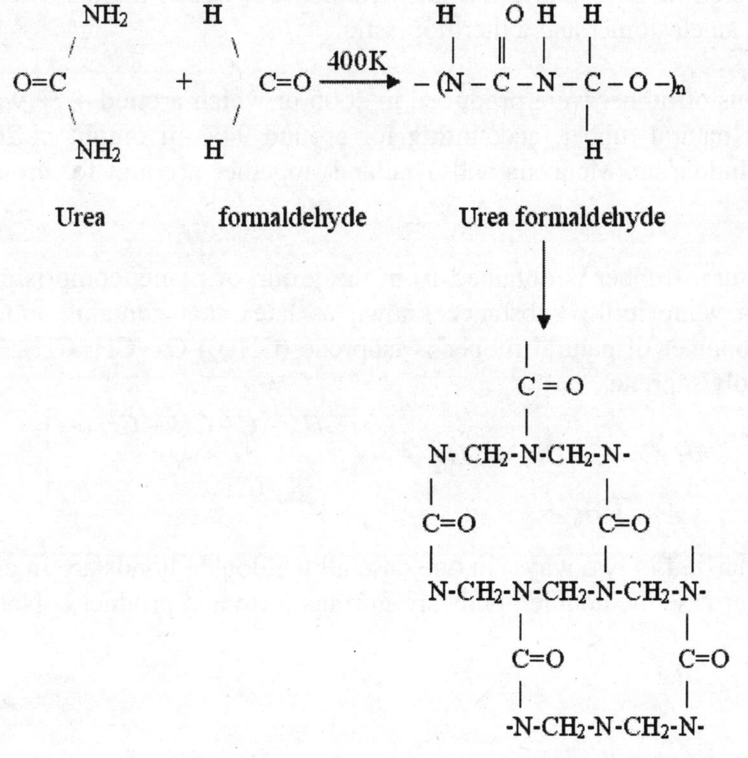

Cross linked structure

Properties

1. They are less resistant to heat and moisture when compared to phenolic resins.
2. They have good insulating properties.
3. They are resistant to oxidation to oil, grease and weak acids.

4. They are light in colour and enable production of light of pastel coloured objects.
5. They are hard. They resist abrasion and scratching.
6. They have high tensile strength, flexural modulus and heat distortion temperature, low water absorption, mould, high surface hardness, elongation at break and volume resistance.

Uses

1. They are mostly used in making moulded articles like vacuum flask, cups, jugs, buttons, bottle caps etc.
2. They are also used for adhesive applications for the production of plywood and laminating.
3. Their applications also include the treatment of textile fibers for improving their shrink and crease resistance.
4. They are also used for the manufacture of coated abrasive paper and binder for foundry cores.
5. Urea formaldehyde was commonly used when producing electrical appliances casing i.e. desk lamps.

4.6 RUBBER

It is an elastic hydrocarbon polymer that naturally occurs as a milky colloidal suspension, or latex, in the sap of some plants. It can also be synthesized. Apart from a few natural product impurities, natural rubber is essentially a polymer of isoprene units, a hydrocarbon diene monomer. Synthetic rubber can be made as a polymer of isoprene or various other monomers. Rubber is believed to have been named by Joseph Priestley, who discovered in 1770 that dried latex rubbed out pencil marks. The material properties of natural rubber make it an elastomer and a thermoplastic.

Close to 21 million tons of rubber were produced in 2005 of which around 42% was natural. Today Asia is the main source of natural rubber, accounting for around 94% of output in 2005. The three largest producing countries (Indonesia, Malaysia and Thailand) together account for around 72% of all natural rubber production.

Natural Rubber: Natural Rubber is obtained from the group of plants comprising nearly 500 different species which yield a white milky substance known as latex that contains about 25-40 % of rubber hydrocarbons. The monomer of natural rubber is isoprene $(CH_3)_2)$ C—$CH=CH_2$. The chemical name of the natural rubber is polyisoprene.

$$nH_2C = \underset{\substack{| \\ CH_3}}{C} - CH = CH_2 \longrightarrow \left[CH_2 - \underset{\substack{| \\ CH_3}}{C} - CH - CH_2 - \right]_n$$

Isoprene can be polymerized in two ways- in one case all the double bonds are in cis form and are known as rubber while in other case the double bonds are in trans form and product is Natural Rubber known as gutta-percha.

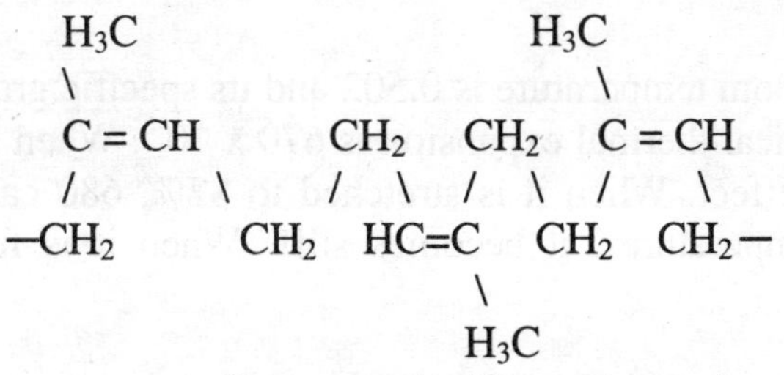

Gutta-percha (Trans-Isomer)

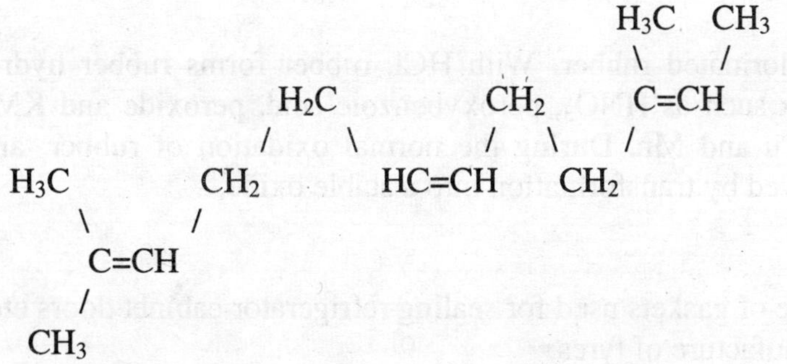

Cis-isomer

Processing of Natural Rubber: The latex can be collected from the plant by making small incisions on the barks of rubber tree like dichopsis gutta and palagum gutta trees. Rubber latex contains 25 to 45% of rubber in the form of milky colloidal emulsion. Tapping is usually done at intervals of about six months. Latex is diluted to contain 15 to 20% of rubber and filtered to remove any dirt present in it. It is then coagulated with 1 kg acetic acid or formic acid per 200 kg of rubber to a soft white mass. The coagulant mass is washed & subjected to any of the following processes:

1. Crepe Rubber: It is prepared by mixing little sodium bisulfite to bleach the rubber and then it is passed through a creeping machine which consists of two rollers with longitudinal grooves. The sheet of 1 mm thickness with rough surface resembling crepe paper is formed. The sheet is then dried at 50^0C in air.

2. Smoked rubber: It is made by mixing rubber with sodium sulphite and rolling the coagulum into thicker sheets having ribbed pattern on its surface. The sheets are dried in smoke house at about 50^0C in the smoke from burning wood or coconut shells. The rubber sheet thus obtained is translucent and amber in colour.

Properties and Uses

Vulcanized rubber has got the ideal elastomeric properties such as rapid extensibility to great elongations, high stiffness and strength when stretched and rapid and complete retraction on release of the external stress. Its chief properties which render it valuable are its resiliency, low thermal and electrical conductivity, low permanent set, resistance to abrasion, resistance to water, bases and dilute acids. Concentrated acids react with rubber and destroy it. Rubber is attacked by oxygen in air and by sunlight and the rate of such attack is reduced by anti-oxidants. Solutions of rubber in benzene are used as adhesives. When rubber is treated with a solvent, the solvent is first absorbed by the rubber, which swells and forms a jelly-like mass and when enough of the solvent has been absorbed, the mass assumes the liquid state. Thus, in a sense the solvent may be said to have dissolved in the rubber.

The specific heat of raw rubber at room temperature is 0.502 and its specific gravity at $0^{o}C$ is 0.950 and at $20^{o}C$ is 0.934. Its coefficient of cubical thermal expansion is 670 x 10^{-6}. When rubber is extended, heat is evolved and this is called Joule's effect. When it is stretched to 82%, 680 calories of heat is liberated. When rubber is cooled to low temperatures, it becomes stiff. When it is frozen, it attains a fibrous structure.

When rubber is heated with about 1% organic sulfonyl chloride or an organic sulfonic acid at about $130^{0}C$, it is converted into a tough, thermoplastic resin which resembles Gutta-percha. Such products are known as thermoprenes.

Rubber reacts with chlorine giving chlorinated rubber. With HCl, rubber forms rubber hydrochloride. Rubber is oxidized by oxidizing agents such as HNO_3, peroxybenzoic acid, peroxide and $KMnO_4$. The oxidation reactions are catalyzed by Cu and Mn. During the normal oxidation of rubber, an unstable peroxide of rubber is first formed followed by transformation into a stable oxide.

Uses

1. Rubber is used for the manufacture of gaskets used for sealing refrigerator cabinet/doors etc.
2. Rubber is mainly used for the manufacture of tyres.
3. It is used for preparing V-belts for the power transmission and conveyor belts for conveying several types of materials. These products are compact, non-slipping, clean and shock-absorbing.
4. Rubber lined tanks (steel, Al, etc.) are widely used in chemical plants where protection from corrosive chemicals is required.
5. Rubber mountings are prepared from sandwiching the rubber between two metal plates. They reduce machine vibrations and prolong the life of the machine besides reducing noise.
6. Rubber is used for manufacturing hoses.
7. Rubber threads and sponge rubber have good shock absorbing and thermal insulation properties. Rubber threads are used in shock absorber cords, heat bands for goggles and helmets golf balls.
8. Rubber is used for various related products like chlorinated rubber, oxidized rubber, rubber hydrochloride, cyclized rubber and ebonites. All these substances have many industrial uses.
9. Foam rubber is used in the manufacture of cushions, mattresses, paddings etc.
10. Rubber is also used for manufacturing toys, sports items etc.
11. Rubbers when blended with plastics give improved strength, hardness, flexibility, chemical and resistance thermal resistance.

Drawbacks of raw rubber

1. Its temperature range is very limited. It becomes soft and sticky in hot summer while hard and brittle in cold weather.
2. It has low tensile strength.
3. It has less elasticity.
4. In organic solvents it undergoes swelling and gradual disintegration.
5. When stretched to a great extent, some molecular chains undergo sliding of slippage over each other hence it suffers from permanent deformation.
6. It is oxidized in air hence it is not durable.

These drawbacks can be improved by vulcanization process.

Vulcanization of Rubber: This process was discovered by Charles Good in year 1839. To improve the properties of rubber, it is compounded with some chemicals like sulphur, hydrogen sulphide, benzoyl chloride etc. Most important is addition of sulphur. The vulcanization process is carried out by heating crude rubber in presence of sulphur at 100^{0}C temperature. The added sulphur combines chemically at the double bonds of different rubber springs. This treatment of sulphur with natural as well as synthetic rubber is called vulcanization process. It improves the properties of the respective rubber. One can control the number of crosslink unit length of the polymer by adjusting quantity of sulphur used. For example when soft rubber articles are required, the quantity of sulphur added is 4% and for hard rubber articles, it is increased up to 45%. The vulcanized rubber has cross-linked structure which is stronger than the unvulcanized rubber.

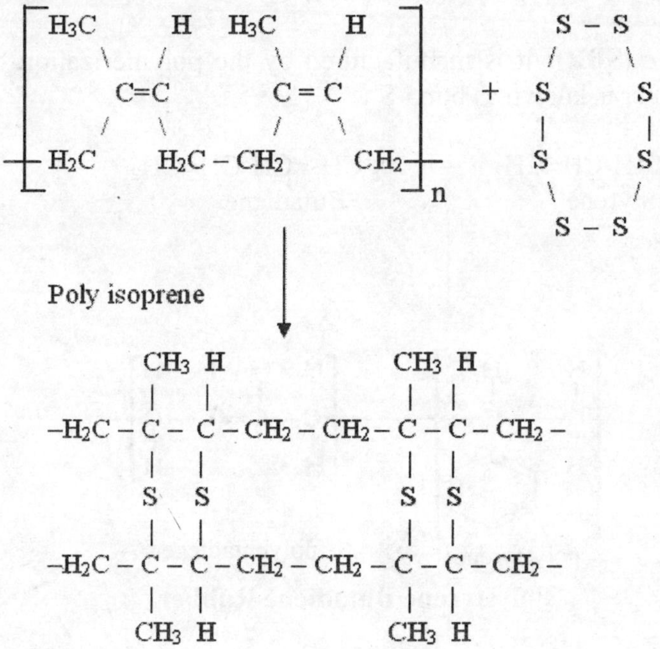

Or

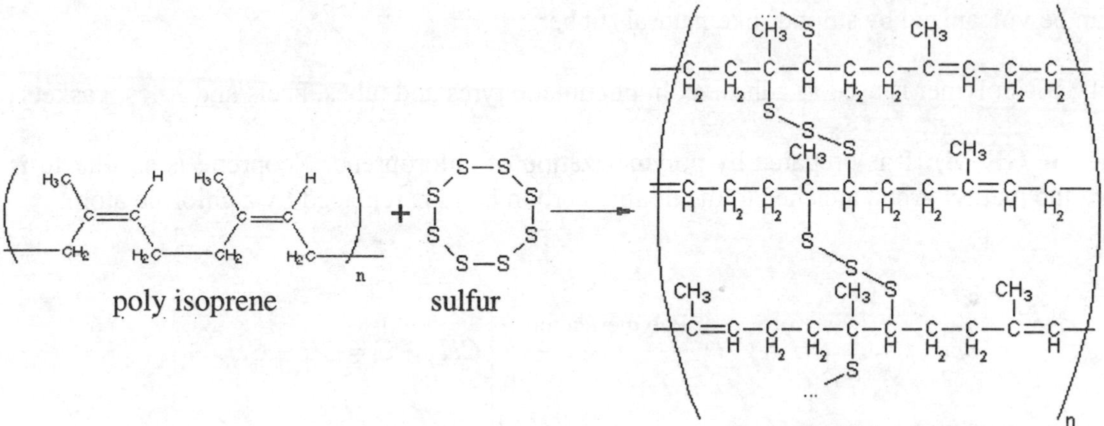

Cross-linked poly isoprene

Advantages of Vulcanization

1. It removes the bad smell of the rubber.
2. Cross-linked structure makes the rubber stronger than unvulcanized form.
3. It can be easily moulded.
4. By adjusting the ratio of sulphur, desired properties of rubber can be produced.

Synthetic Rubber: Synthetic rubber is type of artificially made polymer material which acts as an elastomer. An elastomer is a material with the mechanical (or material) property that can undergo much more elastic deformation under stress than most materials and still returns to its previous size without permanent deformation. Synthetic rubber serves as a substitute for natural rubber in many cases, especially when improved material properties are needed.

Styrene Butadiene Rubber (SBR): It is manufactured by the polymerization of (75%) butadiene and (25%) styrene. This copolymer is known as buna-S

$$x\ C_6H_5CH{=}CH_2 \quad + \quad y\ CH_2{=}CH{-}CH{=}CH_2$$

Styrene Butadiene

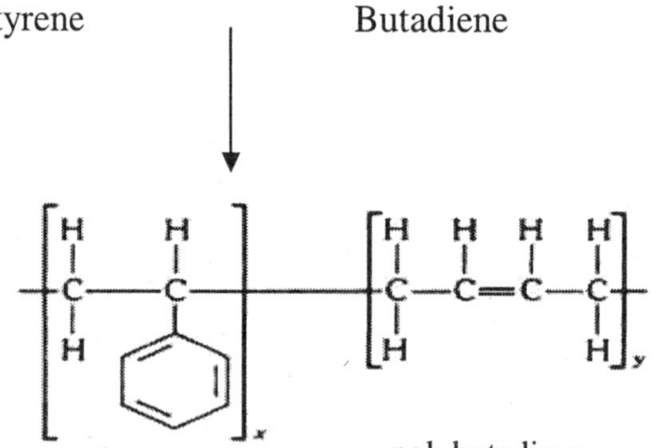

polystyrene polybutadiene

Polystyrene Butadiene Rubber

Properties:

1. High abrasion resistance.
2. High load bearing capacity and resistance.
3. It is oxidized readily in presence of traces of ozone in the atmosphere.
4. It swells in oils and solvents.
5. It can be vulcanized by sulphur like natural rubber.

Uses: Hot SBR polymer is used as adhesive, in pneumatic tyres and tubes, heels and soles, gaskets etc.

Neoprene (or GR-M): It is prepared by polymerization of chloroprene. Neoprene is similar to isoprene except that the methyl group attached to the double carbon bond is replaced by a chlorine atom.

$$nCH_2 = \underset{}{\overset{Cl}{\overset{|}{C}}} - CH = CH_2 \xrightarrow{\text{Polymerization}} -\left[CH_2 - \overset{Cl}{\overset{|}{C}} = CH - CH_2 - \right]_n$$

Chloroprene Neoprene

Properties:

1. It is resistant toward vegetable, mineral oils and high temperature.
2. Being polar polymer, it has greater solubility in polar solvent.
3. It has high tensile strength.
4. It does not undergo oxidative degradation.
5. Resistance to oils is more than rubber but less than nitrile rubber.

Uses: It is used in hose, wire insulation, gaskets, conveyor belts, lining of reaction vessels, adhesive etc.

Butadiene nitrile Rubber (BNR): It is prepared by the copolymerization between 75% butadiene and 25% vinyl cyanide. It is also known as Buna N.

$$nCH_2 = CH - CH = CH_2 + nCH_2 = \underset{\displaystyle CN}{\underset{|}{CH}}$$

Vinyl Cyanide
Or acrylonitrile

$$\downarrow$$

$$\left[-CH_2 - CH = CH - CH_2 - CH_2 - \underset{\displaystyle CN}{\underset{|}{CH}} - \right]_n$$

Buna-N
Polybutadiene-Co-acrylonitrile

Properties:

1. It is resistant towards heat, sunlight, oils, acids and salts.
2. It is less resistant to alkalies than natural rubber due to presence of cyano group.
3. Resistance to acids, salts and oil can be increased by increasing the proportion of acrylonitrile.

Uses: It is used in making tubes and tyres, insulation of high voltage wires and cables, printing rollers, oil resistance foams, automobile parts and high altitude air-craft components hoses and adhesives.

Butyl Rubber (GR-I7)
It is prepared by copolymerization of isobutene with small amount of isoprene (usually 1 to 5%).

$$n_1 \left[CH_2 = \underset{\displaystyle CH_3}{\underset{|}{C}} - CH_3 \right] + n_2 \left[CH_2 = \underset{\displaystyle CH_3}{\underset{|}{C}} - CH = CH_2 \right]$$

Isobutene Isoprene

$$\downarrow$$

$$-\left[CH_2 - \overset{\displaystyle CH_3}{\overset{|}{\underset{\displaystyle CH_3}{\underset{|}{C}}}} - \right]_{n_1} - \left[CH_2 - \underset{\displaystyle CH_3}{\underset{|}{C}} = CH - CH_2 - \right]_{n_2}$$

Polyisobutene-co isoprene (Butyl rubber)

Properties

1. It is amorphous under normal conditions but it crystallizes on stretching.
2. It is resistant to oxidation due to low degree of unsaturation.
3. It can be vulcanized but can not be hardened much.
4. It gets degraded by heat of light.
5. It has good electrical insulation properties.
6. It does not crystallize on cooling and hence remains flexible down to – 50^0C.

Uses: It is used for making automobiles tubes, conveyor belts for food and other materials tanks-linings, insulation for high voltage wires and cables.

5. Polysulphide rubber (or Thiokol or GR-P): It is prepared by the reaction of sodium polysulphide (Na_2S_2) and ethylene dichloride.

$$nClCH_2CH_2Cl + Na-S-S-Na \rightarrow (CH_2-S-S-CH_2)_n + 2NaCl$$

1, 2 Dichloroethane   Sodium polysulphide   Thiocol rubber

Properties

1. It is resistant to mineral oil, fuels, solvents, oxygen, ozone and sunlight.
2. It is impermeable to gases.
3. It can not be vulcanized and hence does not form hard rubber.
4. Polysulphide rubber however, possesses rather poor strength and abrasion resistance.

Uses: The are used for seals, gaskets, cable covering etc. and also used as a solid propellant fuel for rocket motors.

6. Polyurethane rubber (or isocynate rubber): It is produced by reacting poly alcohols with di-isocyanates.

$$nHO-(CH_2)_4-OH + nO{=}C{=}N-(CH_2)_6-N{=}C{=}O$$

1, 4 – Butane- diol   1, 6 Hexa Methylene diisocyanate

$$\downarrow$$

$$[-\overset{O}{\overset{\|}{C}}-\overset{H}{\overset{|}{N}}-(CH_2)_6-\overset{H}{\overset{|}{N}}-\overset{O}{\overset{\|}{C}}-O-(-CH_2)_4-O-]_n$$

Polyurethane rubber

Or

Isocyanate rubber

Properties

1. They are resistant to oxidation because of their saturated character.
2. They are resistant to many solvents but are attacked by acids and alkalies.
3. The polyurethane foams are light. tough and resistant to heat, abrasion chemicals and weathering.

Uses: It is used as coatings and in manufacture of foams and spandex fibers.

4.7 SILICONES

Silicones are more accurately called polymerized siloxanes or polysiloxanes. They are mixed inorganic-organic polymers with the chemical formula $[R_2SiO]_n$, where R = organic groups such as methyl, ethyl and phenyl. These materials consist of an inorganic silicon-oxygen backbone (...-Si-O-Si-O-Si-O-...) with organic side groups attached to the silicon atoms which are four-coordinate. In some cases organic side groups can be used to link two or more of these -Si-O- backbones together. By varying the -Si-O- chain lengths, side groups and cross linking, silicones can be synthesized with a wide variety of properties and compositions. They can vary in consistency from liquid to gel to rubber to hard plastic. The most common siloxane is linear polydimethylsiloxane (PDMS), a silicone oil. The second largest group of silicone materials is based on silicone resins, which are formed by branched and cage-like oligosiloxanes.

Preparation

1. Reacting silicon with alkyl halide of silicon halide with Grignard reagent.

$$CH_3Cl \quad + \quad Si \quad \rightarrow \quad CH_3SiCl_3 : (CH_3)_2\ SiCl_2$$

Methyl Chloride   Silicon

$$SiCl_4 \quad + \quad CH_3MgCl \quad \rightarrow \quad (CH_3)_3\ SiCl \text{ and } (CH_3)_4\ Si$$

Silicon Tetrachloride   Methyl magnesium Chloride   organo silicon chloride and tetra methyl silane

By the help of fractional distillation process, mixture of different organ silicon chloride is separated, which are then polymerized by carefully controlled hydrolysis.

2. Di methyl-silicon dichloride is bifunctional and can yield very long chain polymers.

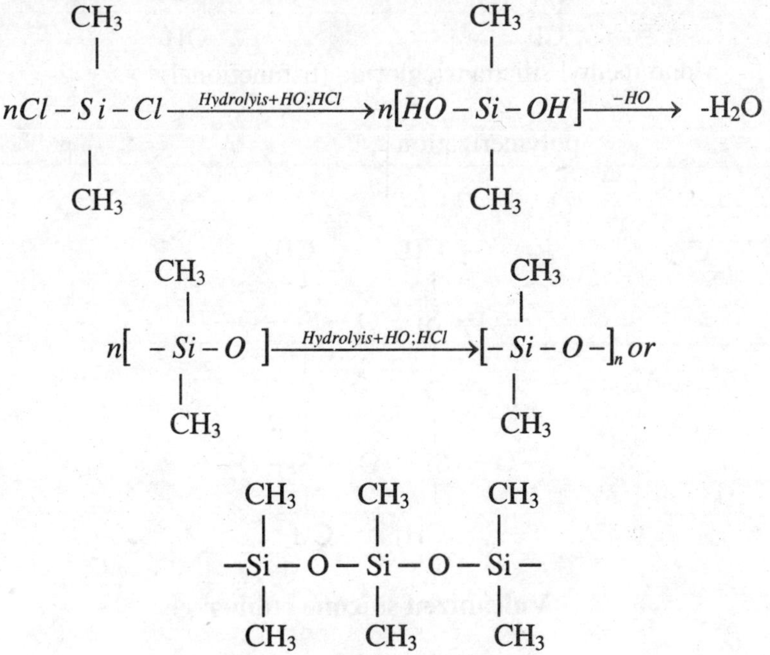

Dimethyl Silicon Polymer
(Silicon rubber)

3. Tri methyl silicon chloride is nonfunctional and hence a chain stopper. This is therefore, used in proportions to limit the chain length.

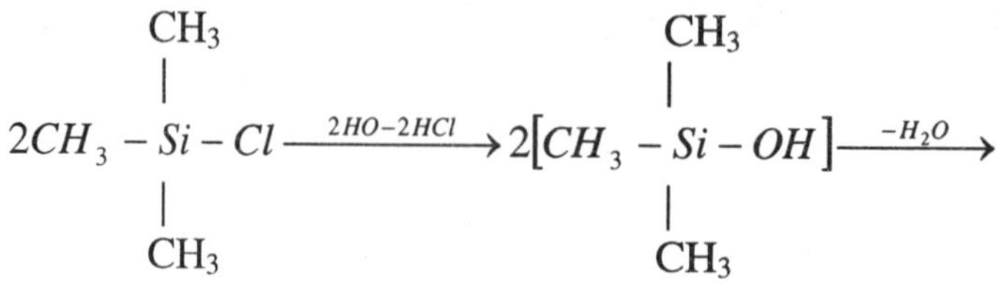

Unstable

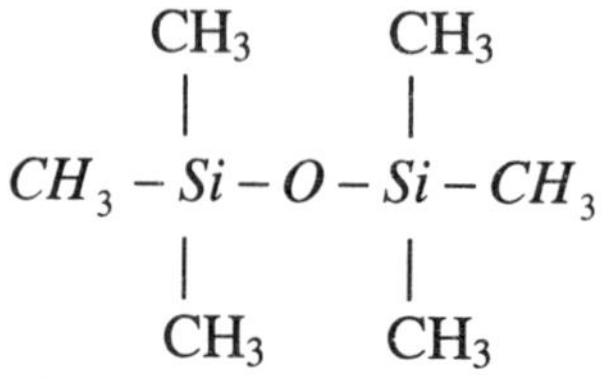

Tri Methyl Silicon Polymer

4. Monomethyl silicon chloride is trifunctional and gives cross linking to the final polymer. Its proportion used in polymerization determines the amount of cross-linking that can be obtained.

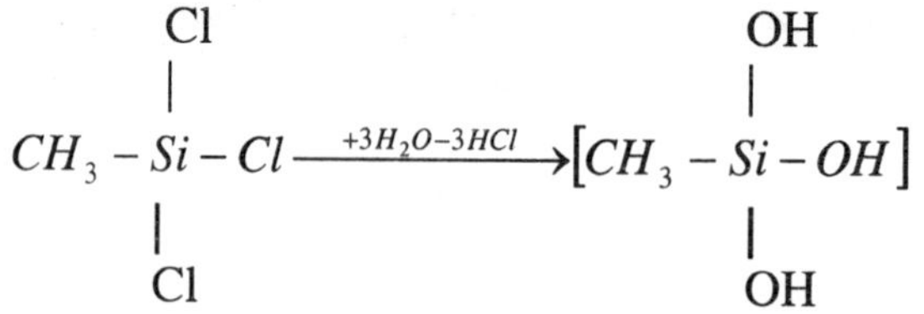

Mono methyl silicon trichloride (trifunctional)

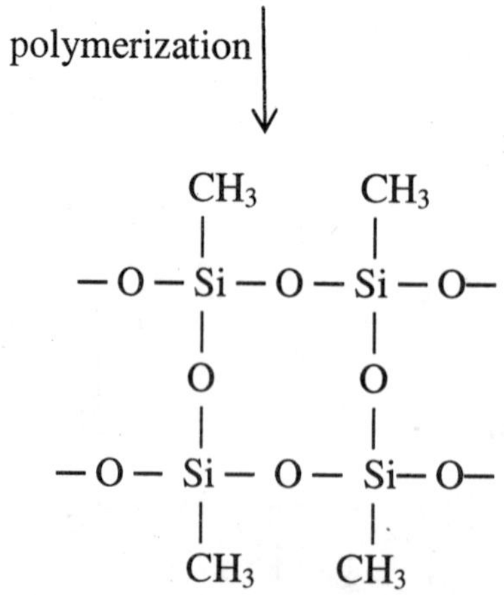

Vulcanized silicone rubber

Properties of silicones

1. Depending on the proportion of various alkyl silicon halides used during their preparation, silicones may be liquids, viscous liquids, semisolid (like greases), rubber-like and solids.

2. Because of silicon oxygen links, they exhibit outstanding stability at high temperature, good water resistance and good oxidation stability.
3. Their chemical resistance is generally lower than that of other plastics.
4. They are non toxic in nature.
5. They are good electrical insulators.
6. They have low chemical resistively.

Uses

1. For making high voltage insulators.
2. They are used as high temperature lubricants, antifoaming agents, water repellent finishes for leather and textiles, heat transfer media, as damping and hydraulic fluids.
3. They are also used in cosmetics and polishes.
4. They are used to seal gaps, joints and crevices in buildings.
5. Silicone grease is often used as a lubricant.
6. Automotive spark plug wires are often insulated by multiple layers of silicone.
7. Silicone is also impregnated into parchment paper and used as a non-stick material for applications such as baking and steaming.
8. Silicone rubber is also used to make utensils (notably spatulas) and bake ware.
9. Pharmacy and medicine.

The total absence of physiological response to the silicones has encouraged investigations regarding their use in pharmacy and medicine. Hand lotions containing silicone fluids are reported to be useful for treating skin affections where contact with water is to be avoided. A dental polyantibiotic silicone paste containing penicillin, bacotracin and streptreptomycin has been developed for root canal therapy. Silicone antifoam has been reported to be useful in treating extreme cases of pneumonia. A lot of development work is now in process in the field of silicones. For example, incorporation of some organic material has been found to alter the siloxane properties. Similarly, the properties of organic acids and amines change by the presence of silicon in the molecule. Thus by superimposing silicone biology on organic biology, materials with entirely new properties can be created. Knowledge of these new products may be helpful in working out better machine design and manufacturing process.

Biodegradable polymers or Biopolymers: A macromolecule derived from natural sources is known as biological polymer. Some biopolymers are used as structural materials, food sources or catalysts. Examples of biopolymers include polypeptides, polysaccharides, polypeptide/polysaccharide hybrids and polynucleotides which are polymers derived from ribonucleic acid (RNA) and deoxyribonucleic acid (DNA), polyhydroxybutyrates are a class of polyesters produced by certain bacteria and cis-1, 4-polyisoprene are the major component of rubber tree latex.

Amino acids are the monomers from which polypeptides are derived. Polypeptides alone, as well as multipolypeptide complexes or complexes with other molecules, are known as proteins and each has a specific biological function. There are numerous examples of biopolymers having a polysaccharide and polypeptide in the same molecule, usually with a polysaccharide as a side chain in a polypeptide or vice versa.

Biopolymers are polymers that are biodegradable. The input materials for the production of these polymers may be either renewable (based on agricultural plant or animal products) or synthetic. There are four main types of biopolymer based on:

(a) Polysaccharide (carbohydrate)

(b) Polyamides (Protein)
(c) Polynucleotides (Nucleic acids)
(d) Polyisoprene (Natural rubber)

(a) **Polysaccharide (carbohydrate):** Polysaccharides are polymeric carbohydrate structures, formed of repeating units (either mono- or di-saccharides) joined together by glycosidic bonds. These structures are often linear, but may contain various degrees of branching. Polysaccharides are often quite heterogeneous containing slight modifications of the repeating unit. Depending on the structure, these macromolecules can have distinct properties from their monosaccharide building blocks. They may be amorphous or even insoluble in water.Examples include storage polysaccharides such as starch, glycogen and structural polysaccharides such as cellulose and chitin. Polysaccharides have a general formula of $C_x(H_2O)_y$ where x is usually a large number between 200 and 2500. Considering that the repeating units in the polymer backbone are often six-carbon monosaccharide, the general formula can also be represented as $(C_6H_{10}O_5)_n$

Starch: Starch or amylum is a polysaccharide carbohydrate consisting of a large number of glucose units joined together by glycosidic bonds. It is a natural polymer which occurs as granules in plant tissue from which it can easily be recovered in large quantities. It is obtained from potatoes, maize, wheat and tapioca and similar sources. Starch is of two types, one being known as α- amylase and the other as β- amylase or amylopectin.

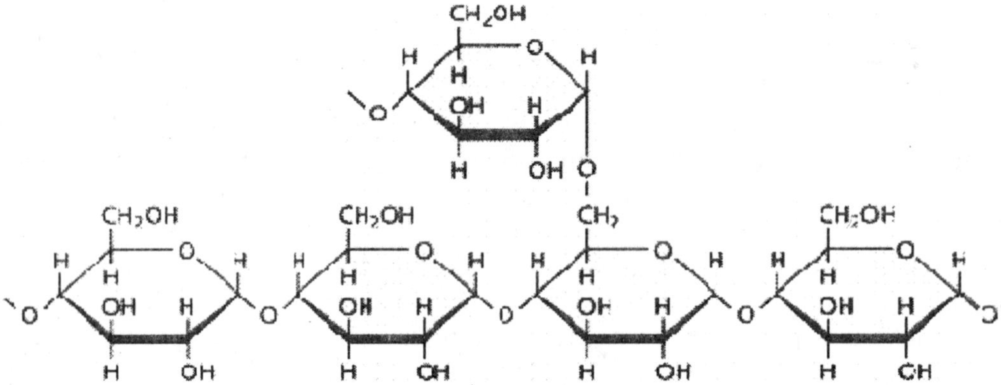

Starch

(i) α- Amylase: α-Amylase is an enzyme that hydrolyses alpha-bonds of large alpha-linked polysaccharides such as starch and glycogen, yielding glucose and maltose. It is the major form of amylase found in humans and other mammals. It is also present in seeds containing starch as a food reserve and is secreted by many fungi.

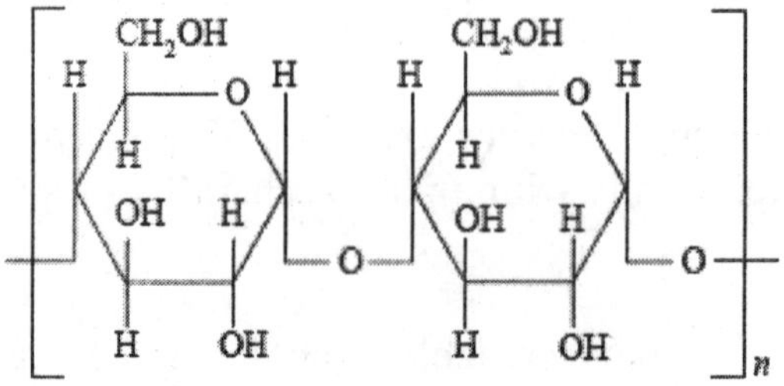

Amylase

(ii) Amylopectin: Amylopectin is a polysaccharide with a varying structure. It is composed of linearly linked alpha 1, 4- linked glucose units (coiled into tubular sections) with occasional alpha 1, 6- glycosidic bonds which provide branching points. Each amylopectin molecule may contain 100,000-200,000 glucose units and each branch is about 20 or 30 glucose units in length, so that these molecules are bushy and nearly spherical in shape.

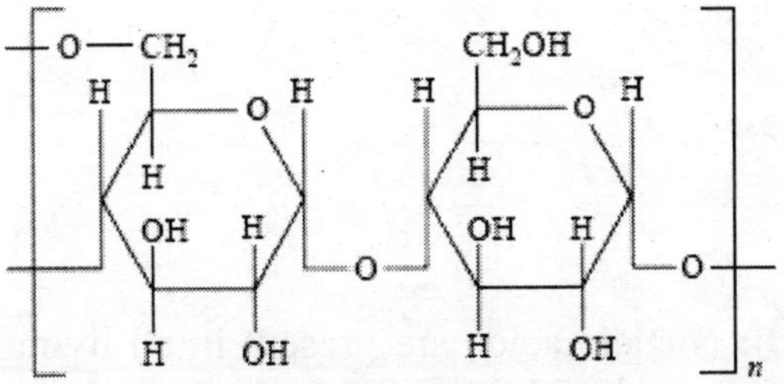

Amylopectin

Thermoplastic starch is unsuitable for packaging liquids. It can sustain only brief contact with water. It has good oxygen barrier properties.

Cellulose: It is the basic structural material of the cell walls of all higher land plants and of some sea weed. The main source of cellulose is cotton and wood. Cellulose is isolated from the plant cell wall and is never in a pure form in nature. It is also associated with lignin and hemi cellulose.

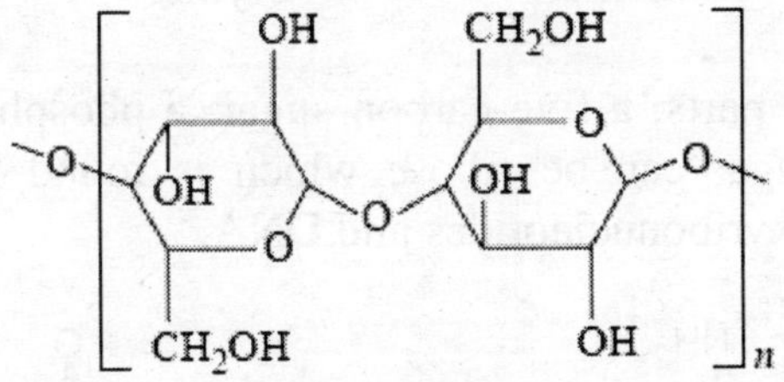

Cellulose

Sources

The use of cellulose for making packaging material such as cellophane is long established. The material is transparent and has good folding properties whereas in the form of pure cellulose or of a nitrocellulose coating, the material is wholly biodegradable and can be composted by existing waste processing plant.

Uses

Familiar applications of cellophane include packaging for CDS, confectionary and cigarettes. The material is gradually falling out of favour however, owing to its high price (about US$6 per kilogram) other cellulose polymer materials (e.g. cellulose film) have also been commercially available for many years but are losing market share to newer polymers such as polypropylene.

(b) **Polyamides (Proteins):** Proteins are natural polymer molecules consisting of amino acid units. The number of amino acids in proteins may range from two to several thousand. Proteins are polypeptides, which are made up of many amino acids linked together as a linear chain. The structure of an amino acid contains an amino group, a carboxyl group, and an R group which is usually carbon based and gives the amino acid.

Proteins occur in every part of plant and animal organisms and are the major constituent of skin, hair, blood, nails etc. In plants they are found in seeds. Proteins form the very basis of life. They regulate a variety of activities in all known organisms, from replication of the genetic code to transporting oxygen and are generally responsible for regulating the cellular machinery and determining the phenotype of an organism. Proteins accomplish their tasks in the body by three-dimensional tertiary and quaternary interactions between various substrates.

Proteins are classified by two types:
(i) Fibrous protein
(ii) Globular protein

(c) Polynucleotide (Nucleic acid): Nucleic acids are present in all living organisms like plants, animals or viruses. They are generally associated with proteins to form nucleoproteins. There are two types of nucleic acids.

1. DNA: Deoxyribose nucleic acid   2. RNA: Ribose nucleic acid
The nucleic acids are very large molecules that have two main parts. The backbone of a nucleic acid is made of alternating sugar and phosphate molecules bonded together in a long chain. DNA is a constituent of the nucleus and RNA present in the cytoplasm outside the nucleus. Nucleotide is a monomer unit of these bio-polymers.

Nucleotide → Poly nucleotide (Nucleic acid)
Monomer   Polymer

Nucleotides are composed of three parts: a five-carbon sugar, a phosphate and a nitrogen-rich structure called a nitrogenous base. The sugar can be ribose which is found in ribonucleotides and RNA or deoxyribose which is found in deoxyribonucleotides and DNA.

Adenie (A)   Guanine (G)

Purine bases (two rings)

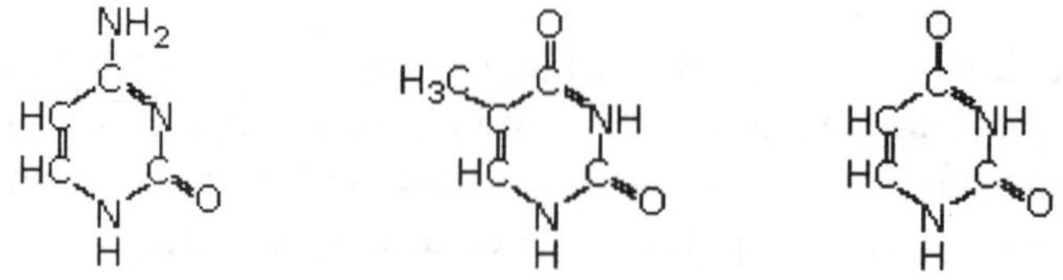

Cytosine (C)   Thymine (T)   Uracil(U)

Pyrimidine bases (one rings)

(d) Polyisoprene (Natural rubber): One of the most well known natural polymers is polyisoprene or natural rubber. Polyisoprene is diene polymer which is a polymer made from a monomer containing two carbon-carbon double bonds. Like most diene polymers it has a carbon-carbon double bond in its backbone chain. Polyisoprene can be harvested from the sap of the hevea tree, but it can also be made by Ziegler-Natta polymerization.

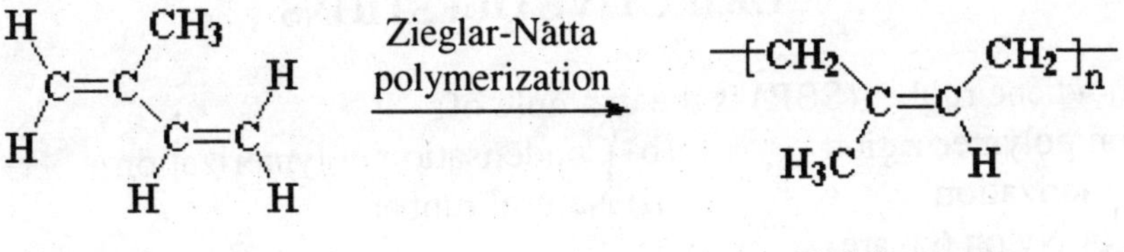

Isoprene Polyisoprene

Uses: cis-1,4-Polyisoprene is used in tyres and tyres products, foam rubber, rubber sheeting, rubber bands, hoses, gasket, belts, molded and mechanical goods, footwear and sporting goods, gloves, sealants, adhesives, bottle nipple, caulking and other typical elastomer application.

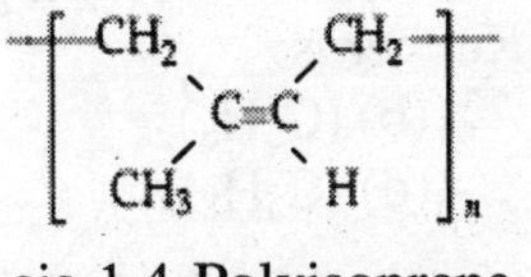

cis-1,4-Polyisoprene

trans-1,4-Polyisoprene: Gutta percha from Malaysia, balata from Brazil (Bolle tree); hard, crystalline, thermoplastic material.

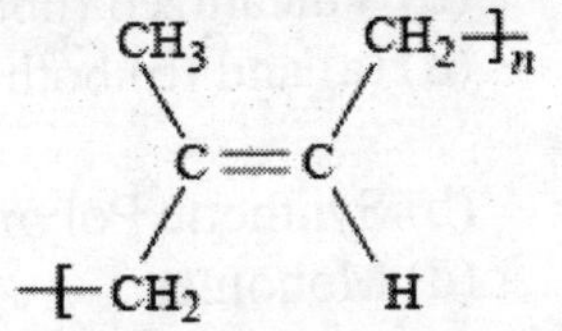

trans-1,4-Polyisoprene

Uses: It is mainly used mainly in high quality golf ball covers and orthopedic devices and splints, in transmission belts, cable coverings, adhesives in prosthetics braces, casts and attachments for artificial limbs.

Synthetic based biopolymers

Synthetic compounds derived from petroleum can also be a starting point for biodegradable polymers e.g. aliphatic aromatic co-polyesters. These polymers have technical properties resembling those of polyethylene (LDPE). Although these polymers are produced from synthetic starting materials, they are fully biodegradable and compostable. The relatively high price of biodegradable polymers of synthetic substances, e.g. aliphatic aromatic co-polyesters has prevented them from reaching a large scale market. The best known application is for making substrate mats.

Applications of Biopolymers: Polymers have properties that make them suitable for use in protecting products from moisture, increasing shelf-life and making products easier to dispense. Every biopolymer has its own material specific properties e.g. barrier properties such as oxygen permeability. The barrier properties are relevant to the choice of biopolymers for the packaging of particular products. Bio-plastics have very promising prospects for use in pesticide soil pins, for packaging in-flight catering products and for packaging dairy products.

OBJECTIVE QUESTIONS

1. Styrene- butadiene rubber (SBR) is the example of:
   (a) Addition polymerization (b) Condensation polymerization
   (c) Copolymerization (d) Natural rubber
2. Monomers of Nylon 6:6 are:
   (a) Adipic acid + Hexamethylene diamine (b) Adipic acid + Diaminobenzene
   (c) Caproic acid + Hexamethylene diamine (d) Anthranilic acid + Urea
3. A plastic which can be softened on heating and hardened on cooling is called:
   (a) Thermite (b) Thermoelastic
   (c) Thermoplastic (d) Thermosetting
4. The chemical formula of Natural Rubber is:
   (a) $(C_5H_8)_n$ (b) $(C_5H_8)_2$
   (c) $(C_5H_8)_3$ (d) $(C_5H_8)_8$
5. Nylon-6:6 is:
   (a) A polyester fiber (b) A polyamide fiber
   (c) A polyethylene derivative (d) None
6. Which of the following has cross- links?
   (a) Urea-formaldehyde resin (b) Vulcanized rubber
   (c) Buna-S (d) (a) and (b) both
7. BUNA- S is
   (a) Natural Polymer (b) Synthetic Polymer
   (c) Semi Synthetic Polymer (d) Monomer
8. Monomer of PTFE is
   (a) Cl_2 $CH\text{-}CH_3$ (b) $F_2C = CF_2$
   (c) $F_3C\text{-}CF_3$ (d) $FClC = CF_2$
9. Which type of polymer is Gutta – Percha?
   (a) Natural Rubber (b) Synthetic Rubber
   (c) Polythene (d) Bakelite
10. The intermolecular forces between chains in Nylon 66 are
    (a) H- bond (b) Ionic bond
    (c) Covalent bond (d) All of above
11. Nylon 66 is which type of polymer?
    (a) Homopolymer (b) Copolymer
    (c) Addition polymer (d) None of above
12. Nylon -66 is a polyamide of:
    (a) Vinyl chloride & Formaldehyde (b) Adipic acid & Methyl amide
    (c) Adipic acid & Hexamethylene diamine (d) Formaldehyde & Urea
13. Which of the following is a condensation polymer?
    (a) Polystyrene (b) Neoprene
    (c) PAN (d) Nylon-66
14. Monomer of PVC is
    (a) Monochloro Ethene (b) Ethyne
    (c) Mono chloro ethane (d) Propane
15. Which is a copolymer?
    (a) Polypropylene (b) Nylon 66
    (c) PVC (d) PTFE
16. Which type of polymer has strongest intermolecular forces?

(a) Fibers (b) Elastomers
(c) Plastic (d) None of above

17. Caprolactum is starting material of
(a) Nylon – 6 (b) Styrene
(c) Terelene (d) Bakelite

18. Which of the following is a natural fiber?
(a) Starch (b) Cellulose
(c) Rubber (d) Nylon 6

19. Natural rubber is a polymer of
(a) Styrene (b) 1, 3 butadiene
(c) TFE (d) 2 methyl 1, 3 butadiene

20. Which of the following is used in bullet proof glass?
(a) PMMA (b) Lexan
(c) Nomex (d) Revlar

21. Soft drink bottles are made up of
(a) Polyester (b) Polyurea
(c) Polystyrene (d) Glyptal

22. Nylon is a
(a) Polyester (b) Polyamide
(c) Polyurea (d) None of above

23. Perlon is
(a) Rubber (b) Nylon
(c) Terelene (d) Oxlon

24. Glyptal is obtained by treating glycerol with
(a) Malonic acid (b) Phthalic anhydride
(c) Maleic acid (d) Acetic acid

25. Which is not a polymer?
(a) DNA (b) Starch
(c) Insulin (d) Sodium Palmitate

26. Which is biodegradable polymer?
(a) Nylon (b) Polyethene
(c) Polystyrene (d) PHBv

27. Which is monomer of Plexiglass?
a) TFE (b) MMA
(c) $CF_2= CF_2$ (d) $CH_2= CH_2$

28. Rubber is vulcanized by adding:
(a) S (b) N_2
(c) O_2 (d) C

29. Which polymer is used for manufacture of unbreakable cups?
(a) Bakelite (b) Nylon 6
(c) Nylon-66 (d) Melamine –Formaldehyde resin

30. Gutta-Percha is:
(a) Trans Polymer of Isoprene (b) Buna – S
(c) Branch Chain Polymer (d) Thermo setting polymer

31. Those polymer during molding get hardened and once they have solidified, they cannot be softened, they are:

(a) Thermoplastic (b) Thermosetting
(c) Elastomer (d) Fibers

32. If the arrangement of functional group is at random around the main chain, then it is
(a) Isotactic polymer (b) Syndiotactic polymer
(c) Atatic polymer (d) None of these

33. Thermoplastic polymers are formed by
(a) Addition polymerization (b) Condensation polymerization
(c) Both of the above (d) None of the above

34. Gutta – Percha is
(a) Atactic polymer (b) Isotactic polymer
(c) Syndiotactic polymer (d) None of the above.

35. Polypropylene is obtained by polymerizing propylene in presence of:
(a) Ziegler – Natta (b) TEL
(c) Diethylteluride (d) None of the above

36. Plastics insoluble in any solvent are
(a) Thermite (b) Thermosets
(c) Thermoplastic (d) Thermoelastics

37. Polymer having medical applications is:
(a) Polyethene (b) Polypropylene
(c) Polystyrene (d) Polymethylmethacrylate

38. A resin which is obtained by the reaction of urea or melamine with formaldehyde is
(a) Amino Resin (b) Bakelite
(c) Phenolic Resin (d) None of these

39. The process used to obtain latex is:
(a) Drilling (b) Tapping
(c) Riveting (d) None

40. Latex is a milky
(a) Solution (b) Colloid
(c) Solid (d) Suspension

Answer Key

1)c	2)a	3)c	4)a	5)b	6)d	7)b	8)b	9)a	10)c	11)b	12)c	13)d	14)a
15)b	16)a	17)a	18)b	19)d	20)b	21)c	22)b	23)b	24)b	25)d	26)d	27)b	28)a
29)d	30)a	31)b	32)c	33)a	34)c	35)a	36)b	37)d	38)a	39)b	40)b		

THEORETICAL QUESTIONS

1. What is condensation polymerization? Explain with example. **[RGPV 07]**
2. Describe in brief the free radical mechanism of polymerization. **[RGPV 07]**
3. Give preparation and uses of the following: **[RGPV 07]**
   Neoprene and PVC
4. Differentiate between Thermoplastic and Thermosetting resin. **[RGPV 07]**
5. Give preparation and uses of Bakelite. **[RGPV 07]**
6. What are amide resins? Explain with example. **[RGPV 07]**
7. Explain mechanism of addition polymerization. **[RGPV 07, 08]**
8. Write preparation, properties and uses of the following: **[RGPV 07]**

(1) Nylon-66
(2) Buna-N
(3) Bakelite
(4) Vulcanized rubber

9. Discuss in brief silicon resins. **[RGPV 07]**
10. Write preparation, properties and uses of the following: **[RGPV 07]**
(1) Nylon-6
(2) Butyl-rubber
(3) Epoxy-resins
(4) PMMA
11. Mention two important types of synthetic rubbers and discuss their synthesis, properties and application. **[RGPV 05]**
12. What are nylons? How is nylon 66 manufactured? Give flow sheet and state some important uses.
13. Discuss the various constituents of plastics and their functions. **[RGPV 05]**
14. Discuss the preparation, properties and uses of the following (any three):
(i) Polystyrene (ii) Buna-N (iii) Plexiglass (iv) Neoprene **[RGPV 07]**
15. Discuss the manufacture of Nylon 66 with flow sheet. **[RGPV 03, 07]**
16. Write short note on vulcanization of rubber. **[RGPV 03, 08]**
17. Define and explain giving at least two examples, the following terms: **[RGPV 07, 08]**
(i) Addition polymerization
(ii) Condensation polymerization
(iii) Copolymerization
18. Describe free radical mechanism of polymerization. **[RGPV 02]**
19. Write short notes on any four of the following: **[RGPV 02]**
(i) Bakelite (ii) Nylon 66 (iii) PVC (iv) Buna-s (v) neoprene
(vi) Polymethyl methacrylate (vii) Natural rubber (viii) Nitrile rubber
20. How is neoprene prepared? Mention its properties and uses.
21. What are silicones? Draw the structure of siloxane polymer obtained by hydrolysing dichlorodimethyl silane. **[RGPV 01]**
22. Discuss the manufacture with flow sheet diagram of the following (any two)
(i) Polyvinyl chloride (PVC) (ii) Nylon 66 (iii) Dacron (or Terylene)
23. Explain why natural rubber needs vulcanization? How is it carried out? **[RGPV 01, 07]**
24. Discuss in brief: (i) Neoprene (ii) Polyurethane (iii) linear branched and cross-linked polymers **[RGPV 01, 07]**
25. Write short answers on the following: **[RGPV 08]**
(i) What is an elastomer?
(ii) Natural rubber needs vulcanization, why?
(iii) GR-S is an example of: (a) Condensation (b) Copolymerization (c) Cross liked polymers (d) Addition polymerization.
26. Write short note on: **[RGPV 01, 07]**
(i) Thermosetting plastics with examples.
(ii) Silicon resin.
27. What is gutta percha? How is it different from Hevea and Guayule rubber? **[RGPV 01]**
28. Name the chemical process which is employed to improve the mechanical strength of natural rubber polymerization.
29. Describe free radical polymerization. **[RGPV 04]**
30. Give flow sheet for producing silicones by Grignard's method.
31. Write short note on P.V.C. **[RGPV 04]**

32. Distinguish between the following:
    i) Mechanism of ionic and radial polymerization.
    ii) Natural and synthetic rubber. **[RGPV 07]**
33. Write preparation, properties & uses of HDPE. **[RGPV 07]**
34. What is Vulcanization? Write the structural changes that takes place due to vulcanization. Give applications of vulcanization. **[RGPV 08]**
35. Write the structure of four addition polymers and four condensation polymer with their respective monomers. **[RGPV 08]**
36. Explain why:
    i) Bakelite is used in electrical appliances?
    ii) PVC is tougher and stronger than polyethylene? **[RGPV 08]**
37. What are polymers? Classify polymers on the basis of different parameters giving suitable examples? **[RGPV 08]**

........*........

Unit – V

Spectroscopy

[A] INSTRUMENTAL TECHNIQUES IN CHEMICAL ANALYSIS

5.1 SPECTROSCOPY

Spectroscopy is the study of the interaction between radiation (electromagnetic radiation, or light, as well as particle radiation) and matter. Spectrometry is the measurement of these interactions and an instrument which performs such measurements is a spectrometer or spectrograph. A plot of the interaction is referred to as a spectrogram, or, informally, a spectrum. Historically spectroscopy was referred to a branch of science in which visible light was used for the theoretical study of the structure of matter and for qualitative and quantitative analysis. Recently, however, the definition has broadened as new techniques have been developed that utilise not only visible light, but many other forms of radiation.

Spectroscopy is a general methodology that can be adopted in many ways to extract the information we need (energies of electronic, vibrational, rotational state, structure and symmetry of molecule, dynamic information). Spectroscopy is the most powerful tool available for the study of atomic and molecular structure and is used in the analysis of a wide range of the samples. The study of spectroscopy is carried out under following headings:

(1) **Atomic spectroscopy:** It is concerned with interaction of electromagnetic radiations with atoms which are commonly in their lowest energy state called the ground state.

(2) **Molecular spectroscopy:** It deals with the interaction of electromagnetic radiation with molecules. This results in transition between rotational and vibrational energy levels in addition to electronic transition.

The spectroscopic method is used in the elucidation of structure of organic compounds. It is advantageous over other conventional methods because of following reasons:

- The method is used to find the spectra of the organic compound.
- Very small amounts (mg or less) of the organic compounds are required for the determination of spectra and even this amount is recovered without any change at the end of the experiment.
- The method is very sensitive and the results obtained are very accurate and reliable.

Electromagnetic radiation consists of waves of energy whose parameters are.

(1) Wavelength (λ): It is the distance between adjacent peaks (or troughs) and may be designated in meters, centimeters or nanometers (10^{-9} meters).

(2) Wave number ($\acute{\upsilon}$): It is the number of wave cycles that travel past a fixed point per unit of time and is usually given in cycles per second, or hertz (Hz).

(3) Frequency (υ): It is the number of waves per second. It is expressed in cycles per second or hertz. These three quantities are related as:

$$1/\lambda = \acute{\upsilon} = \upsilon/c, \qquad \text{where } c = \text{velocity of light}$$

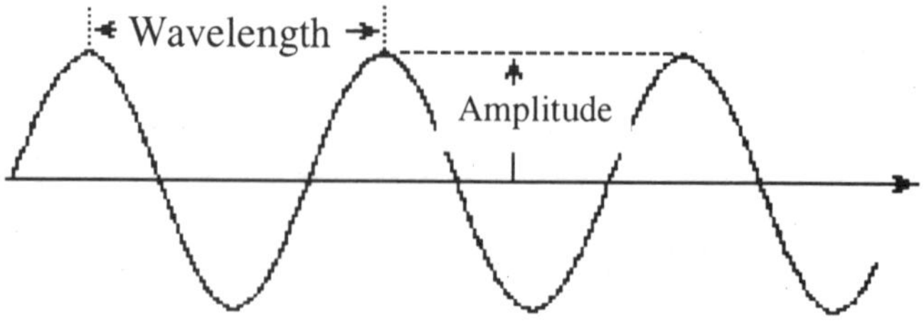

Fig: 5.1 Wave Motion

5.2 ELECTROMAGNETIC SPECTRUM

The electromagnetic (EM) spectrum gives the information about the radiation. Radiation is energy that travels and spreads out as it goes-- visible light that comes from a lamp in our house and radio waves that come from a radio station.Other examples of EM radiation are microwaves, infrared and ultraviolet light, X-rays and gamma-rays. Hotter objects create higher energy radiation than cool objects. Only extremely hot objects or particles moving at very high velocities can create high-energy radiation like X-rays and gamma-rays.

Electromagnetic radiation can be described in terms of a stream of photons which are massless particles each traveling in a wave-like pattern and moving at the speed of light. Each photon contains a certain amount (or bundle) of energy and all electromagnetic radiation consists of these photons. The only difference between the various types of electromagnetic radiation is the amount of energy found in the photons. Radio waves have photons with low energies, microwaves have a little more energy than radio waves, infrared has still more, then visible, ultraviolet, X-rays and the most energetic of all is gamma-rays. Actually, the electromagnetic spectrum can be expressed in terms of energy, wavelength, or frequency Since electromagnetic radiation is a form of energy, its absorption by a molecule leads to an increase in its internal energy.

The electromagnetic radiation contains radiation of different wavelength possessing different energy therefore when a molecule is exposed to an electromagnetic energy, it does not absorb all the radiation, only a particular portion of the radiation is absorbed depending upon the structure of the molecule. The amount of absorption of energy also depends upon the frequency of the radiation.

Thus it is clear that molecules depending upon their structure absorb different types of excitation. The absorption of energy of some radiation results in electronic excitation, i.e. the electron moves from one energy level to another level, some energy absorption may produce vibrational excitation and some may produce rotational excitation. Depending upon the type of energy absorption, different spectra are obtained.

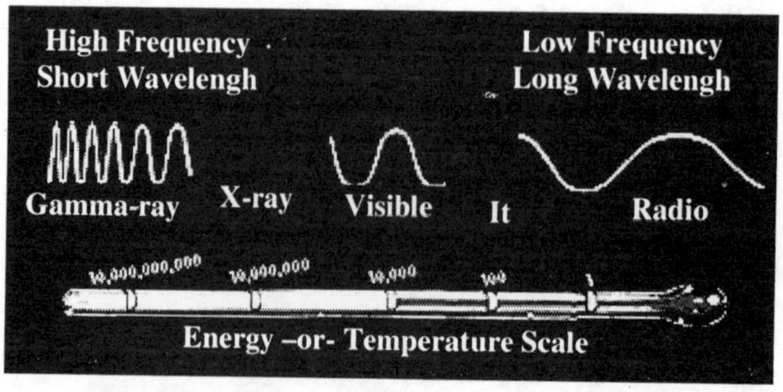

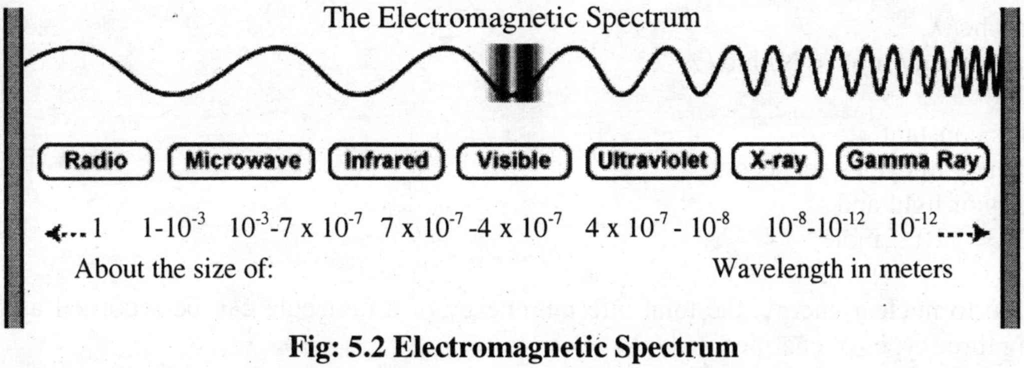

Fig: 5.2 Electromagnetic Spectrum

5.3 ORIGIN OF ELECTRONIC SPECTRA

Emission Spectra: When a substance is subjected to intense heat or an electric discharge is passed through it, its atoms or molecules absorb energy (energized photons) and get excited. When these excited atoms or molecules return to their ground state, they emit radiations which when passed through a prism give rise to a spectrum. This spectrum is known as emission spectrum.

When this type of spectrum is recorded on a photographic plate, then bright lines are obtained on the black background in the case of atoms and bands are obtained in the case of molecules. Similarly, when white light is passed through a prism, a continuous spectrum made up of seven colours is obtained. Sodium light gives a line spectrum having two D-lines (Yellow) of a definite wavelength.

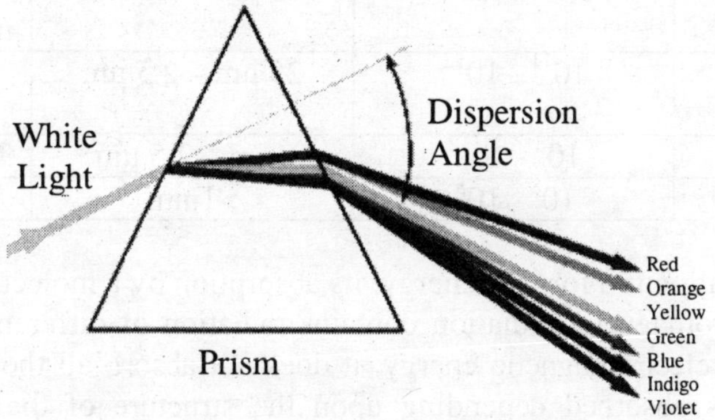

Fig: 5.3 Dispersion of White Light

Absorption Spectrum: When white light is passed through a prism, a spectrum consisting of seven colours is obtained but when white light is passed through a sodium flame before reaching the prism, a continuous spectrum with two black lines in place of yellow lines is obtained from sodium flame. Here sodium flame absorb two wavelengths from white light which itself emits. This type of spectrum is known as absorption spectrum.Such spectrum contains black (dark) lines or bands on lighted background because some radiations are absorbed by the medium.

The phenomenon can be understood by the following principle:

When rays of light or electromagnetic radiations (which are source of energy) are passed through a substance, the molecules falling in the path of the incident light absorb some energy (in the form of photons) of the light due to which the spectrum of the remaining radiations or light is found to contain black lines or bands in it. In this process only those photons are absorbed whose energy is equal to the energy difference (ΔE) between two energy levels of the molecule of the substance.

$\Delta E = h\nu = hc/\lambda$
Energy absorbed / mole = $N_A h c / \lambda$
where
h= plank's constant
ν = frequency in cycles per second
c= velocity of light and
$N_A = 6.023 \times 10^{23}$ $mole^{-1}$

In addition to nuclear energy, the total internal energy of a molecule can be recorded as the sum of following three types of energies.

$E = E_{ele} + E_{vib} + E_{Rotational}$

Table 1: Electromagnetic spectrum

Types of Radiation	Frequency range (Hz)	Wavelength range	Types of transition
Gamma- rays	$10^{20} - 10^{24}$	$<10^{12}$ m	Nuclear
X-rays	$10^{17} - 10^{20}$	1 nm – 1 pm	Inner electron
Ultraviolet	$10^{15} - 10^{17}$	400nm – 1 nm	Outer electron
Visible	$4 - 7.5 \times 10^{14}$	750nm – 400nm	Outer electron
Near- infrared	$10^{12} - 4 \times 10^{14}$	25 μm - 750 μm	Outer electron molecular vibrations
Infrared	$10^{11} - 10^{12}$	25 μm – 2.5 μm	Molecular vibrations
Microwaves	$10^{8} - 10^{12}$	1nm – 2.5 μm	Molecular rotations
Radio waves	$10^{8} - 10^{8}$	>1mm	Nuclear spin flips*

Since electromagnetic radiation is a form of energy, its absorption by a molecule leads to an increase in its internal energy. The electromagnetic radiation contains radiation of different energy, therefore when a molecule is exposed to an electromagnetic energy, it does not absorb all the radiation, only a particular portion of the radiation is absorbed depending upon the structure of the molecule. The amount of absorption of energy depends upon the frequency of the radiation also.

Thus it is clear that molecules, depending upon their structure absorb different types of radiation, possessing different energy and therefore undergo different types of excitations. The absorption of energy of some radiation results in electronic excitation. Depending upon the type of energy absorption, different spectra are obtained.

5.4 UV SPECTROSCOPY

Introduction: UV-visible spectroscopy is the measurement of the wavelength and intensity of absorption of near-ultraviolet and visible light by a sample. Ultraviolet and visible light are energetic enough to promote outer electrons to higher energy levels. UV-visible spectroscopy is usually applied to molecules and inorganic ions or complexes in solution. The uv-visible spectra have broad features that are of limited use for sample identification but are very useful for quantitative measurements. The concentration of an analyte in solution can be determined by measuring the absorbance at some wavelength and applying the Beer-Lambert Law.

$$A = \epsilon Cl$$

When electromagnetic radiation of UV region (λ= 200-400 nm) or visible region (λ= 400-800 nm) is passed through a compound containing a multiple bond, a part of the incident radiation is absorbed by the compound. The amount of absorbed radiation energy depends upon the nature of the compound and wave length of the radiation. The energy of absorbed radiation promotes electron from the lower energy level to higher energy level. The organic compound may undergo $\sigma \rightarrow \sigma^*$, $n \rightarrow \sigma^*$, $n \rightarrow \pi^*$, $\pi \rightarrow \pi^*$ transitions. The amount of radiation of UV and visible region absorbed is measured by spectrophotometer.

Instrumentation

Source of Radiation: The tungsten filament incident lamp is commonly used as a spectrophotometeric source through the visible region and adjacent parts of the ultraviolet and infra red region. (approx 320 nm to 3.5 μm). For the ultraviolet, hydrogen or deuterium discharge lamps are generally used. They are useful from about 160- 360 nm. Continuously spectrum in the ultraviolet region is conveniently produced by the excitation of hydrogen at low pressure with an electric discharge.

Monochrometers: Monochrometers for radiant energy of the ultra violet region have no glass optics, so either prisms, quartz or fused silica must be used as the dispersive device.

Detector: The photomultiplier tube is most widely used detector in the ultraviolet spectroscopy. It consists of a cathode to which a thin layer of selected semi conductive material containing alkali metal such as CS_3Sb, K_2CSSb and Na_2KSb with a trace of Cs is deposited.

Sample and reference compartments: Only double beam instruments have a reference compartment, the high stability of modern light sources coupled with rapid measurement systems permits many high quality instruments to incorporate a single beam optical system without significantly sacrificing measurement stability and the additional expense of the double beam optics system. A well designed cell compartment has a highly collimated light beam traversing the cell holder. To reduce reflective light losses and multiple reflection errors, the cell holder should position the cell in such a way that both faces are at right angles to the incident and exciting light beams.

Detector: Either photoelectric detector or photo- voltaic detectors can be used. These days these detectors have been largely replaced by the photomultiplier and certain solid state detectors.

Output and Data Processing: Such devices can be an analog absorbance or transmittance meter or logic circuitry. Now-a-days microprocessor is incorporated in the spectrometers for control and monitoring of the operations.

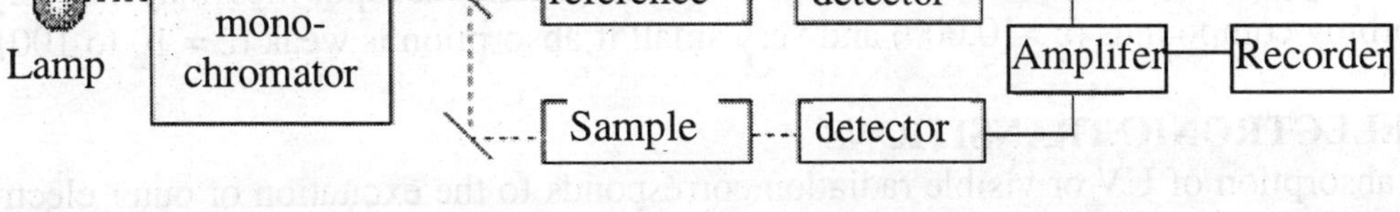

Fig 5.4: Scheme of a Dual-Beam UV-Visible Spectrophotometer

Working of UV-Visible Spectrophotometer: A diagram of the components of a typical spectrometer is shown in fig 5.5. The functioning of this instrument is relatively straightforward. A beam of light from a visible and/or UV light source is separated into its component wavelengths by a prism or diffraction grating. Each monochromatic (single wavelength) beam in turn is split into two equal intensity beams by a half-mirrored device. The sample beam passes through a small transparent container (cuvette) containing a solution of the compound being studied in a transparent solvent. The other beam, the reference, passes through an identical cuvette containing only the solvent. The intensities of these light beams are then measured by electronic detectors and then compared. The intensity of the reference beam, which should have suffered little or no light absorption, is defined as I_0. The intensity of the sample beam is defined as I. Over a short period of time, the spectrometer automatically scans all the component wavelengths in the manner described. The ultraviolet (UV) region scanned is normally from 200 to 400 nm and the visible portion is from 400 to 800 nm.

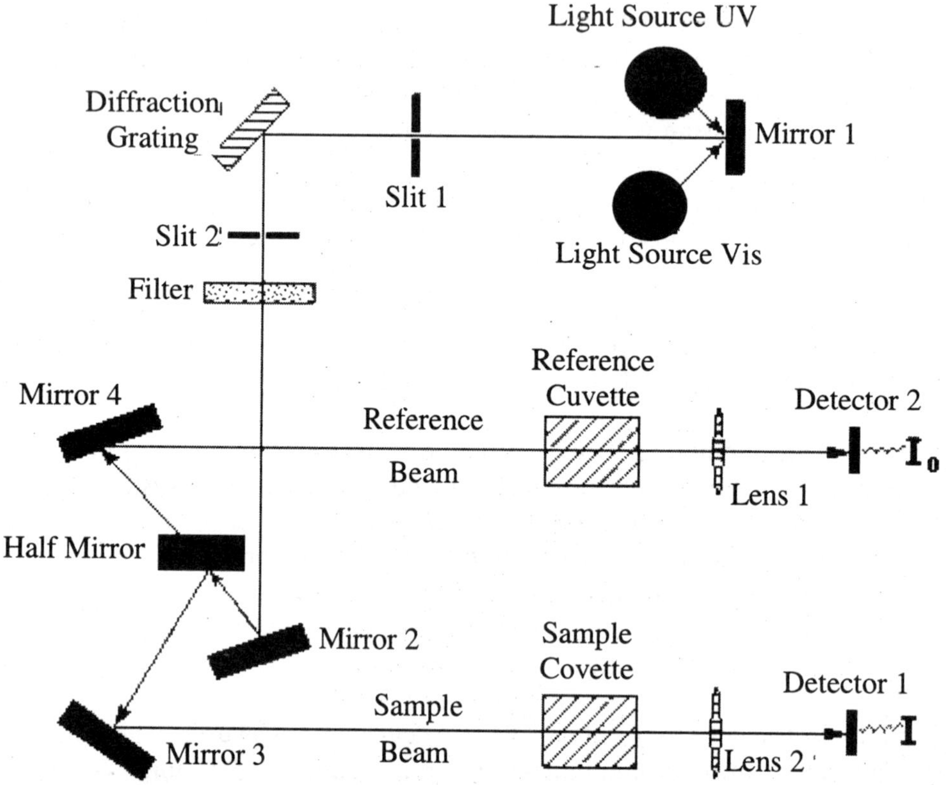

Fig. 5.5 : UV Spectrometer

For the spectrum, a solution of 0.249 mg of the unsaturated aldehyde in 95% ethanol was placed in a 1 cm cuvette for measuement. Using the above formula, we get ε = 36,600 for the 395 nm peak and 14,000 for the 255 nm peak. Note that the absorption extends into the visible region of the spectrum, so it is not surprising that this compound is orange coloured. Molar absoptivities may be very large for strongly absorbing compounds (ε >10,000) and very small if absorption is weak (ε = 10 to 100).

5.5 ELECTRONIC TRANSITIONS

The absorption of UV or visible radiation corresponds to the excitation of outer electrons. There are three types of electronic transition which can be considered:

1. Transitions involving π, σ and *n* electrons
2. Transitions involving charge-transfer electrons
3. Transitions involving *d* and *f* electrons (not covered in this unit)

When an atom or molecule absorbs energy, electrons are promoted from their ground state to an excited state. In a molecule, the atoms can rotate and vibrate with respect to each other. These vibrations and rotations also have discrete energy levels which can be considered as being packed on top of each electronic level.

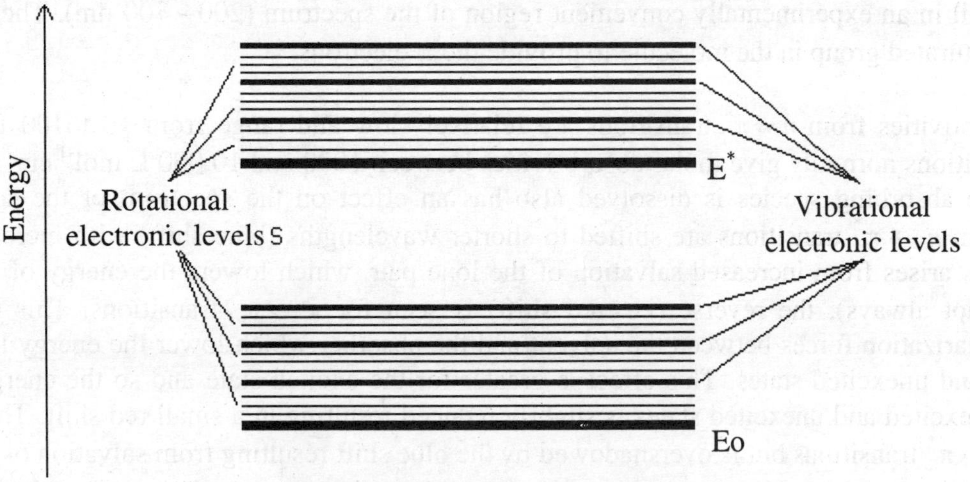

Fig 5.6: Electronic Transitions

Absorbing species containing π, σ, and *n* electrons: Absorption of ultraviolet and visible radiation in organic molecules is restricted to certain functional groups (*chromophores*) that contain valence electrons of low excitation energy. The spectrum of a molecule containing these chromophores is complex. This is because the superposition of rotational and vibrational transitions on the electronic transitions gives a combination of overlapping lines. This appears as a continuous absorption band.

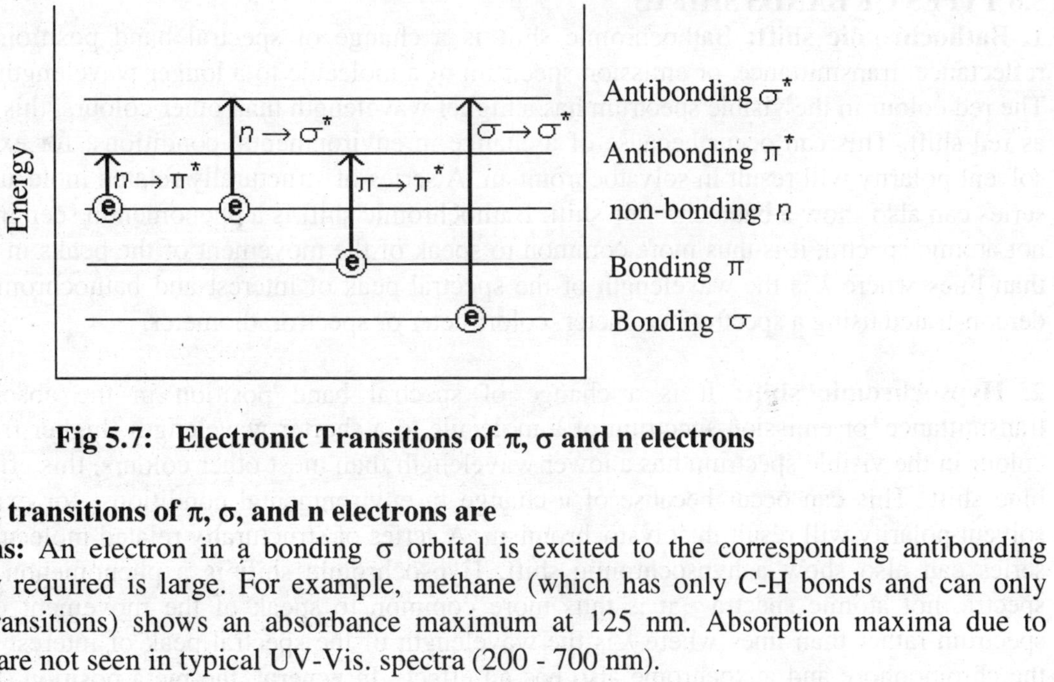

Fig 5.7: Electronic Transitions of π, σ and n electrons

Possible electronic transitions of π, σ, and n electrons are

$\sigma \rightarrow \sigma^*$ Transitions: An electron in a bonding σ orbital is excited to the corresponding antibonding orbital. The energy required is large. For example, methane (which has only C-H bonds and can only undergo $\sigma \rightarrow \sigma^*$ transitions) shows an absorbance maximum at 125 nm. Absorption maxima due to $\sigma \rightarrow \sigma^*$ transitions are not seen in typical UV-Vis. spectra (200 - 700 nm).

$n \rightarrow \sigma^*$ Transitions: Saturated compounds containing atoms with lone pairs (non-bonding electrons) are capable of $n \rightarrow \sigma^*$ transitions. These transitions usually need less energy than $\sigma \rightarrow \sigma^*$ transitions. They can be initiated by light whose wavelength is in the range of 150 - 250 nm. The number of organic functional groups with $n \rightarrow \sigma^*$ peaks in the UV region is small.

$n \rightarrow \pi^*$ and $\pi \rightarrow \pi^*$ Transitions: Most absorption spectroscopy of organic compounds is based on transitions of n or π electrons to the π^* excited state. This is because the absorption peaks for these transitions fall in an experimentally convenient region of the spectrum (200 - 700 nm). These transitions need an unsaturated group in the molecule to provide the π electrons.

Molar absorbtivities from $n \rightarrow \pi^*$ transitions are relatively low and range from 10 to100 L mol^{-1} cm^{-1}. $\pi \rightarrow \pi^*$ transitions normally give molar absorbtivities between 1000 and 10,000 L mol^{-1} cm^{-1}. The solvent in which the absorbing species is dissolved also has an effect on the spectrum of the species. Peaks resulting from $n \rightarrow \pi^*$ transitions arc shifted to shorter wavelengths (blue shift) with increasing solvent polarity. This arises from increased salvation of the lone pair, which lowers the energy of the n orbital. Often (but not always), the reverse (i.e. red shift) is seen for $\pi \rightarrow \pi^*$ transitions. This is caused by attractive polarization forces between the solvent and the absorber which lower the energy levels of both the excited and unexcited states. This effect is greater for the excited state and so the energy difference between the excited and unexcited states is slightly reduced resulting in a small red shift. This effect also influences $n \rightarrow \pi^*$ transitions but is overshadowed by the blue shift resulting from salvation of lone pairs.

Charge Transfer Absorption: Many inorganic species show charge-transfer absorption and are called charge-transfer complexes. For a complex to demonstrate charge-transfer behaviour one of its components must have electron donating properties and another component must be able to accept electrons. Absorption of radiation then involves the transfer of an electron from the donor to an orbital associated with the acceptor. Molar absorbtivities from charge-transfer absorption are large (greater that 10,000 L mol^{-1} cm-1).

5.6 TYPES OF BANDS SHIFTS

1. Bathochromic shift: Bathochromic shift is a change of spectral band position in the absorption, reflectance, transmittance, or emission spectrum of a molecule to a longer wavelength (lower frequency). The red colour in the visible spectrum has a higher wavelength than other colours, this effect is also called as red shift. This can occur because of a change in environmental conditions: for example, a change in solvent polarity will result in solvatochromism. A series of structurally related molecules in a substitution series can also show a bathochromic shift. Bathochromic shift is a phenomenon seen in molecular spectra, not atomic spectra, it is thus more common to speak of the movement of the peaks in the spectrum rather than lines where λ is the wavelength of the spectral peak of interest and bathochromic shift is typically demonstrated using a spectrophotometer, colorimeter or spectroradiometer.

2. Hypsochromic shift: It is a change of spectral band position in the absorption, reflectance, transmittance, or emission spectrum of a molecule to a shorter wavelength (higher frequency). The blue colour in the visible spectrum has a lower wavelength than most other colours, this effect is also called as blue shift. This can occur because of a change in environmental conditions: for example, a change in solvent polarity will result in solvatochromism. A series of structurally related molecules in a substitution series can also show a hypsochromic shift. Hypsochromic shift is a phenomenon seen in molecular spectra, not atomic spectra - it is thus more common to speak of the movement of the peaks in the spectrum rather than lines where λ is the wavelength of the spectral peak of interest and the position of the chromophore and auxochrome also has an effect. In general, the meta position (M) has the shortest wavelength and the para (P) and ortho (O) absorption wavelengths are approximately equal and longer than meta. Again this is due to resonance forms.

3. Hyperchromic shift: If the presence of group increases the intensity of band, it is known as hyperchromic shift.

4. Hypochromic shift: If the presence of group decreases the intensity of band, it is known as hypochromic shift.

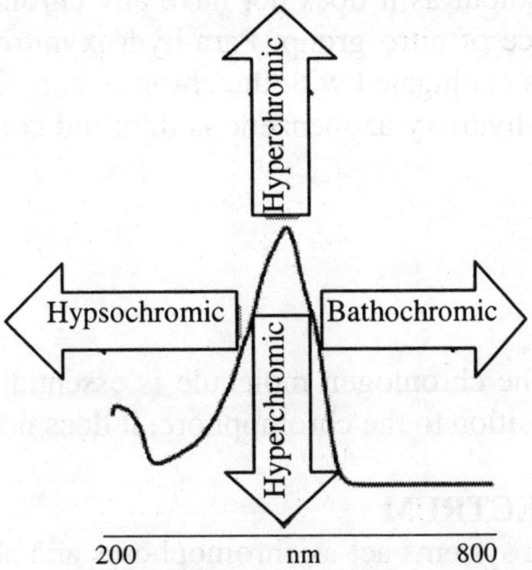

Fig 5.8: Diagram of Band Shift

Table 5.2: Terminology for Absorption Shifts

Nature of Shift	Descriptive Term
To Longer Wavelength	Bathochromic
To Shorter Wavelength	Hypsochromic
To Greater Absorbance	Hyperchromic
To Lower Absorbance	Hypochromic

Chromophores: Chromophore is a part of a molecule responsible for its colour. When a molecule absorbs certain wavelengths of visible light and transmits or reflects others, the molecule has a colour. A chromophore is a region in a molecule where the energy difference between two different molecular orbitals falls within the range of the visible spectrum. Visible light that hits the chromophore can thus be absorbed by exciting an electron from its ground state into an excited state. In biological molecules that serve to capture or detect light energy, the chromophore is the part that causes a conformational change of the molecule when hit by light. Chromophores always arise in one of two forms: conjugated pi systems and metal complexes. In the former, the energy levels that the electrons jump between are extended pi orbitals created by a series of alternating single and double bonds, often in aromatic systems. Common examples include retinal (used in the eye to detect light), various food colourings, fabric dyes (azo compounds), lycopene, β-carotene and anthocyanins.

The metal complex chromophores arise from the splitting of d-orbitals by binding of a transition metal to ligands. Examples of such chromophores can be seen in chlorophyll (used by plants for photosynthesis), hemoglobin, hemocyanin and colourful minerals such as malachite and amethyst.

Auxochrome: This is a group of atoms attached to a chromophore which modifies the ability of that chromophore to absorb light. Example: -OH , - NH_2 , Aldehydes. An auxochrome is a functional group of atoms with nonbonded electrons which, when attached to a chromophore, alters both the wavelength and intensity of absorption. If these groups are in direct conjugation with the pi-system of the chromophore, they may increase the wavelength at which the light is absorbed and as a result intensify the absorption. A feature of these auxochromes is the presence of at least one lone pair of electrons which can be viewed as extending the conjugated system by resonance. It increases the colour of any organic compound. For example, benzene does not display colour as it does not have any chromophore but nitrobenzene is pale yellow colour because of the presence of nitro group. Para-hydroxynitrobenzene exhibits a deep yellow colour. Here an auxochrome (-OH) is conjugated with the chromophore $-NO_2$. Similar behaviour happens in azo benzene (red colour) but para-hydroxy azobenzene is dark red colour. There are mainly two types of auxochromes

(1) Acidic -COOH, -OH, $-SO_3H$
(2) Basic -NHR, $-NR_2$, $-NH_2$

The presence of an auxochrome in the chromogen molecule is essential to make a dye. However, if an auxochrome is present in the meta position to the chromophore, it does not affect the colour.

EXAMPLES OF UV-VISIBLE SPECTRUM

Many kinds of conjugated pi-electron systems act as chromophores and absorb light in the 200 to 800 nm region. These include unsaturated aldehydes and ketones and aromatic ring compounds. The spectrum of the unsaturated ketone illustrates the advantage of a logarithmic display of molar absorptivity. The $\pi \rightarrow \pi^*$ absorption located at 242 nm is very strong with $\varepsilon = 18,000$. The weak $n \rightarrow \pi^*$ absorption near 300 nm has $\varepsilon = 100$.

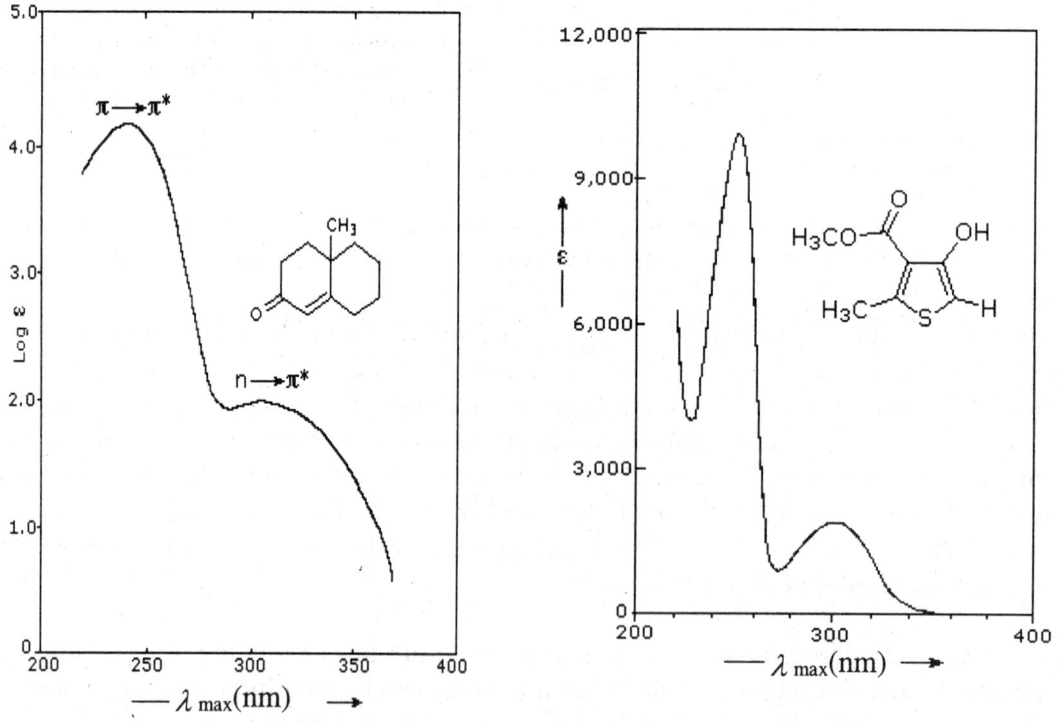

Fig 5.9: Spectrum of Unsaturated Ketones

Benzene exhibits very strong light absorption near 180 nm ($\varepsilon > 65,000$), weaker absorption at 200 nm ($\varepsilon = 8,000$) and a group of much weaker bands at 254 nm ($\varepsilon = 240$). Only the last groups of absorptions are completely shown because of the 200 nm cut-off characteristic of most of the spectrophotometers. The added conjugation in naphthalene, anthracene and tetracene causes bathochromic shifts of these absorption bands, as shown in the fig 5.10.

The spectrum of the bicyclic diene shows some vibrational fine structure, but in general is similar in appearance to that of isoprene. Closer inspection discloses that the absorption maximum of the more highly substituted diene has moved to a longer wavelength by about 15 nm. This "substituent effect" is general for dienes and trienes and is even more pronounced for enone chromophores.

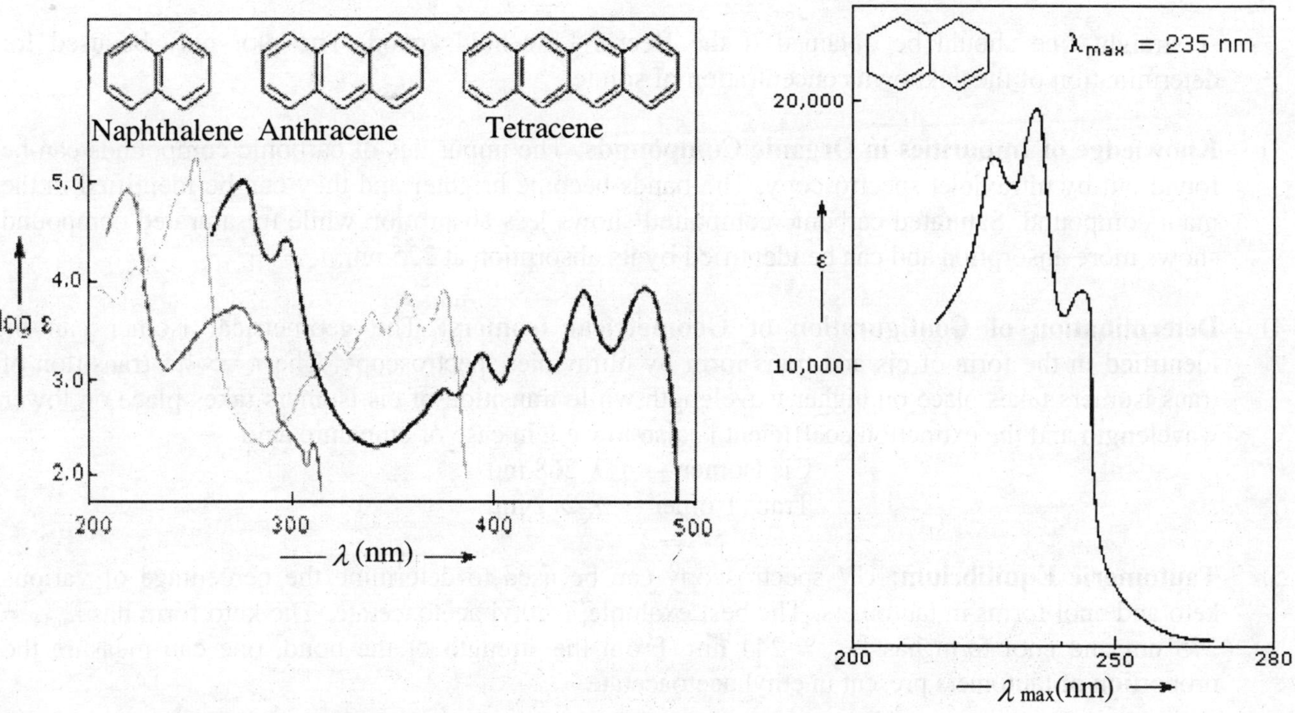

Fig 5.10: UV-Visible Spectra of Some Aromatic Compounds

5.7 APPLICATIONS OF ULTRAVIOLET SPECTROSCOPY

1) **Qualitative Analysis**: Ultraviolet spectroscopy is used for characterisation of aromatic compounds and conjugated olefins. Identification is done by comparing the absorption spectra with the spectra of known compound. Since the absorption spectra of each pure compound are characteristic property of that compound, it can be used for the identification of that compound. A very common use of spectophotometry is in the structural problems, especially of organic molecules. According to Hartley's rule, compounds of similar structure give analogous absorption spectra e.g. Isatin can have the following (I) and (II) two structures.

```
            CO                                  CO
           /  \                                /  \
  C6H4        C(OH)                  C6H4         C(OH)
       \    //                            \     /
         N                                  NH
     I Lactim                           II Lactam
```

Fig 5.11: Structure of Isatin

On comparing the absorption spectra of these two with those of their methyl ether derivatives, it was observed that the absorption spectra of N-methyl ether were similar to that of structure II. This shows that Isatin has a lactam structure i.e. structure (II)

2) **Quantitative Analysis:** Ultraviolet spectroscopy is generally used for the quantitative determination of compound that absorbs ultraviolet radiation. The determination is based on Beer's Law:

$$A = -\log T = \log \; I_0/ I_t = cl$$

A straight line should be obtained if the Beer's Law holds good. The plot may be used for determination of the unknown concentration of solute.

3) **Knowledge of Impurities in Organic Compounds:** The impurities of carbonic compounds can be found out by ultraviolet spectroscopy. The bands become brighter and they can be identified in the main compound. Saturated carbonic compound shows less absorption while unsaturated compound shows more absorption and can be identified by its absorption at 225 nm.

4) **Determination of Configuration of Geometrical Isomers:** The geometrical isomer can be identified in the form of cis and trans form by ultraviolet spectroscopy. The $\pi \rightarrow \pi^*$ transition of trans isomers takes place on higher wavelength while transition of cis isomers takes place on lower wavelength and the extinction coefficient is also low e.g in case of cinnamic acid

Cis Isomer – λ-268 mμ
Trans Isomer - λ-272 mμ

5) **Tautomeric Equilibrium:** UV spectroscopy can be used to determine the percentage of various keto and enol forms in tautomers. The best example is ethyl acetoacetate. The keto form has λ_{max} = 275 nm and enol form has λ_{max} = 244 nm. From the strength of the bond, one can measure the proportion of tautomers present in ethyl acetoacetate.

6) **Determination of Ozone in environment:** The ozone concentration present in (smog) smoke fog in environment can be calculated by measuring its absorption at 260 nm .

7) **Determination of Dissociation Constants of weak acids or bases:** UV spectroscopy can be used to determine the dissociation constants of acids or bases.The dissociation constant of an acid [HA] is determined by determining the ratio [HA] / [A] spectrometrically from the graph plotted between absorbance and wavelength at different pH.

$$pKa = pH + \log \; [HA] / [A]$$

UV/Visible spectroscopy is routinely used in the quantitative determination of solutions of transition metal ions and highly conjugated organic compounds. The application of ultra violet and visible spectroscopy to qualitative analysis is more limited due to the fact that the absorption bands tend to be broad and hence details are lost. However spectral investigations in this region provide useful qualitative information regarding the presence or absence of functional groups such as carbonyl, nitro, aromatic, aldehyde or conjugated dienes in organic compounds. Highly absorbing impurities in non absorbing media can also be detected e.g. if an absorption peak for the contaminant has a sufficiently high absorptivity, the presence of trace amounts can be readily established.

8) **Elucidation of structure:** UV absorption spectrometry has been used for the determination of organic substances. Unsaturated hydrocarbons, alcohols, ethers and amines exhibit near UV absorptive particularly if conjugation of double bond exists. It has also been used in biochemistry and has also been applied for the determination of inorganic substances.

   The most common use of UV spectroscopy is for the elucidation of structures of organic compounds. The selective absorption serves as an identifying finger print for a particular structure e.g. if there is no appreciable absorption in the region of 270 to 280 nm, then the compound does not contain a benzene ring. Similarly if the compound contains no absorption from about 210 nm to the visible region, isolated double bonds must be absent if transparency extends down to 180 nm.

9) **Determination of pKa value:** The pKa value of indicator can be determined successfully by variation of the absorption spectrum of an acid base indicator as function of pH. Since pKa may be defined as the pH value for which one half of the indicator is in the acid form and one half is in the basic form, it may be determined by a point mid-way between the left and right horizontal segments (pH 7 in this case). The dissociation constants of compounds with absorption in the ultra violet rather than the visible can often be determined similarly e.g. the opylline (λ 240) and benzotriazole (λ=274). Data in such case are usually plotted in three dimensions and the presentation is called stereo- spectrogram in which three axes refer to wavelength, pH and absorbance.

10) **To determine the calcium in blood serum:** Calcium in blood can be indirectly determined by converting the calcium present in one ml of serum as its oxalate, redissolving it into sulphuric acid and treating it with dilute ceric sulphate . The absorption of the excess ceric ion is measured at 315 nm. The amount of calcium in the blood serum can thus be indirectly calculated.

5.8 COLOURIMETRY

It is a device invented by Jan Szczepanik. This is a measurement of the absorbance of a specific solution. It allows the absorbance of a solution at a particular wavelength of light to be determined. The most common application of a colorimeter is to determine the concentration of unknown solution with the help of known solute. Different chemical substances absorb different wavelengths of light. The concentration of a solute is proportional to the absorbance. This is known as the Beer-Lambert law.

Colorimetry is the measurement of the wavelength and the intensity of electromagnetic radiation in the visible region of the spectrum. Colorimetry can help us to find the concentration of substances, since the amount and colour of the light that is absorbed or transmitted depends on properties of the solution, including the concentration of particles in it. A colorimeter is an instrument that compares the amount of light getting through a solution with the amount that can get through a sample of pure solvent. A colorimeter contains a photocell which is able to detect the amount of light which passes through the solution under investigation. The more light that hits the photocell, the higher the current it produces, hence showing the absorbance of light. A colorimeter takes three wideband readings along the visible spectrum to obtain a rough estimate of a colour sample. Pigments absorb light at different wavelengths.

Apparatus:

The essential parts of a colorimeter are:

- A light source (often an ordinary low-voltage filament lamp).
- An adjustable aperture.
- A set of coloured filters.
- A cuvette to hold the working solution.

- A detector (usually a photoresistor} to measure the transmitted light.
- A meter to display the output from the detector.
- A voltage regulator, to protect the instrument from fluctuations in mains voltage.
- A second light path, cuvette and detector. This enables comparison between the working solution and a "blank", consisting of pure solvent to improve accuracy.

Filters: Changeable optics filters are used in the colorimeter to select the wavelength of light which the solute absorbs the most in order to maximize accuracy. The usual wavelength range is from 400 to 700 nanometres (nm). If it is necessary to operate in the ultraviolet range (below 400 nm), then some modifications to the colorimeter are needed. In modern colorimeters, the filament lamp and filters may be replaced by several light-emitting diodes of different colours.

Cuvettes: In a manual colorimeter, the cuvettes are inserted and removed by hand. An automated colorimeter (as used in an Auto Analyzer) is fitted with a flowcell through which solution flows continuously.

Output: The output from a colorimeter may be displayed by an analogue or digitalmeter and may be shown as transmittance (a linear scale from 0-100%) or as absorbance (a logarithmic scale from zero to infinity). The useful range of the absorbance scale is from 0-2 but it is desirable to keep within the range 0-1 because at value above 1, the results become unreliable due to scattering of light. In addition, the output may be sent to a chart recorder, data logger, or computer.

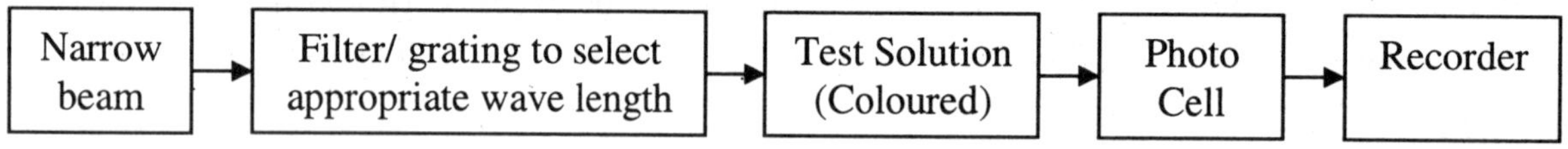

Fig 5.12: Block Diagram of Colorimeter

Using Colorimeter: A colorimeter is the device used in colorimetry. To use this device, different solutions must be made and a control (usually a mixture of distilled water and another solution) is first filled into a cuvette and placed inside a colorimeter to calibrate the machine. Only after the device has been calibrated, one can use it to find the densities and/or concentrations of the other solutions. A colorimeter takes three wideband readings along the visible spectrum to obtain a rough estimate of a colour sample. For critical colour matching, a spectrophotometer that takes readings three times along the visible spectrum would be employed. A densitometer is sufficient to measure lightness and darkness. A spectroradiometer measures the colours of light sources.

Applications: Colourimetry is used in chemistry and in industries such as colour printing, textile manufacturing, paint manufacturing and in the food industry.

5.9 BEER-LAMBERT LAW

In optics, the Beer-Lambert Law, also known as Beer's law or the Lambert-Beer law or the Beer-Lambert-Bouguer law is an empirical relationship that relates the absorption of light to the properties of the material through which the light is travelling.There are several ways in which the law can be expressed:

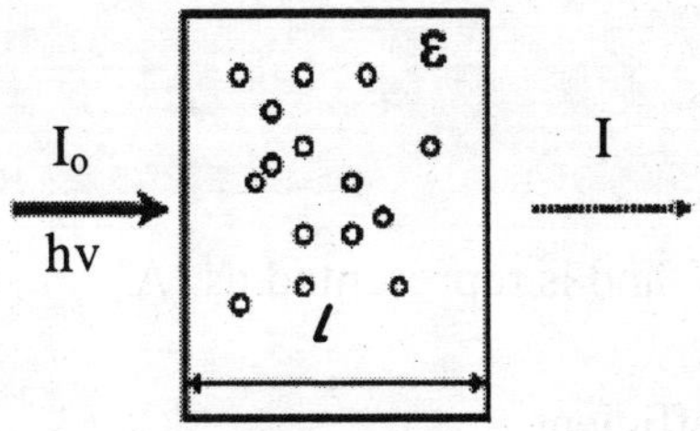

Fig: 5.13

$$A = €cl$$

$$\text{or} \quad \frac{I_1}{I_0} = 10^{-A} = 10^{-lc}$$

$$\text{or} \quad A = \log_{10}\left(\frac{I_0}{I_1}\right)$$

$$\text{or} \quad \alpha = \frac{4\pi k}{\lambda}$$

where, A is absorbance; I_o is the intensity of the incident light, I is the intensity after passing through the material, l is the distance that the light travels through the material (the path length), c is the concentration of absorbing species in the material, € is the absorption coefficient or the molar absorptivity of the absorber; λ is the wavelength of the light and *k* is the extinction coefficient.

1) Lamberts law: When a monochromatic radiation is passed through a solution, the decrease in intensity of radiation with the thickness of the solution is directly proportional to the intensity of the incident radiation.

∴ Rate of decrease in intensity of incident radiation with the thickness of the medium

$$= \frac{-dI}{dx}$$

Thus $\frac{-dI}{dx} \alpha I$ -------------- (I)

Or $\frac{-dI}{dx} = KI$ ----------- (II)

where K is the proportionality constant

Further $\frac{-dI}{I} = Kdx$ ------- (III)

on integrating equation (III) between limits I= I_o at x=0 and I= I at x= l we get

$$In \frac{I}{I_0} = -Kl$$

$$2.303 \log \frac{I}{I_0} = -Kl$$

$$\log \frac{I}{I_0} = \frac{-K}{2.303} l$$

Or

$$\log \frac{I_0}{I} = \frac{K}{2.303} l$$

Where $\log \frac{I_0}{I}$ is called 'Absorbance' and is represented as 'A'

and $\frac{K}{2.303} = \in$ is absorption coefficient

$\therefore$ A=$\in$cl

2) **Beer's Law:** Beer's law takes into consideration the concentration of solution along with thickness of the solution. The law states that when a monochromatic light is passed through a solution, the decrease in intensity of radiation with the thickness of the solution is directly proportional to the incident light as well as concentration of the solution. Let a monochromatic light passes through a solution whose concentration is C molar and thickness d_x, then rate of decrease of intensity of radiation is given by:

$$\frac{-dI}{dx} \alpha CI$$

$$\frac{-dI}{dx} = K'CI$$

$$\frac{-dI}{I} = K'C\ dx$$

On integrating the equation (x) between the limits
I = I_o at x= 0 and I=I at x= l, we get

$$\int_{I_0}^{I} \frac{dI}{I} = -KC \int_{o}^{l} dx$$

$$In \frac{I}{I_o} = -K'Cl$$

$$2.303 \log \frac{I}{I_o} = K'Cl$$

$$\log \frac{I}{I_o} = -K'Cl$$

$$\log \frac{I}{I_o} = \frac{K}{2.303} Cl$$

$$A = \in C\, l$$

where c is the concentration of solute expressed in mole/litre, l=length of the cell containing the sample and € is molar extinction coefficient.

Limitation: The Beer-Lambert Law is useful for characterizing many compounds but does not hold as a universal relationship for the concentration and absorption of all substances. The law tends to break down at very high concentrations, especially if the material is highly scattering. If the light is especially intense, nonlinear optical processes can also cause variations. The linearity of the Beer-Lambert law is limited by chemical and instrumental factors. Causes of nonlinearity include:

- Deviations in absorptivity coefficients at high concentrations (>0.01M) due to electrostatic interactions between molecules in close proximity.
- Scattering of light due to particulates in the sample.
- Fluorescence or phosphorescence of the sample.
- Changes in refractive index at high analyte concentration.
- Shifts in chemical equilibria as a function of concentration.
- Non-monochromatic radiation, deviations can be minimized by using a relatively flat part of the absorption spectrum such as the maximum of an absorption band.
- Stray light.

5.10 INFRARED SPECTROSCOPY

Infrared spectroscopy (IR Spectroscopy) is the subset of spectroscopy that deals with the IR region of the electromagnetic spectrum. It covers a range of techniques, with the most common type by far being a form of absorption spectroscopy. As with all spectroscopic techniques, it can be used to identify a compound and to investigate the composition of a sample.

Atoms in a molecule are continuously vibrating. Molecules vibrate in several ways (Modes). Vibrational changes depend upon the masses of the atoms and their spatial arrangement in the molecule. Almost all organic molecules absorb radiations of various wavelengths in the intermediate infrared region of the electromagnetic spectrum (λ = 1.5 to 20 μm). Every compound shows characteristic absorption band in the IR region of the spectrum. Different functional groups produce easily recognizable band at nearly definite position of the spectral range. Consequently, IR spectra are often characterized as molecular finger prints which detect the presence of functional groups

Theory: The infrared portion of the electromagnetic spectrum is divided into three regions, the near, mid and far infrared. The far-infrared, (approx. 400-10 cm^{-1}) lying adjacent to the microwave region, has low energy and may be used for rotational spectroscopy. The mid- infrared (approx. 4000-400 cm^{-1}) may be used to study the fundamental vibrations and associated rotational-vibrational structure, while the higher energy near IR (14000-4000 cm^{-1}) can excite overtone or harmonic vibrations.

An invaluable tool in organic structure determination and verification involves the class of electromagnetic (EM) radiation with frequencies between 4000 and 400 cm^{-1} (wave numbers). Radiation in this region can be utilized in organic structure determination by making use of the fact that it is absorbed by interatomic bonds in organic compounds. Chemical bonds in different environments will absorb varying intensities and at varying frequencies. Thus IR spectroscopy involves collecting absorption information and analyzing it in the form of a spectrum. The frequencies at which there are absorptions of IR radiation ("peaks" or "signals") can be correlated directly to bonds within the compound. The interatomic bond may vibrate in several different motions (stretching or bending), individual bonds may absorb at more than one IR frequency. Stretching absorptions usually produce stronger peaks than bending, however the weaker bending absorptions can be useful in differentiating similar types of bonds (e.g. aromatic substitution). It is also important to note that symmetrical vibrations do not cause absorption of IR radiation. For example, neither of the carbon-carbon bonds in ethene or ethyne absorbs IR radiation.

Molecular Vibration and Origin of IR Spectra: The infrared spectrum yields the most of information concerning the structure of organic molecules. A molecule is constantly vibrating. All vibrations fall into the basic categories of stretching and bending. Stretching vibrations are of two types viz symmetric and asymmetric.

Symmetric vibrations (Stretching) involve the movement of the atoms with repeated particular atom in a molecule in the same direction while asymmetric stretching involves continuous change in the inner atomic distance along the excess of the bond between two atoms not in the same direction as shown below in the figure 5.14.

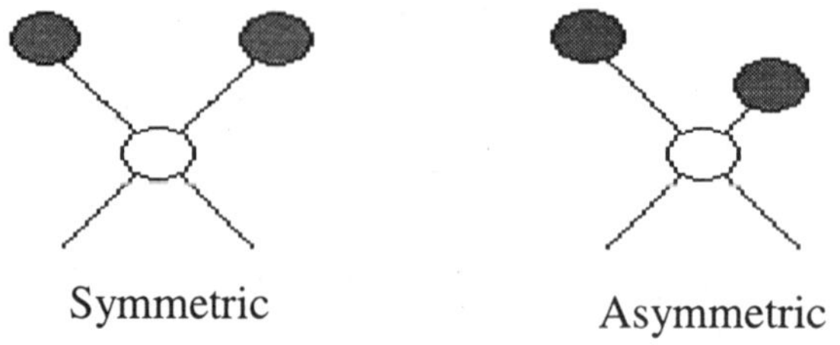

Fig. 5.14: Stretching Vibrations

Bending of vibrations (deformations): They are characterized by a change in the angle between two bonds and are of four types as shown below:

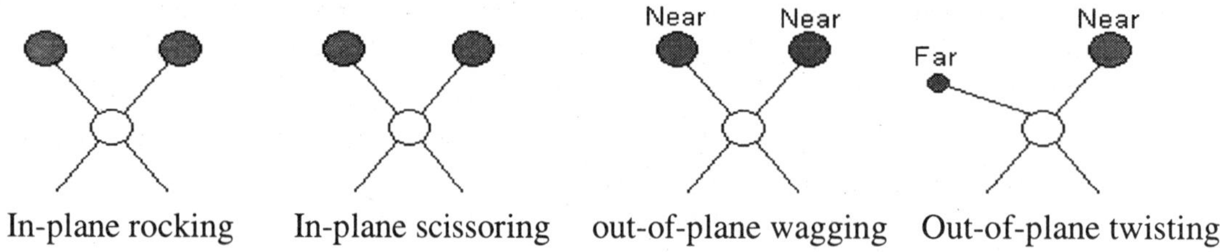

Fig. 5.15: Bending Vibrations

(1) Rocking involves the movement of the atoms in the same direction.

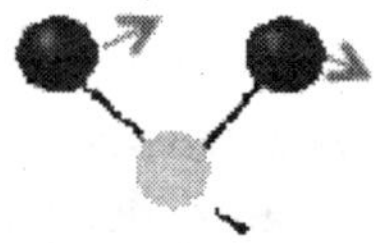

Fig. 5.16: Rocking Vibrations

(2) Scissoring in which two atoms approach each other.

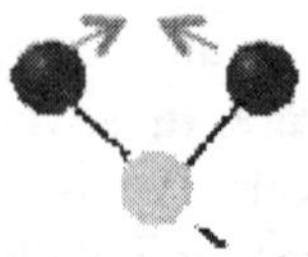

Fig. 5.17: Scissoring Vibrations

(3) Wagging involves the movement of atoms (Both) up and below the plane with respect to control atom.

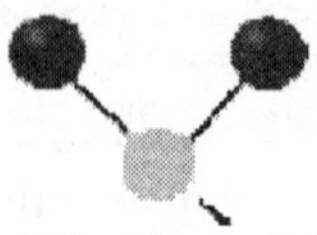

Fig. 5.18: Wagging Vibrations

(4) Twisting involves the movement of one atom up and the other down the plane with respect to the central atom.

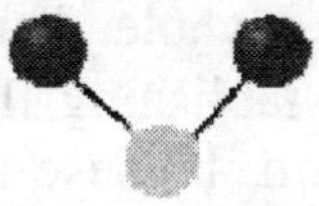

Fig. 5.19: Twisting Vibrations

Bending vibration requires lesser energy then the stretching vibrations. Vibrational frequency is given by the Hook's law.

$Vm = 1/2\pi \sqrt{k/\mu} = 1/2\pi\sqrt{k(m_1+m_2)/m_1+m_2}$

where k is the force constant, μ is the reduced mass and represented as $\mu = m_1+m_2 / m_1+m_2$

where m_1 and m_2 are the masses of two atoms (in gm).

From the above equation, it is clear that the vibrations of a bond occur at certain quantized frequencies. When IR light of that same frequency is incident on the molecule, energy is absorbed and the amplitude of that vibration is increased. When the molecule reverts from the excited state to the original ground state, absorbed energy is released as heat. A non linear molecule that contains n atom, has 3n - 6 possible fundamental vibration modes that can be responsible for absorption of IR light. Thus such simple molecule as methane (CH_4) and benzene (C_6H_6) have theoretically 9-30 possible fundamental absorption bands respectively.

Instrument:

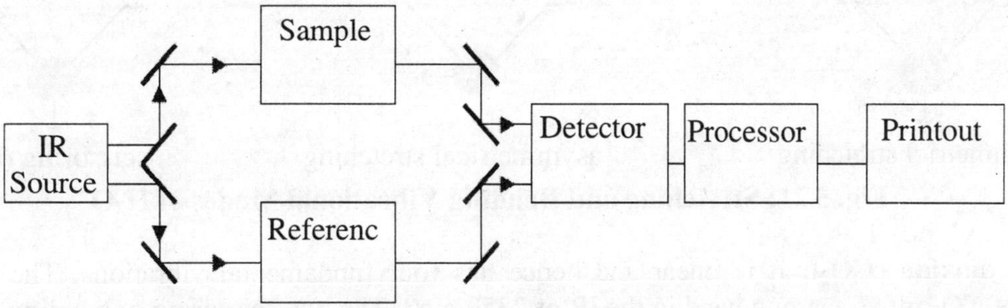

Fig. 5. 20: Block Diagram of IR Spectrophotometer

Infrared absorption spectra are usually obtained by placing the sample in on beam of a double beam IR spectrophotometer and measuring the relative intensity of transmitted light energy vs wavelength or (wave number) A common light source for IR radiation is the Nernst Glower which is a moulded rod containing a mixture of zirconium oxide and erbium oxide that is heated around 1500^0C by electrical means. Metal halides (NaCl) are commonly used for this purpose. Recording spectrophotometer, record the complete spectrum (2.5-25μ, 4000-400 cm^{-1}) of matter.

Technique: For the IR spectrum of solid substance, a very small amount of the organic substances (some miligrams) is grinded with a drop of nuzol and the paste so obtained is compressed between two plates. Nuzol itself gives a simple IR spectrum. Nuzol is a mixture of liquid alkanes of high molecular weight. The absorption that takes place by it, are C-H bending vibration at 6.8 μm and 7.98 μm. Hexachlorobutadiene is another mullifer since it does not contain C-H bond. Therefore it is transparent in that region where nuzol absorbs.

Finger print region: The region of IR spectrum extending from 2.5 to 8 μm (4000- 1250 cm^{-1}) is a characteristicof bonds and groups present in the compounds. On the other hand, the region beyond 8 μm (1250 cm^{-1}) is characteristic of the molecule as a whole. This latter region is called far finger print region. The study of this region is very useful for establishing the identification of two compounds. No two different compounds have identical IR spectrum. If these spectra are identical i.e. superimposible, then both the compounds should be identical.

Nujol mull: A mull is a suspension of a solid in a liquid. Under these conditions, light can be transmitted through the sample to afford an acceptable infrared spectrum. The commercial sample of nujol, or mineral oil, which is a long chain hydrocarbon, is often used for this purpose. Most solids do not dissolve in this medium but can be ground up in its presence. A small mortar and pestle is used for this purpose. The major disadvantage of using a nujol mull is that the information in the C-H stretching region is lost because of the absorptions of the mulling agent. To eliminate this problem, it may be necessary to run a second spectrum in a different mulling agent that does not contain any C-H bonds. Typical mulling agents that are used for this purpose are perfluoro or perchlorohydrocarbons. Examples include perchlorobutadiene, perfluorokerosene or perfluorohydrocarbon oil.

Examples of Infrared absorption spectra:

1. Water (H_2O): The fundamental vibrations for water (H_2O) are shown below in fig. 5.21.Water molecule is nonlinear and has three fundamental vibrations.

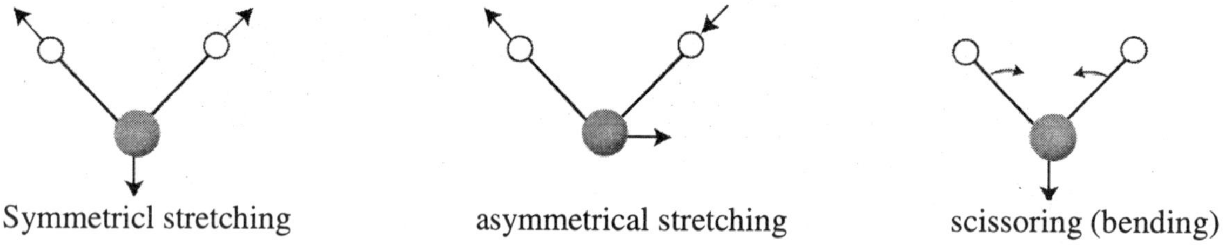

Fig. 5.21: Stretching and Bending Vibrational Modes of H_2O

2. Carbon dioxide (CO_2): It is linear and hence has four fundamental vibrations. The asymmetrical stretching of CO_2 gives a strong band in the IR at 2350 cm^{-1}. The two scissoring or bending vibrations are equivalent and therefore have same frequency and are said to be degenerate, appearing in an IR spectrum at 666 cm^{-1}.

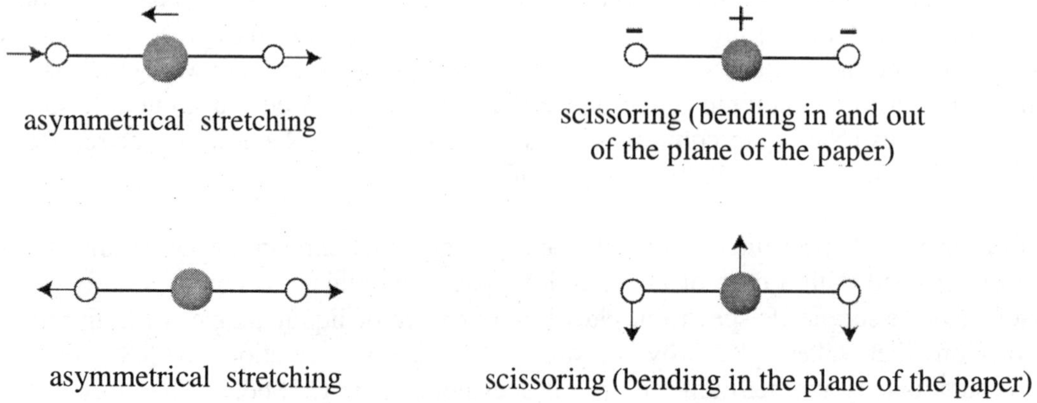

Fig. 5.22: Stretching and Bending Vibrational Modes for CO_2

Spectra of alkanes: The spectra of simple alkanes are characterized by absorptions due to C–H stretching and bending (the C–C stretching and bending bands are either too weak or of too low frequency to be detected in IR spectroscopy). In simple alkanes, which have very few bands, each band in the spectrum can be assigned.

- C–H stretch from 3000–2850 cm^{-1}
- C–H bend or scissoring from 1470-1450 cm^{-1}
- C–H rock, methyl from 1370-1350 cm^{-1}
- C–H rock, methyl, seen only in long chain alkanes, from 725-720 cm^{-1}

The IR spectrum of octane is shown below in fig 5.23. The strong bands in the region of 3000-2850 cm^{-1} are due to C-H stretching. The C-H scissoring (1470cm^{-1}), methyl rock (1383 cm^{-1}) and long-chain methyl rock (728 cm^{-1}) are noted on the spectrum. Since most organic compounds have these features, these C-H vibrations are usually not noted when interpreting a routine IR spectrum.

The region from 1300-900 cm^{-1} is called the fingerprint region. The bands in this region originate in interacting vibrational modes resulting in a complex absorption pattern. Usually, this region is quite complex and often difficult to interpret however each organic compound has its own unique absorption pattern (or fingerprint) in this region and thus an IR spectrum can be used to identify a compound by matching it with a sample of a known compound.

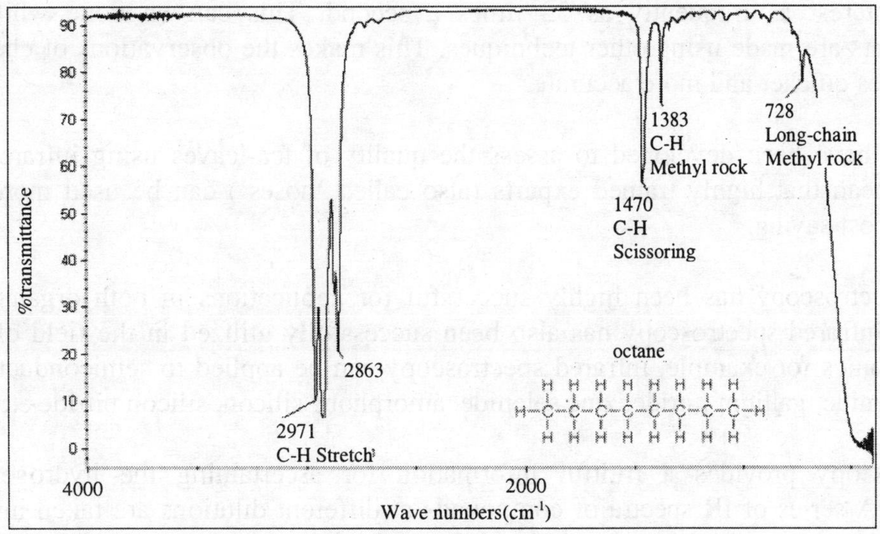

Fig. 5.23: The IR Spectrum of Octane

ANALYSIS OF AN INFRARED SPECTRUM

An example of an infrared spectrum for octane (C_8H_{18}) is shown in fig 5.23. Molecules absorb infrared light when one of six possible bonding vibrations occurs, bonds can have symmetrical and asymmetrical stretching, scissoring, rocking, wagging and twisting. The energies of the peaks must be matched to known bond vibrations. The C-H stretching and bending energies are clearly visible, but the C-C bands are not seen, as they are either too weak or too low in energy.

Examples of some common bond vibration energies:

Peak Position	**Bond**
3500- 3300 cm^{-1}	N-H Stretch (amines)
3300- 3200 cm^{-1}	O-H Stretch (alcohols)
3100- 3000 cm^{-1}	C-H Stretch (alkenes)
3000- 2850 cm^{-1}	C-H Stretch (alkanes)
1760- 1665 cm^{-1}	C=O Stretch (ketones, aldehydes, esters)
1680- 1640 cm^{-1}	C=C Stretch (alkenes)

Uses and Applications:

1) Infrared spectroscopy is widely used in both research and industry as a simple and reliable technique for measurement, quality control and dynamic measurement. The instruments are now small and can be transported, even for use in field trials. With increasing technology in computer filtering and manipulation of the results, samples in solution can now be measured accurately (water produces a broad absorbance across the range of interest and thus renders the spectra unreadable without this computer treatment). Some machines will also automatically tell what substance is being measured from a store of thousands of reference spectra held in storage.

2) By measuring at a specific frequency over time, changes in the character or quantity of a particular bond can be measured. This is especially useful in measuring the degree of polymerization in polymer manufacture. Modern research machines can take infrared measurements across the whole range of interest as frequently as 32 times a second. This can be done while simultaneous measurements are made using other techniques. This makes the observations of chemical reactions and processes quicker and more accurate.

3) Techniques have been developed to assess the quality of tea-leaves using infrared spectroscopy. This will mean that highly trained experts (also called 'noses') can be used more sparingly at a significant cost saving.

4) Infrared spectroscopy has been highly successful for applications in both organic and inorganic chemistry. Infrared spectroscopy has also been successfully utilized in the field of semiconductor microelectronics for example, infrared spectroscopy can be applied to semiconductors like silicon, gallium arsenide, gallium nitride, zinc selenide, amorphous silicon, silicon nitride etc.

5) IR spectroscopy provides a fruitful information for ascertaining the hydrogen bond in the compound. A series of IR spectra of compounds at different dilutions are taken into consideration and comparison among them makes it easier because if dilution is increased, the absorption band, due to intermolecular hydrogen bonding decreases while that due to intramolecular hydrogen bonding remains unchanged.

6) IR spectroscopy is useful to study the progress of chromatographic separation.

7) The difference in the wavelength of overtones of C-H bands in different environments can be used to determine the relative proportions of unsaturated and saturated rings present in hydrocarbons and also to determine the percentage of aromatics or olefins present in the mixtures.

8) Determination of Force constant and Bond length from vibrational spectrum depends upon -

$$\nu = \frac{1}{2\pi}\sqrt{\frac{k}{\mu}}$$

Frequency of absoption is directly proportional to force constant which is considered to be the strength of bond i.e. more is the frequency, more is the strength of bond. μ is the reduced mass which is inversly proportional to frequency, so more is the mass, less is the vibrational frequency.

9) Identification of unknown compound is made by fingerprint technique which involves matching the spectrum (IR) of unknown compound with that of the known compound.

10) As different functional groups in organic compounds have different characterstic values of k and μ, hence they will absorb at characterstic frequencies in the IR spectrum. Thus, from the IR-spectrum of a compound, the presence and absence of functional groups in the compound is known.

5.11 NUCLEAR MAGNETIC RESONANCE SPECTROSCOPY(NMR)

NMR is a spectroscopic technique which uses electromagnetic radiation and magnetic fields to determine the structure of organic compounds. Radio-frequency radiation is used to stimulate nuclei present within the molecule and by this information we can determine where the carbon atoms and hydrogen atoms are located. The effect was first noticed in 1902 by P. Zeeman, a physicist, who won a Nobel Prize for noticing that nuclei of certain atoms behave strangely in a magnetic field. Fifty years later F. Bloch and E. Purcell, both physicists put this idea in constructing the first NMR spectrometer. They too received a Nobel Prize for this work.

Principle of NMR: The principle of NMR is based upon the spin of atomic nuclei in an external magnetic field. It has been observed that a nucleus of atom having an odd number of protons or a neutron, or both unpaired proton and neutron, spins on its own axis owing to its positive charge. Not all nuclei possess this ability. The nuclear magnetic resonance of a substance is concerned with nuclear spin associated with nuclei (proton or neutron). This is because spinning nuclei generate a circulating electric current which in turn develops a magnetic field around nuclei which makes it a tiny magnet. When these nuclei are placed in a strong magnetic field they line up processing in the direction of the applied field. There are two possible orientations which the nuclei can adopt, either lined up with the field (parallel), or against the field (anti-parallel). The two orientations are not exactly of the same energy. The parallel alignment is slightly lower in energy than the anti-parallel one.

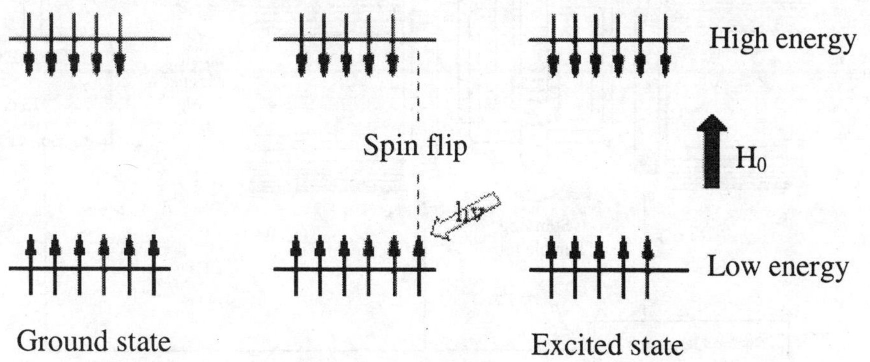

Fig. 5.24: Orientations of Atomic Nuclei in External Magnetic Field.

The energy difference between the two orientations is the basis of NMR spectroscopy study because the difference of energy if provided to the nucleus, its transition from low energy state to high energy state is brought about. Thus, it requires supply of energy equal to the difference in energy between two states. When the nuclei are irradiated with radio frequency radiation, the lower energy nuclei flip up to the higher energy state. When this occurs, the nuclei are said to be in resonance. For determining resonance frequency of nucleus, the energy absorbed by nucleus is measured and the applied magnetic field is changed (increased or decreased). When applied magnetic field is increased, the frequency of nucleus also increases and if the frequency absorbed by nucleus equalizes the frequency of applied magnetic field, transition is said to occur. The energy absorbed gives a signal in detector which is recorded as a particular band in the spectra providing useful information. This information is recorded as NMR spectra.

- An NMR spectrum is a plot of the radio frequency applied against absorption.
- A signal in the spectrum is referred to as a resonance.
- The frequency of a signal is known as its chemical shift.

The NMR spectra give information to identify and characterize the molecule.

- The number of signals in absorption spectra equals to the number of different kinds of protons in the molecule.
- The position of signal in terms of frequency provides information about the electronic environment or surroundings of each proton.
- The intensity of signal depicts the concentration that is the number of protons.
- Splitting in peaks indicates environment of proton with respect to other proton.

NMR Instrumentation

NMR spectrometers are very complex instruments, containing many parts which all work in concert to produce a spectrum.

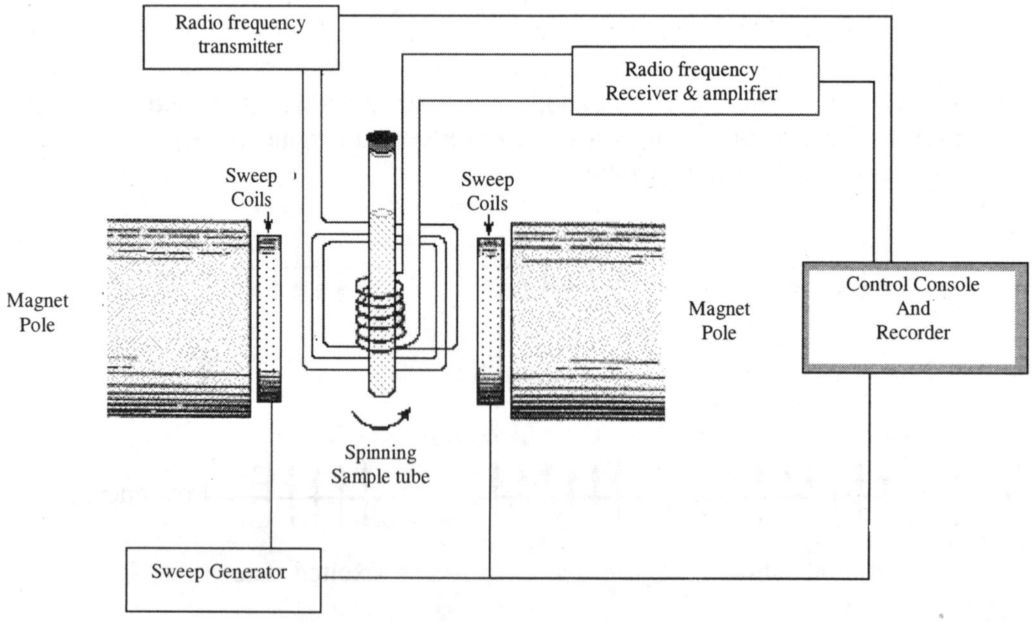

Fig. 5.25: A Schematic Diagram of NMR Spectrometer

The Components of a NMR Instrument:

The NMR instrument consists mainly of the following parts:

- The magnet
- Radiofrequency sources
- Sweep Circuit
- Detector
- Recorder
- Amplifiers
- Analog-digital converters (ADC's)
- A computer system

The first requirement for NMR is a strong magnet, usually a superconducting magnet which generates a strong focused magnetic field. The purpose of the magnet is to align all the NMR active nuclei and split them into their respective spin states. Sweep circuits are there to supply additional field required to bring the field up to the resonance condition. Receiver receives the resonance signals and sends them to amplifier and detector. Recorder finally records the spectrum. Sample holder holds the spinning sample. NMR can be studied under chemical shift against absorption. The protons in TMS are all equivalent and its NMR spectrum exhibits a single resonance line at a high applied field. In addition TMS is chemically inert, relatively volatile (B.P.= 27^{0}C) and soluble in most organic solvent. For exact position of absorption caused by protons, a small amount of (TMS) tetra methyl silane is mixed with the sample and NMR spectra is recorded.

Nuclear Shielding and Deshielding: The magnetic field at the nucleus is not equal to the applied magnetic field, electrons around the nucleus shield it from the applied field. The difference between the applied magnetic field and the field at the nucleus is termed as nuclear shielding. Consider the s-electrons in a molecule. They have spherical symmetry and circulate in the applied field producing a magnetic field which opposes the applied field. This means that the applied field strength must be increased for the nucleus to absorb at its transition frequency. This upfield shift is also termed as diamagnetic shift.

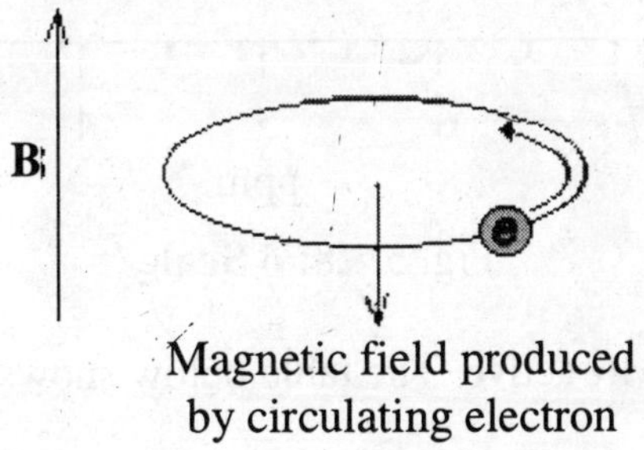

Fig. 5.26: Diamagnetic shift

Electrons in p-orbital have no spherical symmetry. They produce comparatively large magnetic fields at the nucleus, which give a low field shift. This "deshielding" is termed as paramagnetic shift.

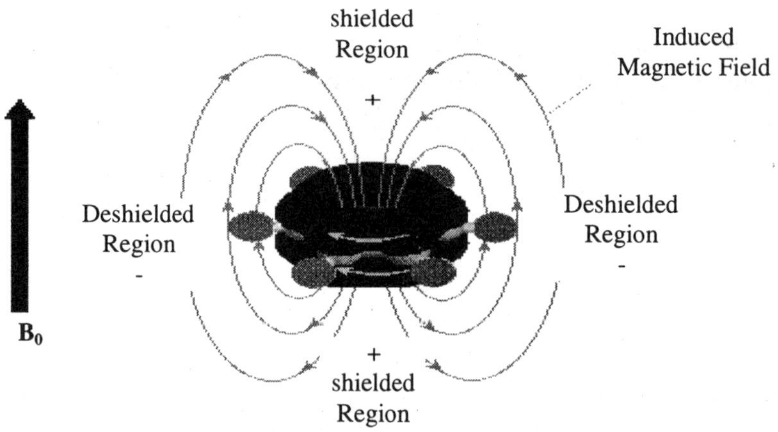

Fig. 5.27: Nuclear Shielding and Deshielding

Chemical Shift: It is defined as nuclear shielding or applied magnetic field. The chemical shift in absolute terms is defined by the frequency of the resonance expressed with reference to a standard compound which is defined to be at 0 ppm. The scale is made more manageable by expressing it in parts per million (ppm) and is independent of the spectrometer frequency.

$$\text{Chemical shift, } \partial = \frac{\text{frequency of signal - frequency of reference}}{\text{spectrometer frequency}} \times 10^6$$

It is often convenient to describe the relative positions of the resonances in an NMR spectrum. For example, a peak at a chemical shift of 10 ppm is said to be downfield or deshielded with respect to a peak at 5 ppm, or if the peak is at 5 ppm, it is upfield or shielded with respect to the peak at 10 ppm.

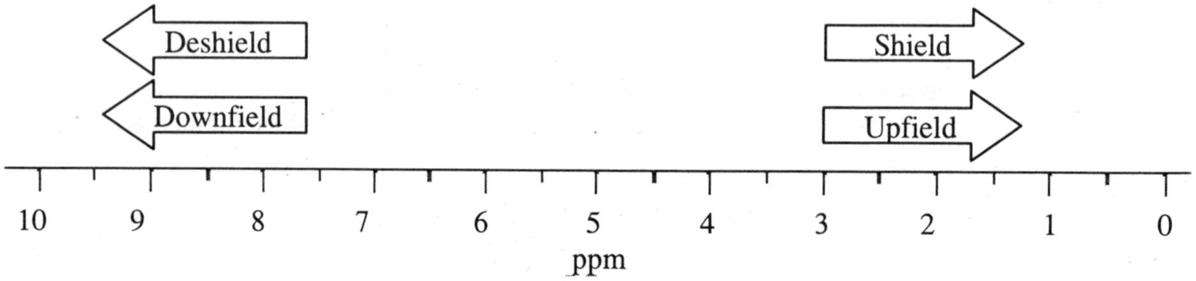

Fig. **5. 28: δ Scale**

Types of Nuclei and Nuclear spin:

There are many nuclei which are NMR active. The table below shows some of the common ones.

Table 5.3 Nuclei and Nuclear Spin

Isotope	% abund	Nuclear spin
1 H	99.985	1/2
13C	1.108	1/2
2H	0.015	1
11B	80.42	3/2
14N	99.63	1
19F	100	1/2
31P	100	1/2
Nuclear Active Isotopes		

Subatomic particles (electrons, protons and neutrons) can be imagined as spinning on their axes. In many atoms (such as 12C), these spins are paired against each other, such that the nucleus of the atom has no overall spin. However, in some atoms (such as 1H and 13C), the nucleus does possess an overall spin.

The rules for determining the net spin of a nucleus are as follows:

1. If the number of neutrons and the number of protons are both even, then the nucleus has no spin. (I is not equal to 0)
2. If the number of neutrons plus the number of protons is odd, then the nucleus has a half-integer spin (i.e. I = 1/2, 3/2, 5/2)
3. If the number of neutrons and the number of protons are both odd, then the nucleus has an integer spin (i.e. I = 1, 2, 3)

The overall spin I, is important. Quantum mechanics tells us that a nucleus of spin I will have 2I + 1 possible orientations. A nucleus with spin 1/2 will have 2 possible orientations. In the absence of an external magnetic field, these orientations are of equal energy. If a magnetic field is applied, then the energy levels split. Each level is given a magnetic quantum number, m.

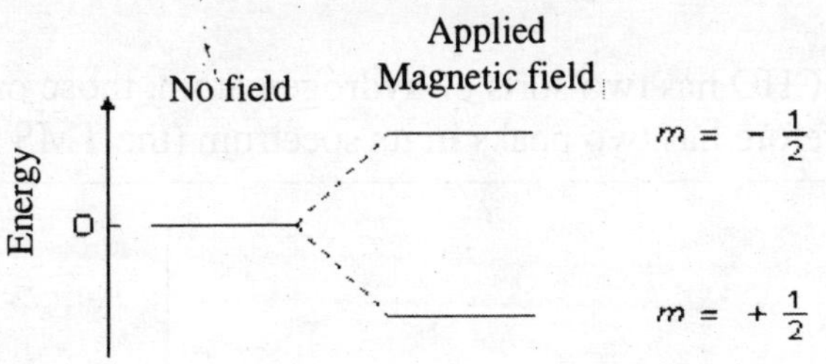

Fig. 5.29: Energy Levels for a Nucleus with Spin Quantum Number 1/2

When the nucleus is in a magnetic field, the initial populations of the energy levels are determined by thermodynamics as described by the Boltzmann distribution. This is very important and it means that the lower energy level will contain slightly more nuclei than the higher energy level. It is possible to excite these nuclei into the higher level with electromagnetic radiation. The frequency of radiation needed is determined by the difference in energy between the energy levels.

Examples of NMR Spectra

The number of peaks in the low-resolution spectrum depends on the number of different environments that the hydrogen atoms have in the molecule.

One environment: Benzene, C_6H_6 has only one sort of hydrogen atom; so that the NMR spectrum shows a single peak (the TMS peak is omitted)

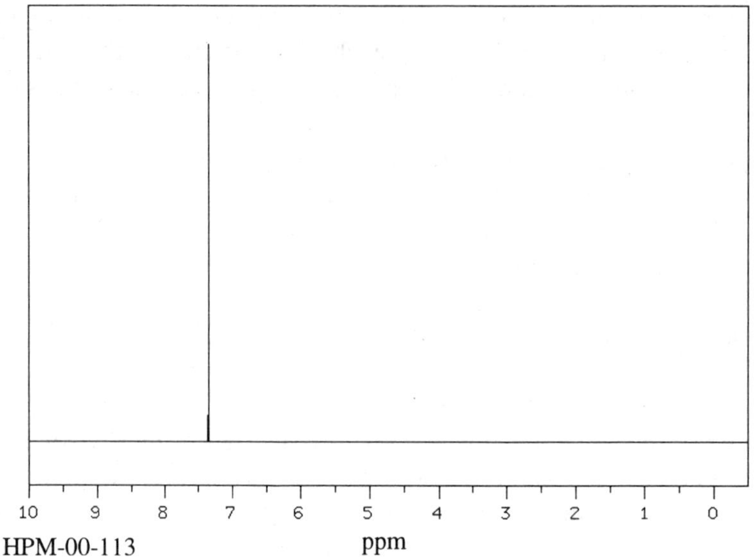

Fig. 5.30 NMR Spectra of benzene

Two environments: Ethanal CH_3CHO has two sorts of hydrogen atom, those on the methyl group and that on the aldehyde group. It therefore has two peaks in its spectrum (the TMS peak is omitted):

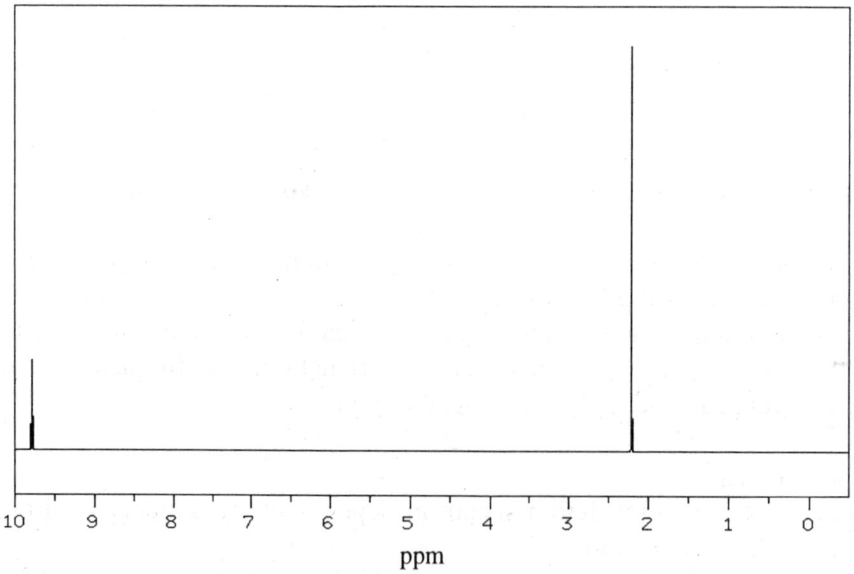

Fig. 5.31: NMR Spectra of ethanal

Three environments: Ethanol CH_3CH_2OH has methyl hydrogen, methylene hydrogen and hydroxyl hydrogen. It therefore has three peaks in its spectrum (the TMS peak is omitted). However, this spectrum is the high-resolution spectrum, which shows spin-spin coupling.

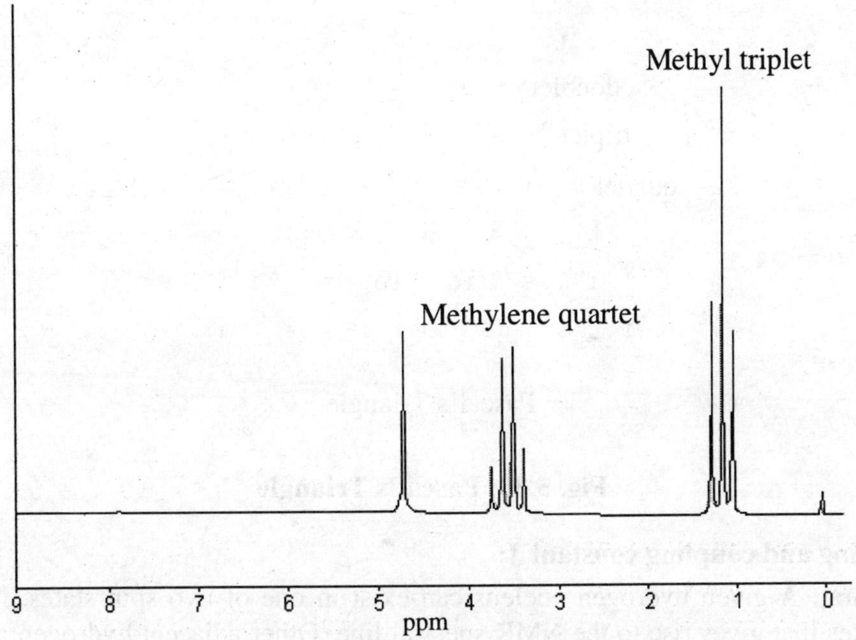

Fig. 5.32 NMR Spectrum of Ethanol

Integration of NMR Spectra:

- The area of a peak is proportional to the number of H that the peak represents.
- The integral measures the area of the peak.
- The integral gives the relative ratio of the number of H for each peak.

Spin-Spin Splitting

NMR provides information on how many hydrogen neighbours exist for a particular hydrogen or group of equivalent hydrogen. In general, an NMR resonance will split into N + 1 peaks where N = number of hydrogen on the adjacent atom or atoms.

- If there is no hydrogen on the adjacent atoms, then the resonance will remain a single peak, a singlet.
- If there is one hydrogen on the adjacent atoms, the resonance will be split into two peaks of equal size, a doublet.
- If there are two hydrogen on the adjacent atoms, the resonance will split into three peaks with an area in the ratio of 1:2:1, a triplet.
- If there are three hydrogen on the adjacent atoms, the resonance will split into four peaks with an area in the ratio of 1:3:3:1, a quartet.

Generally we use Pascal's Triangle for determination of splitting of peaks.

Pascal's Triangle

The relative intensities of the lines in a coupling pattern are given by a binomial expansion or more continently by Pascal's triangle. To drive Pascal's triangle, start at the apex and generate each lower row by creating each number by adding the two numbers above and to either side in the row above together. The first six rows are shown to the right. So for H-NMR a proton with zero neighbours, n=0, appears as a single line, a proton with one neighbours, n=1 as two lines of equal intensity, a proton with two neighbours, n=2, as three lines of intensities 1: 2: 1, etc.

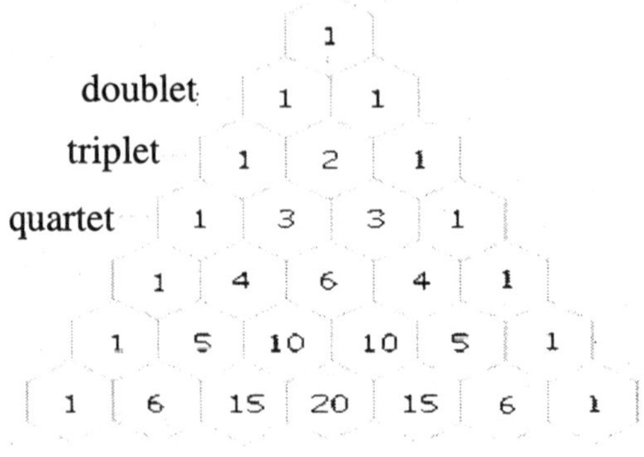

Pascal's Triangle

Fig. 5.33: Pascal's Triangle

Spin - spin coupling and coupling constant J:

Spin-spin Coupling: A given hydrogen nucleus can exist in one of two spin states, it is the transition between these states that gives rise to the NMR spectral line. Other adjacent hydrogen atoms in the same environment, for example all the methyl hydrogen atoms in ethanol, do not affect the absorption. However this is no longer true when the hydrogen atoms are non-equivalent. In ethanol, for example, the hydrogen atoms on the methyl group interact with those on the methylene group, their magnetic fields couple. The effect of coupling on the spectrum is that the lines are split into multiplets. Most coupling occurs between hydrogen atoms on adjacent carbon atoms, so in the ethanol spectrum there is splitting of the lines due to the methyl and methylene hydrogen atoms, but not that of the hydroxyl hydrogen, it is too far away. The spectra are commonly integrated, that is the area under each peak (or set of peaks in a multiplet) is measured. This gives information about the number of hydrogen atoms that has given rise toeach absorption.

Consider the structure of ethanol:

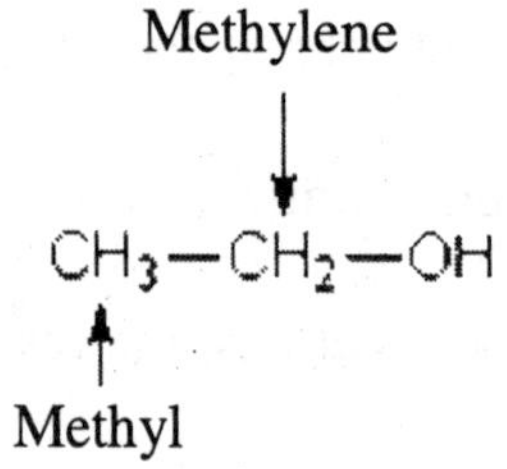

The ^{1}H NMR spectrum of ethanol (below) shows that the methyl peak has been split into three peaks (a triplet) and the methylene peak has been split into four peaks (a quartet). This occurs because there is a small interaction (coupling) between the two groups of protons. The spacing between the peaks of the methyl triplet is equal to the spacing between the peaks of the methylene quartet. This spacing is measured in Hertz and is called the coupling constant J.

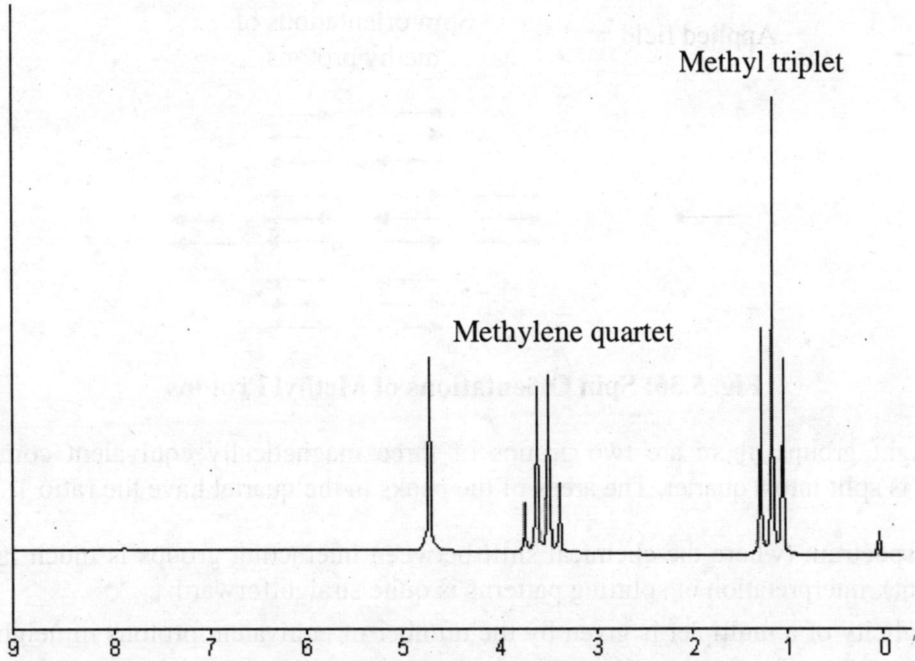

Fig. 5.34 NMR Spectrum of Ethanol

To see why the methyl peak is split into a triplet, let us look at the methylene protons. There are two of them and each can have one of two possible orientations (aligned with or opposed against the applied field). This gives a total of four possible states;

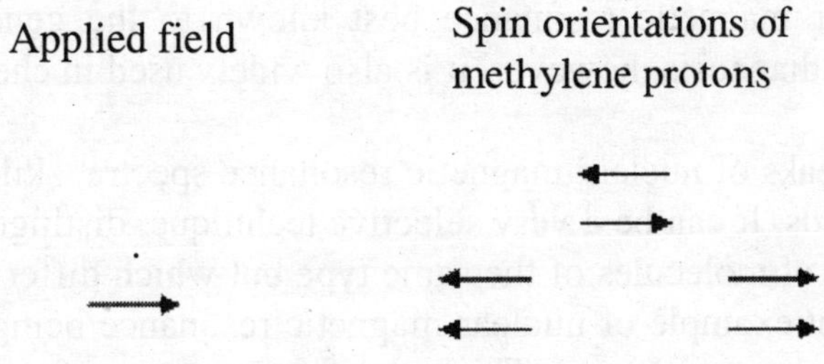

Fig. 5.35: Spin Orientation of Methylene Protons

In the first possible combination, spins are paired and opposed to the field. This has the effect of reducing the field experienced by the methyl protons; therefore a slightly higher field is needed to bring them to resonance, resulting in an upfield shift. Neither combination of spins opposed to each other has an effect on the methyl peak. The spins paired in the direction of the field produce a downfield shift. Hence, the methyl peak is split into three, with the ratio of areas 1:2:1.

Similarly, the effect of the methyl protons on the methylene protons is such that there are eight possible spin combinations for the three methyl protons;

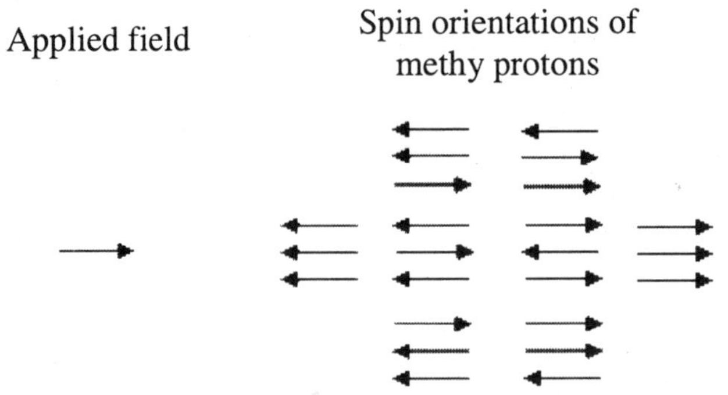

Fig. 5.36: Spin Orientations of Methyl Protons

Out of these eight groups, there are two groups of three magnetically equivalent combinations. The methylene peak is split into a quartet. The areas of the peaks in the quartet have the ratio 1:3:3:1.

In a first-order spectrum (where the chemical shift between interacting groups is much larger than their coupling constant), interpretation of splitting patterns is quite straightforward:

- The multiplicity of a multiplet is given by the number of equivalent protons in neighbouring atoms plus one, i.e. the n + 1 rule.
- Equivalent nuclei do not interact with each other. The three methyl protons in ethanol cause splitting of the neighbouring methylene protons, they do not cause splitting among themselves.
- The coupling constant is not dependant on the applied field. Multiplets can be easily distinguished from closely spaced chemical shift peaks.

Applications:

Medicine: The use of nuclear magnetic resonance best known to the general public is in magnetic resonance imaging for medical diagnosis, however, it is also widely used in chemical studies.

Chemistry: By studying the peaks of nuclear magnetic resonance spectra, skilled chemists can determine the structure of many compounds. It can be a very selective technique, distinguishing among many atoms within a molecule or collection of molecules of the same type but which differ only in terms of their local chemical environment. A recent example of nuclear magnetic resonance being used in the determination of a structure is that of buckminsterfullerene. This now famous form of carbon has 60 carbon atoms forming a sphere. The carbon atoms are all in identical environments and so should see the same internal H field. Unfortunately, buckminsterfullerene contains no hydrogen and so ^{13}C nuclear magnetic resonance has to be used. ^{13}C spectra are more difficult to obtain because carbon-13 is not the common isotope of carbon (unlike hydrogen, where ^{1}H is the common isotope). However, in 1990 the spectrum was obtained by R. Taylor and co-workers at the University of Sussex and was found to contain a single peak, confirming the unusual structure of C_{60}.

Non-destructive testing: Nuclear magnetic resonance is extremely useful for analyzing samples non-destructively. Radio waves and static magnetic fields easily penetrate many types of matter and anything that is not inherently ferromagnetic. For example, various expensive biological samples such as nucleic acids, including RNA and DNA, or proteins, can be studied using nuclear magnetic resonance for weeks or months before using destructive biochemical experiments. This also makes nuclear magnetic resonance a good choice for analyzing dangerous samples.

Data acquisition in the petroleum industry: Another use for nuclear magnetic resonance is data acquisition in the petroleum industry for petroleum and natural gas exploration and recovery. A borehole is drilled into rock and sedimentary strata into which nuclear magnetic resonance logging equipment is lowered. Nuclear magnetic resonance analysis of these boreholes is used to measure rock porosity, to estimate permeability from pore size distribution and to identify pore fluids (water, oil and gas).

Process control: NMR has now entered the arena of real-time process control and process optimization in oil refineries and petrochemical plants. Two different types of NMR analysis are utilized to provide real time analysis of feeds and products in order to control and optimize unit operations. Time-domain NMR (TD-NMR) spectrometers operating at low field (2-20 MHz for ^1H) yield free induction decay data that can be used to determine absolute hydrogen content values, rheological information and component composition. These spectrometers are used in mining, polymer production, cosmetics and food manufacturing as well as coal analysis. High resolution FT-NMR spectrometers operating in the 60 MHz range with shielded permanent magnet systems yield high resolution ^1H NMR spectra of refinery and petrochemical streams. The variation observed in these spectra with changing physical and chemical properties is modelled utilizing chemometrics to yield predictions on unknown samples. The prediction results are provided to control systems via analogue or digital outputs from the spectrometer.

5.12 ELECTRON PARAMAGNETIC SPECTROSCOPY

EPR is Electron Paramagnetic Resonance. It is a spectroscopic method that detects the presence of unpaired electrons in samples. It can yield meaningful structural and dynamic information, even from ongoing chemical or physical processes without influencing the process itself. It is an ideal technique to complement other analytical methods in a wide range of application areas. These areas include Chemistry, Physics, Materials Research, Biology and Medicine and Ionizing Radiation.

Introduction: In the absence of an external magnetic field, the two possible electron spin states (spin up and spin down) degenerate. When an atom or molecule with an unpaired electron is placed in a magnetic field, the spin of the unpaired electron can become aligned either in the same direction or in the opposite direction of the applied field. These two possible electron alignments have different energies (i.e. are no longer degenerate) and are directly proportional to the applied magnetic field strength. This is called the Zeeman effect.

Electron-paramagnetic-resonance (EPR) also referred to as electron-spin-resonance (ESR) spectroscopy measures the absorption of microwave radiation corresponding to the energy splitting of the unpaired electron when it is placed in a strong magnetic field. Species that contain unpaired electrons are:

1. Free radicals
2. Odd electron molecules.
3. Transition-metal complexes
4. Lanthanide ions
5. Triplet-state molecules

The EPR instrument: In a typical EPR instrument, a klystron tube is used to generate monochromatic microwave radiation in the ~9.75 GHz (known as the X-band) region. Other regions of interest are the L-band (~1.1 GHz), the S-band (~3.0 GHz), the Q-band (~34.0 GHz), and the W-band (~94.0 GHz). The microwave radiation travels down a waveguide to the sample, which is held in place in a microwave 'cavity' held between the poles of two magnets. Spectra are obtained by measuring the absorption of the microwave radiation while sweeping the magnetic field strength. EPR spectra are usually displayed in derivative form to improve the signal-to-noise ratio.

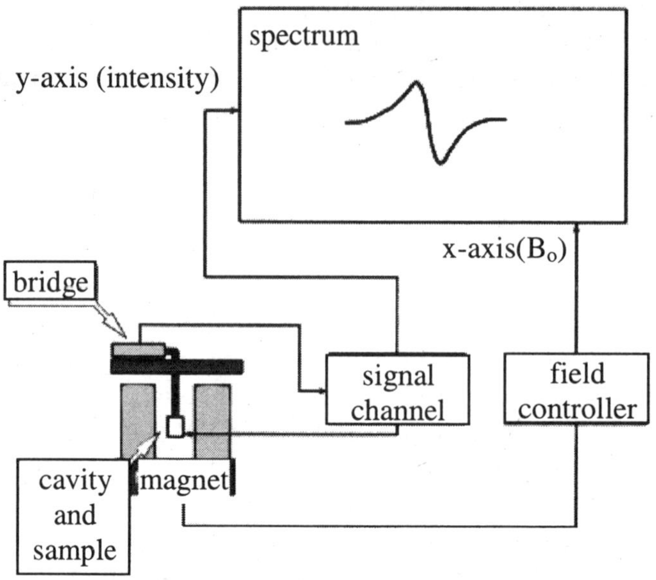

Fig. 5.37 Block Diagram of EPR Instrument

Units and constants: Magnetic field strength is denoted by B or B_0 and is measured in tesla (T) in the SI system. However, in EPR spectroscopy fields are commonly reported using the CGS unit the gauss (G), where 1 G = 10^{-4} T.

Planck's constant $h = 6.6261 \times 10^{-34}$ J s
Boltzmann constant $k = 1.3807 \times 10^{-23}$ J K^{-1}
Bohr magneton $\mu_B = 9.2740 \times 10^{-24}$ J T^{-1}

Origin of an EPR signal: Every electron has a magnetic moment and spin quantum number s = 1/2 , with magnetic components m_s = +1/2 and m_s = -1/2. In the presence of an external magnetic field with strength B_0, the electron's magnetic moment aligns itself either parallel (m_s = -1/2) or antiparallel (m_s = +1/2) to the field, each alignment having a specific energy (Zeeman effect). The parallel alignment corresponds to the lower energy state and the separation between it and the upper state is $\Delta E = g_e \mu_B B_0$, where g_e is the electron's so-called g-factor (Landé *g*-factor). This equation implies that the splitting of the energy levels is directly proportional to the magnetic field's strength as shown in the diagram below:

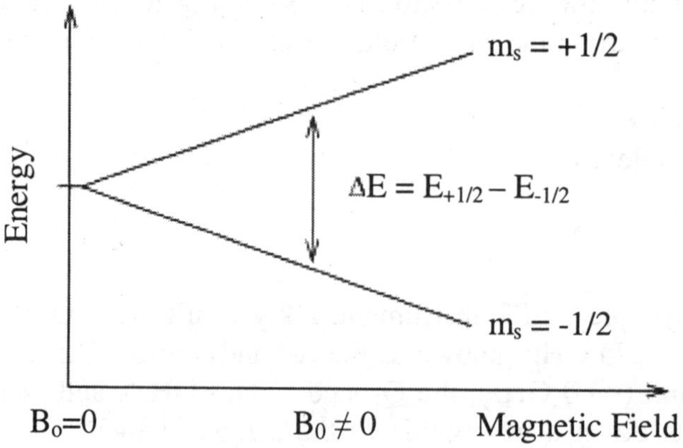

Fig. 5.38: Splitting under Magnetic Field

An unpaired electron can move between the two energy levels by either absorbing or emitting electromagnetic radiation of energy. Substituting in $\varepsilon = h\nu$ and $\Delta E = g_e\mu_B B_0$ leads to the fundamental equation of EPR spectroscopy: $h\nu = g_e\mu_B B_0$. Experimentally, this equation permits a large combination of frequency and magnetic field values, but the great majority of EPR measurements is made with microwaves in the 9000 - 10000 MHz (9 - 10 GHz) region with fields corresponding to about 3500 G (0.3500 T).

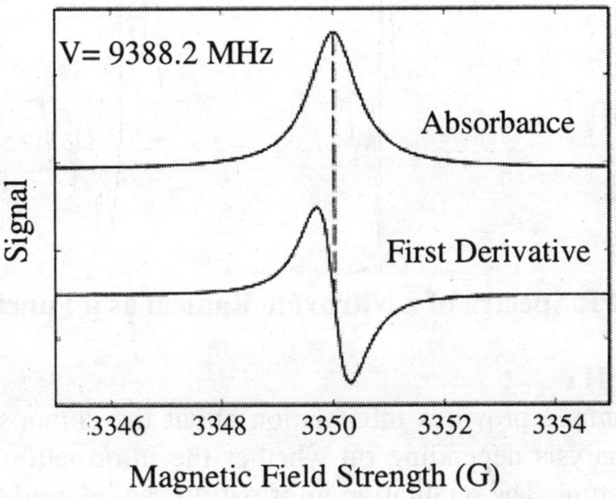

Fig. 5.39: Relation Between Frequency and Magnetic Field Value

As an example of how $h\nu = g_e\mu_B B_0$ can be used, consider the case of a free electron, which has g_e = 2.0023 and the simulated spectrum in two different forms. For the microwave frequency of 9388.2 MHz, the predicted resonance position is a magnetic field of about $B_0 = h\nu / g_e\mu_B$ = 0.3350 tesla = 3350 gauss as shown. Note that while two forms of the same spectrum are presented in the figure, most EPR spectra are recorded and published only as first derivatives.

EPR applications: EPR is used in solid-state physics for the identification and quantification of radicals, in chemistry to identify reaction pathways, as well as in biology and medicine for tagging biological spin probes. Since radicals are very reactive, they do not normally occur in high concentrations in biological environments. With the help of specially designed non reactive radical molecules that attach to specific sites in a biological cell, it is possible to obtain information on the environment of these so-called spin-label or spin-probe molecules.

Table 5.4: Chart of waveband withλ, ν and magnetic field strength

Waveband	**L**	**S**	**C**	**X**	**P**	**K**	**Q**	**U**	**V**	**E**	**W**	**F**	**D**	**—**	**J**	**—**
λ / mm	300	100	75	30	20	12.5	8.5	6	4.6	4	3.2	2.7	2.1	1.6	1.1	0.83
ν / GHz	1	3	4	10	15	24	35	50	65	75	95	111	140	190	285	360
B_0 / T	0.03	0.11	0.14	0.33	0.54	0.86	1.25	1.8	2.3	2.7	3.5	3.9	4.9	6.8	10.2	12.8

The EPR waveband is stipulated by the frequency or wavelength of a spectrometer's microwave source.EPR experiments often are conducted at X and less commonly, Q bands, mainly due to the ready availability of the necessary microwave components (which originally were developed for radar applications). A second reason for widespread X and Q band measurements is that electromagnets can reliably generate fields up to about 1 tesla. However, the low spectral resolution over g-factor at these wavebands limits the study of paramagnetic centers with comparatively low anisotropic magnetic parameters.

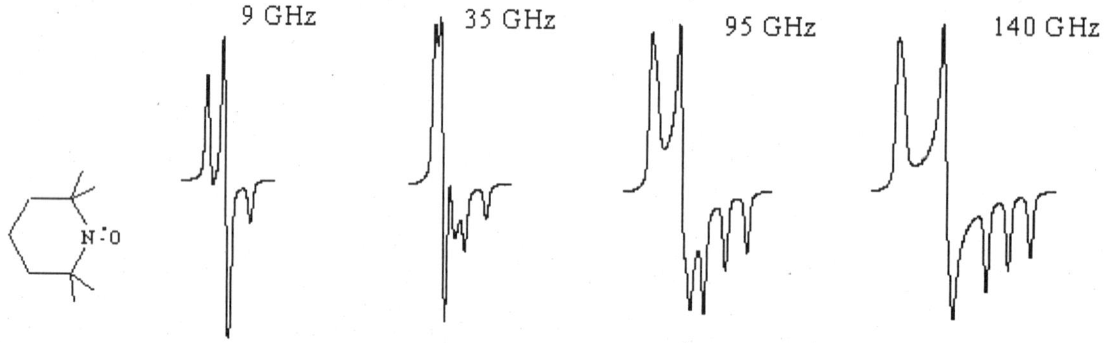

Fig. 5.40: EPR Spectra of a Nitroxide Radical as a Function of Frequency

5.13 CHROMATOGRAPHY

The analysis of a given sample provides information about the composition of the sample. It could be classified as qualitative analysis depending on whether the information provided by it is of qualitative nature or of quantitative nature. The qualitative information can be used to deduce the structural features, atomic species and the functional groups present in a given sample. The results of quantitative analysis take the form of numerical data in units such as %, ppm, mg/l etc. in either type of analysis, the required information is obtained by measurement of some physical property that is characteristically related to the component or component of interest.

These properties which are useful in determination of chemical composition of a sample are called analytical signals. A lot of advancement is taking place in analytical methods. Chromatography is mostly used for the identification and characterization of organic compound. It is used as qualitative as well as quantitative method.

This method for the first time was given by David Day (a Geologist) and Michel Tswett (a Botanist) in 1906. Both of them were trying separation of substances from their mixtures. Day called the method followed by him as frictional diffusion. Michel Tswett named it as chromatography derived from Greek word (*Chroma* meaning colour) and (*Graphein* meaning write).

Chromatography can be defined as an analytical technique used for the separation and identification of solutes from a mixture based on their affinity towards solvent acting as a stationary phase or moving phase. In chromatography technique, there are two phases- one is stationary phase (steady phase) while other one is moving phase (mobile phase). The mixture to be purified can be applied to either a solid or liquid phase acting as a stationary phase, another liquid or gas phase acts as a moving phase and moves slowly over the stationary phase. This movement of moving phase over stationary phase brings about separation of components of mixture by adsorption partition method or ion exchange process.

Classification of Chromatography:

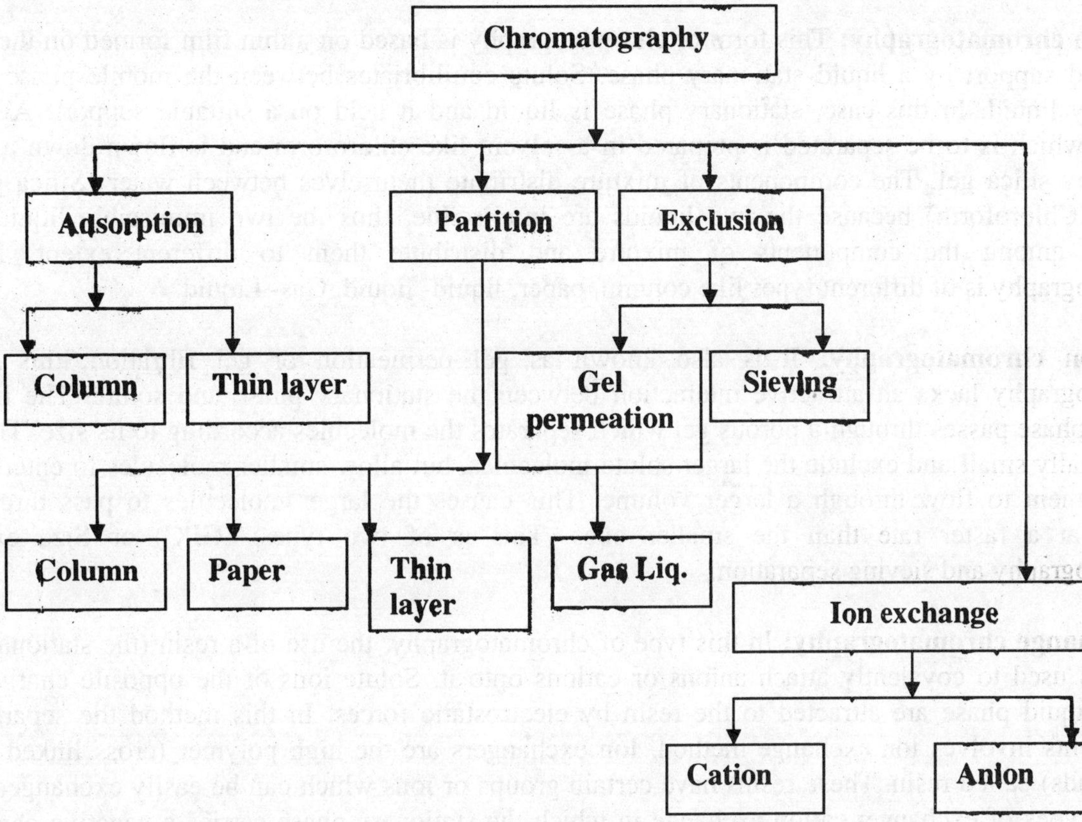

Adsorption chromatography: Adsorption chromatography is probably one of the oldest types of chromatography. It utilizes a mobile liquid or gaseous phase that is adsorbed onto the surface of a stationary solid phase. The equilibrium between the mobile and stationary phase accounts for the separation of different solutes.

This method of separation of components from mixture is carried out by using stationary phase in the form of packed column (e.g. alumina) or thin layer and mobile phase in the solvent form. The mobile is allowed to flow down over the stationary phase, the component which is readily adsorped by the stationary phase remains adsorbed at the top and the other components according to their adsorption on stationary phase. Thus the component having more affinity for stationary phase is retained at the top (upper end) of stationary phase and the component having less affinity or adsorption tendency for the stationary phase penetrates the column to a larger distance and is retained at the bottom (lower end) of stationary phase.

The colourless components of mixture are made visible by a process called development. Thus development is a process of detecting colourless components of a mixture present on stationary phase by spraying a suitable reagent (normally ninhydrin is used as developing agent). This process of visualization of a colourless chromatogram, by spraying with a developing reagent is called development of chromatogram.

Adsorption chromatography includes:
1.Column chromatography (by using packed column)
2.Thin layer chromatography (by using thin layer of liquid steady phase)

3.Ion- exchange chromatography (by using ion exchange as steady phase).

Partition chromatography: This form of chromatography is based on a thin film formed on the surface of a solid support by a liquid stationary phase. Solute equilibriates between the mobile phase and the stationary liquid. In this case, stationary phase is liquid and it held on a suitable support. A solution mixture which is to be separated is prepared in a solvent like chloroform and is flown down a column packed by silica gel. The components of mixture distribute themselves between water (Silica gel) and solvent (Chloroform) because the two liquids are immiscible, thus the two immiscible liquids cause partition among the components of mixture and distribute them to different extent. Partition chromatography is of different types like column, paper, liquid- liquid, Gas- Liquid.

Exclusion chromatography: It is also known as gel permeation or gel filtration, this type of chromatography lacks an attractive interaction between the stationary phase and solute. The liquid or gaseous phase passes through a porous gel which separates the molecules according to its size. The pores are normally small and exclude the larger solute molecules, but allow smaller molecules to enter the gel, causing them to flow through a larger volume. This causes the larger molecules to pass through the column at a faster rate than the smaller ones. This is of two types: (GPC) or Size exclusion chromatography and sieving separation.

Ion-exchange chromatography: In this type of chromatography, the use of a resin (the stationary solid phase) is used to covalently attach anions or cations onto it. Solute ions of the opposite charge in the mobile liquid phase are attracted to the resin by electrostatic forces. In this method the separation of components involves ion exchange method. Ion exchangers are the high polymer (cross linked organic compounds) called resin. These resins have certain groups or ions which can be easily exchanged. There are two types of exchange: cation exchange in which the stationary phase carries a negative charge and anion exchange in which the stationary phase carries a positive charge. Charged molecules in the liquid phase pass through the column until a binding site in the stationary phase appears. The molecule will not elute from the column until a solution of varying pH or ionic strength is passed through it. Separation by this method is highly selective. Since the resins are fairly inexpensive and high capacities can be used, this method of separation is applied early in the overall process.

Affinity Chromatography: This is the most selective type of chromatography employed. It utilizes the specific interaction between one kind of solute molecule and a second molecule that is immobilized on a stationary phase. For example, the immobilized molecule may be an antibody to some specific protein. When solute containing a mixture of proteins is passed by this molecule, only the specific protein is reacted to this antibody, binding it to the stationary phase. This protein is later extracted by changing the ionic strength or pH.

Liquid Chromatography: There are many types of liquid chromatography. There is liquid adsorption chromatography in which an adsorbent is used. This method is used in large-scale applications since adsorbents are relatively inexpensive. There is also liquid-liquid chromatography which is analogous to gas-liquid chromatography. The three types that will be considered here fall under the category of modern liquid chromatography. They are reverse phase, high performance and size exclusion liquid chromatography, along with supercritical fluid chromatography.

Reverse phase chromatography is a powerful analytical tool and involves a hydrophobic, low polarity stationary phase which is chemically bonded to an inert solid such as silica. The separation is essentially an extraction operation and is useful for separating non-volatile components.

High performance liquid chromatography (HPLC) is similar to reverse phase only in this method, the process is conducted at a high velocity and pressure drop. The column is shorter and has a small diameter, but it is equivalent to possessing a large number of equilibrium stages.

Size exclusion chromatography, also known as gel permeation or filtration chromatography does not involve any adsorption and is extremely fast. The packing is a porous gel and is capable of separating large molecules from smaller ones. The larger molecules elute first since they cannot penetrate the pores. This method is common in protein separation and purification.

Supercritical fluid chromatography is a relatively new analytical tool. In this method, the carrier is a supercritical fluid such as carbon dioxide mixed with a modifier. Compared to liquids, supercritical fluids have solubilities and densities as large and they have diffusivities and viscosities quite a bit larger. This type of chromatography has not yet been implemented on a large scale.

Gas Chromatography: Gas chromatography makes use of a pressurized gas cylinder and a carrier gas, such as helium, to carry the solute through the column. The most common detectors used in this type of chromatography are thermal conductivity and flame ionization detectors. There are three types of gas chromatography that will be discussed here: gas adsorption, gas-liquid and capillary gas chromatography.

Gas adsorption chromatography involves a packed bed comprised of an adsorbent used as the stationary phase. Common adsorbents are zeolite, silica gel and activated alumina. This method is commonly used to separate mixtures of gases.

Gas-liquid chromatography is a more common type of analytical gas chromatography. In this type of column, an inert porous solid is coated with a viscous liquid which acts as the stationary phase. Diatomaceous earth is the most common solid used. Solutes in the feed stream dissolve into the liquid phase and eventually vaporize. The separation is thus based on relative volatilities.

Capillary gas chromatography is the most common analytical method. Glass or fused silica comprises the capillary walls which are coated with an absorbent or other solvent. Because of the small amount of stationary phase, the column can contain only a limited capacity. However, this method also yields rapid separation of mixtures.

Theory: Gas chromatography (GC) is a type of chromatography in which the mobile phase is a carrier gas, usually an inert gas such as helium or an unreactive gas such as nitrogen, and the stationary phase is a microscopic layer of liquid or polymer on an inert solid support, inside glass or metal tubing, called a column. The instrument used to perform gas chromatographic separations is called a gas chromatograph.

Retention: The retention is a measure of the speed at which a substance moves in a chromatographic system. In continuous development systems like HPLC or GC, where the compounds are eluted with the eluent, the retention is usually measured as the retention time R_t or t_R, the time between injection and detection. In interrupted development systems like TLC the retention is measured as the retention factor R_f, the run length of the compound divided by the run length of the eluent front:

$$R_f = \frac{\text{Distance moved by compound}}{\text{Distance moved by solvent}}$$

The retention of a compound often differs considerably between experiments due to variations of the eluent, the stationary phase, temperature, sample matrix and the setup. It is therefore important to compare the retention of the test compound to that of several standard compounds under absolutely identical conditions.

Instrument: A gas chromatograph is a chemical analysis instrument for separating chemicals in a complex sample. A gas chromatograph uses a flow-through narrow tube known as the column, through which different chemical constituents of a sample pass in a gas stream (carrier gas, mobile phase) at different rates depending on their various chemical and physical properties and their interaction with a specific column filling, called the stationary phase. As the chemicals exit the end of the column, they are detected and identified electronically. The function of the stationary phase in the column is to separate different components, causing each one to exit the column at a different time (retention time). Other parameters that can be used to alter the order or time of retention are the carrier gas flow rate and the temperature.

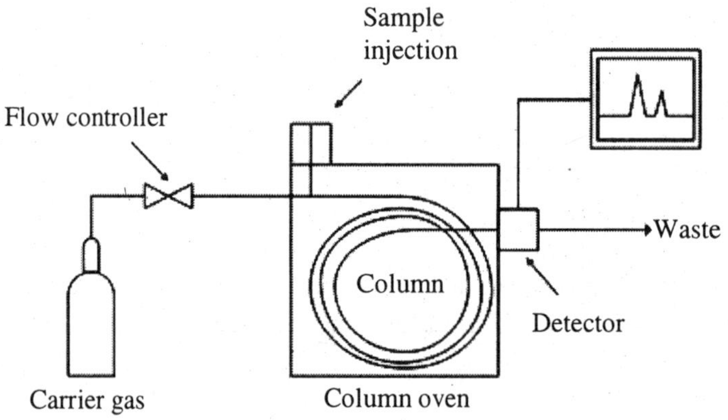

Fig. 5.41: Diagram of a Gas Chromatograph

Columns: Two types of columns are used in GC:

1. **Packed columns:** These columns are 1.5 - 10 m in length and have an internal diameter of 2 - 4 mm. The tubing is usually made of stainless steel or glass and contains a packing of finely divided, inert, solid support material (e.g. diatomaceous earth) that is coated with a liquid or solid stationary phase. The nature of the coating material determines what type of materials will be most strongly adsorbed. Thus numerous columns are available that are designed to separate specific types of compounds.
2. **Capillary columns:** Capillary columns have a very small internal diameter of the order of a few tenths of millimeters and lengths between 25-60 meters. The inner column walls are coated with the active materials. Most capillary columns are made of fused-silica with a polyimide outer coating. These columns are flexible, so a very long column can be wound into a small coil.

Carrier Gas: The choice of carrier gas (mobile phase) is important, with hydrogen being the most efficient and providing the best separation. Typical carrier gases include helium, nitrogen, argon, hydrogen and air. However, helium has a larger range of flow rates that are comparable to hydrogen in efficiency, with the added advantage that helium is non-flammable and works with a greater number of detectors. Therefore, helium is the most common carrier gas used.

Detectors: A number of detectors are used in gas chromatography. The most common are the flame ionization detector (FID) and the thermal conductivity detector (TCD). Both are sensitive to a wide range of components and both work over a wide range of concentrations.

Working: In a GC analysis, a known volume of gaseous or liquid analyte is injected into the "entrance" (head) of the column, usually using a microsyringe (or, solid phase microextraction fibers, or a gas source switching system). As the carrier gas sweeps the analyte molecules through the column, this motion is inhibited by the adsorption of the analyte molecules either onto the column walls or onto packing materials in the column. The rate at which the molecules progress along the column depends on the strength of adsorption, which in turn depends on the type of molecule and on the stationary phase materials. Since each type of molecule has a different rate of progression, the various components of the analyte mixture are separated as they progress along the column and reach the end of the column at different times (retention time). A detector is used to monitor the outlet stream from the column; thus, the time at which each component reaches the outlet and the amount of that component can be determined. Generally, substances are identified (qualitatively) by the order in which they emerge (elute) from the column and by the retention time of the analyte in the column. A chromatogram is the visual output of the chromatograph. In the case of an optimal separation, different peaks or patterns on the chromatogram correspond to different components of the separated mixture.

Applications:

1) **Qualitative analysis:** Generally chromatographic data is presented as a graph of detector response (y-axis) against retention time (x-axis). This provides a spectrum of peaks for a sample representing the analytes present in a sample eluting from the column at different times. Retention time can be used to identify analytes if the method conditions are constant. Also, the pattern of peaks will be constant for a sample under constant conditions and can identify complex mixtures of analytes. In most modern applications however the GC is connected to a mass spectrometer or similar detector that is capable of identifying the analytes represented by the peaks.

2) **Quantitative analysis:** The area under a peak is proportional to the amount of analyte present. By calculating the area of the peak using the mathematical function of integration, the concentration of an analyte in the original sample can be determined. Concentration can be calculated using a calibration curve created by finding the response for a series of concentrations of analyte or by determining the response factor of an analyte. The response factor is the expected ratio of an analyte to an internal standard and is calculated by finding the response of a known amount of analyte and a constant amount of internal standard (a chemical added to the sample at a constant concentration, with a distinct retention time to the analyte).

3) In most modern GC-MS systems, computer software is used to draw and integrate peaks and match MS spectra to library spectra. In general, substances that vaporize below 300°C (and therefore are stable up to that temperature) can be measured quantitatively. The samples are also required to be salt-free, they should not contain ions. Very minute amounts of a substance can be measured but it is often required that the sample must be measured in comparison to a sample containing the pure substance.Various temperature programs can be used to make the readings more meaningful for example to differentiate between substances that behave similarly during the GC process.

4) Professionals working with GC analyze the content of a chemical product, for example in assuring the quality of products in the chemical industry; or measuring toxic substances in soil, air or water. GC is very accurate if used properly and can measure picomoles of a substance in a 1 ml liquid sample or parts-per-billion concentrations in gaseous samples.

5) It is used to study the contents of Lavender oil or measuring the ethylene that is secreted by Nicotiana benthamiana plants after artificially injuring their leaves. GC analyses hydrocarbons (C_2-C_{40}+).

6) Gas chromatography is successfully used for the separation and determination of many components in petroleum products.

Advantages:

- In gas chromatography, single sharp peak per component, maximum height per peak, minimum peak width and minimum retention time are observed in chromatogram.
- The method is highly sensitive and requires very small amount of sample mixture.
- The method is quick and easy.
- The method gives good precision and accuracy.
- It is most suitable for routine analysis because the results of chromatography are highly reliable.

Disadvantages:

- It is generally suitable for easily vaporizable and thermally stable components.
- The low boiling components elute quickly a bunch on records chart.
- Components having same characteristics but having widely varying volatility, create difficulty in their separation.

Here are chromatograms of Sulphur hexa fluoride and unresolved complex mixture:

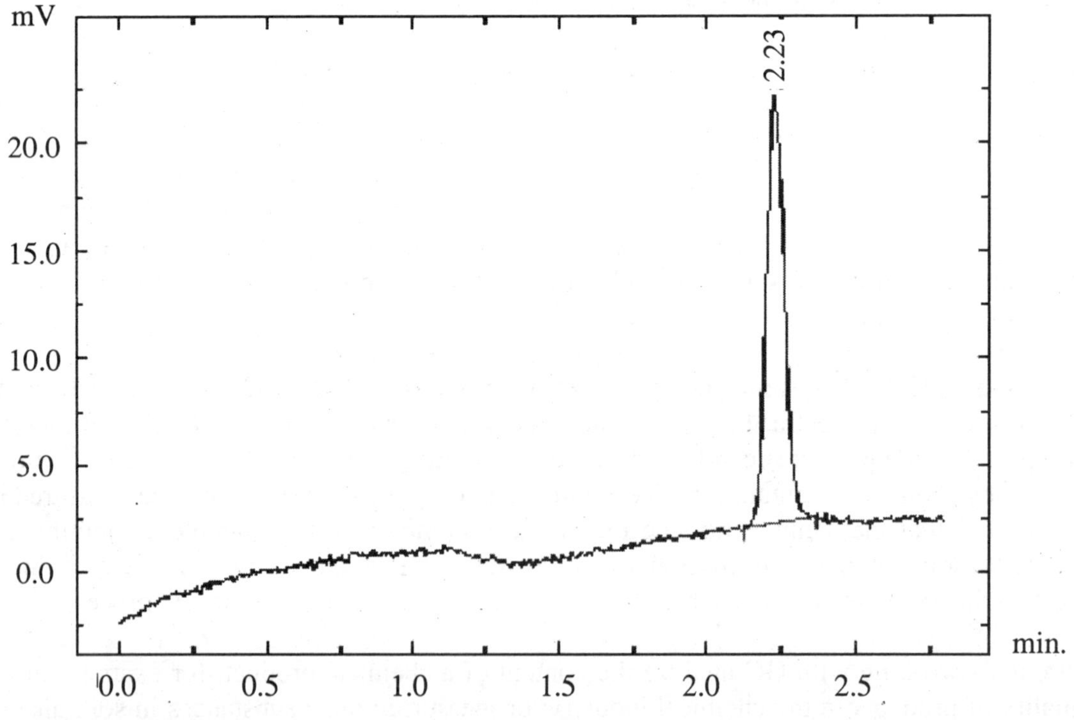

Fig. 5.42: Chromatogram of SF_6 Extracted from 950 Cc of Water

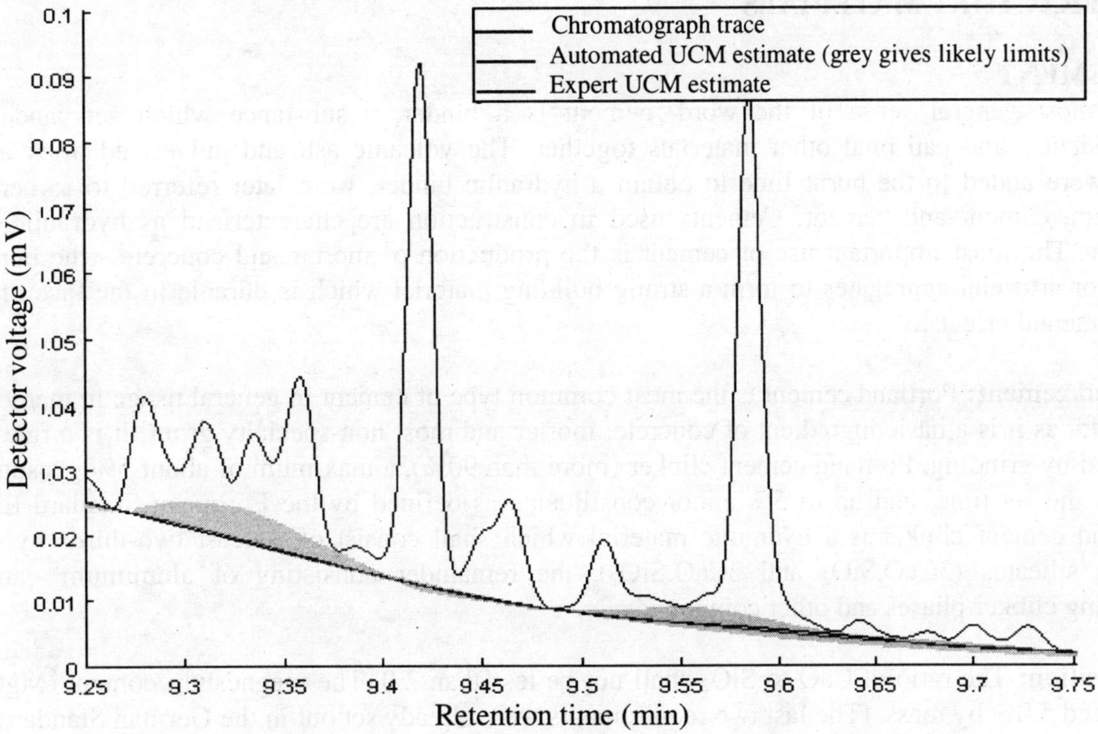

Fig. 5.43: Estimation of Unresolved Complex Mixture

[B] REFRACTORY MATERIALS

5.14 CEMENT

In the most general sense of the word, cement is a binder, a substance which sets and hardens independently and can bind other materials together. The volcanic ash and pulverized brick additives which were added to the burnt lime to obtain a hydraulic binder, were later referred to as cementum, cimentum, cäment and cement. Cements used in construction are characterized as hydraulic or non-hydraulic.The most important use of cement is the production of mortar and concrete - the bonding of natural or artificial aggregates to form a strong building material which is durable in the face of normal environmental effects.

Portland cement: Portland cement is the most common type of cement in general usage in many parts of the world, as it is a basic ingredient of concrete, mortar and most non-specialty grout. It is a fine powder produced by grinding. Portland cement clinker (more than 90%), a maximum of about 5% gypsum which controls the set time, and up to 5% minor constituents as defined by the European Standard EN197.1, "Portland cement clinker is a hydraulic material which shall consist of at least two-thirds by mass of calcium silicates ($3CaO.SiO_2$ and $2CaO.SiO_2$), the remainder consisting of aluminium and iron-containing clinker phases and other compounds.

Composition: The ratio of CaO to SiO_2 shall not be less than 2.0. The magnesium content (MgO) shall not exceed 5.0% by mass. (The last two requirements were already set out in the German Standard, issued in 1909). Portland cement clinker is made by heating in a kiln, a homogeneous mixture of raw materials to a sintering temperature, which is about 1450°C for modern cements. The aluminium oxide and iron oxide are present as a flux and contribute little to the strength. For special cements, such as Low Heat (LH) and Sulfate Resistant (SR) types, it is necessary to limit the amount of tricalcium aluminate ($3CaO.Al_2O_3$) formed. The major raw material for the clinker-making is usually limestone ($CaCO_3$). Normally, an impure limestone which contains SiO_2, is used. The $CaCO_3$ content can be even 80%. Secondary raw materials (materials in the raw mix other than limestone) depend on the purity of the limestone. Some of the secondary raw materials used are clay, shale, sand, iron ore, bauxite, fly ash and slag. When a cement kiln is fired by coal, the ash of coal acts as secondary raw material.

ISI Specification of Portland cement:

i) Lime saturation factor $= \dfrac{CaO - 0.7SO_3}{2.8SiO_2 + 1.2Al_2O_3 + Fe_2O_3} = 0.66$ to 1.02

ii) The ratio $\dfrac{Al_2O_3}{Fe_2O_3}$ shall not be less that 0.66.

iii) Insoluble residue should not exceed 2%.

iv) Total sulphur contents calculated as sulphuric anhydride (SO_3) shall not be more than 2.75%.

v) The weight of magnesia (MgO) should not exceed 6%.

vi) Loss on ignition shall not exceed 4%.

vii) Fineness not to exceed 10 %, after sieving the residue (by weight) on B.S. 170- mesh test seive.

viii) Setting times: Initial = 30 minutes, Final = 10 hrs.

ix) Heat of hydration:
After seven days: < 65 cal/gm
After twenty eight days: < 75 cal/ gm

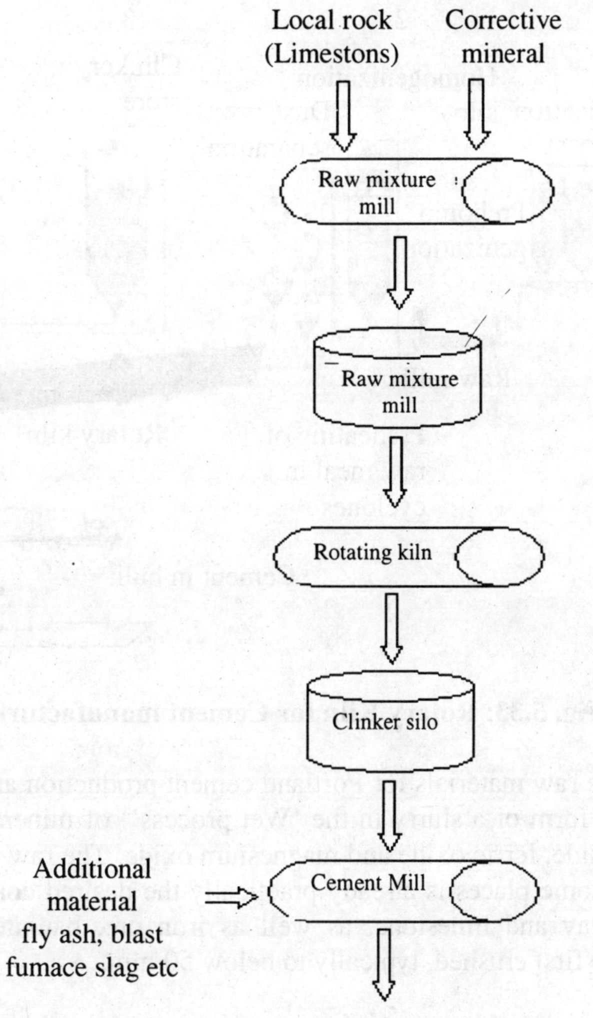

Fig. 5.32: Flow Sheet of Cement Manufacturing

Schematic explanation of Portland cement production: There are three fundamental stages in the production of Portland cement:

- Preparation of the raw mixture
- Production of the clinker
- Preparation of the cement

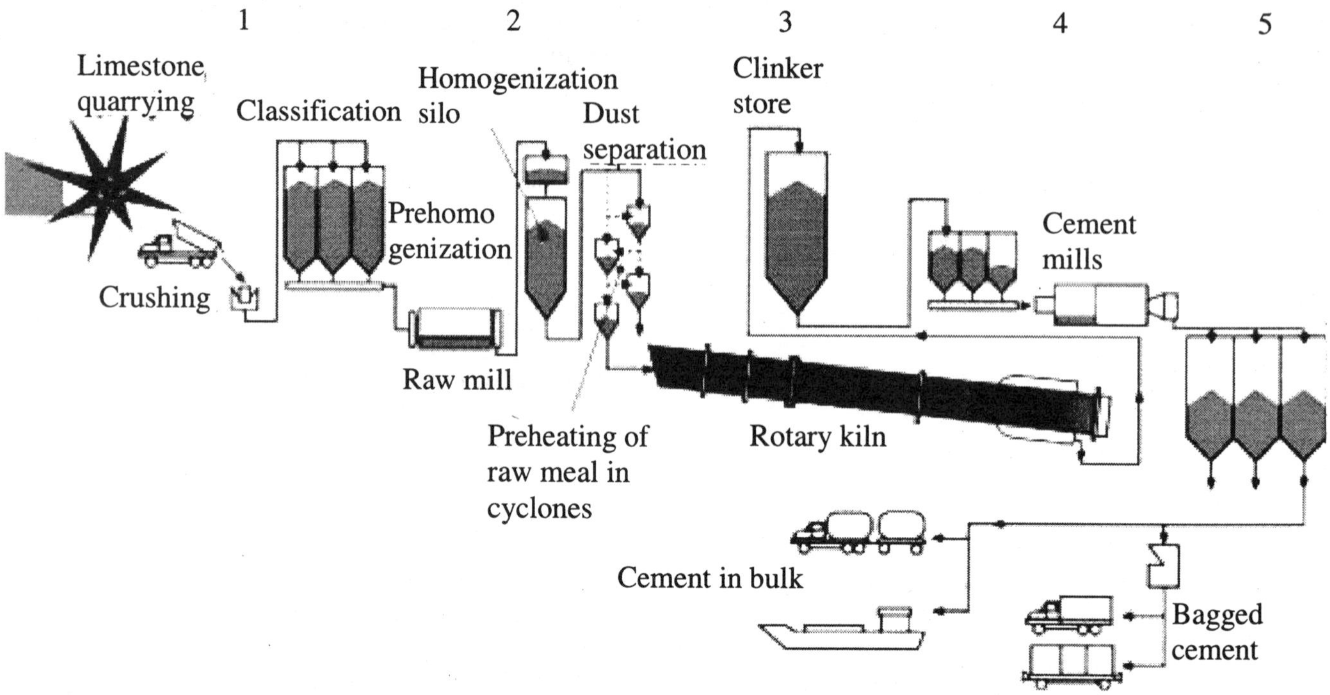

Fig. 5.33: Rotary Kiln for Cement manufacturing

Raw mix preparation: The raw materials for Portland cement production are mixture (as fine powder in the 'Dry process' or in the form of a slurry in the 'Wet process') of minerals containing calcium oxide, silicon oxide, aluminium oxide, ferric oxide and magnesium oxide. The raw materials are usually quarried from local rock, which in some places is already practically the desired composition and in other places requires the addition of clay and limestone, as well as iron ore, bauxite or recycled materials. The individual raw materials are first crushed, typically to below 50 mm.

The raw materials are next ground together in a rawmill. Silos of individual raw materials are arranged over the feed conveyor belt. Accurately controlled proportions of each material are delivered onto the belt by weigh-feeders. Passing into the rawmill, the mixture is ground to raw mix. The fineness of raw mix is specified in terms of the size of the largest particles and is usually controlled so that there are less than 5-15% by mass of particles exceeding 90 μm in diameter. It is important that the raw mix contains no large particles in order to complete the chemical reactions in the kiln and to ensure the mix is chemically homogenous.

In the case of a dry process, the rawmill also dries the raw materials, usually by passing hot exhaust gases from the kiln through the mill, so that the raw mix emerges as a fine powder. This is conveyed to the blending system by conveyor belt or by a powder pump. In the case of wet process, water is added to the rawmill feed and the mill product is slurry with moisture content usually in the range of 25-45% by mass. This slurry is conveyed to the blending system by conventional liquid pumps.

Raw mix blending: The raw mix is formulated to a very tight chemical specification. Typically, the content of individual components in the raw mix must be controlled within 0.1% . Calcium and silicon are present in order to form the strength-producing calcium silicates. Aluminium and iron are used in order to produce liquid ("flux") in the kiln burning zone. The liquid acts as a solvent for the silicate-forming reactions and allows these to occur at an economically low temperature. Insufficient aluminium and iron lead to difficult burning of the clinker, while excessive amounts lead to low strength due to dilution of the silicates by aluminates and ferrites.

Formation of clinker: The raw mixture is heated in a cement kiln, a slowly rotating and sloped cylinder, with temperatures increasing over the length of the cylinder upto a peak temperature of 1400-1450 °C. A complex succession of chemical reactions takes place as the temperature rises. The peak temperature is regulated so that the product contains sintered but not fused lumps. Sintering consists of the melting of 25-30% of the mass of the material. The resulting liquid draws the remaining solid particles together by surface tension and acts as a solvent for the final chemical reaction in which alite is formed. Too low temperature causes insufficient sintering and incomplete reaction, but too high temperature results in a molten mass or glass destruction of the kiln lining and waste of fuel. The resulting material is clinker.

On cooling, it is conveyed to storage. The clinker can be stored for a number of years before use. Prolonged exposure to water decreases the reactivity of cement produced from weathered clinker. The high energy requirements and the release of significant amounts of carbon dioxide make cement production a concern for global warming.

Cement Grinding: In order to achieve the desired setting qualities in the finished product, a quantity (2-8%, but typically 5%) of calcium sulfate (usually gypsum or anhydride) is added to the clinker and the mixture is finely ground to form the finished cement powder. This is achieved in a cement mill. The grinding process is controlled to obtain a powder with a particle size range, in which typically 15% by mass consists of particles below 5 μm diameter and 5% of particles above 45 μm.

The cement is conveyed by belt or powder pump to a silo for storage. Cement plants normally have sufficient silo space for 1-20 weeks production, depending upon local demand cycles. The cement is delivered to end-users either in bags or as bulk powder blown from a pressure vehicle into the customer's silo. In developed countries, 80% or more of cement is delivered in bulk and many cement plants have no bag-packing facility. In developing countries, bags are the normal mode of delivery.

Table 5.6:Typical constituents of Portland clinker and Portland cement

Clinker	Mass%	Cement	Mass%
Tricalcium silicate $(CaO)_3.SiO_2$, C_3S	45-75%	Calcium oxide, CaO, *C*	61-67%
Dicalcium silicate $(CaO)_2.SiO_2$, C_2S	7-32%	Silicon oxide, SiO_2, *S*	19-23%
Tricalcium aluminate $(CaO)_3.Al_2O_3$, C_3A	0-13%	Aluminium oxide, Al_2O_3, *A*	2.5-6%
Tetracalcium aluminoferrite $(CaO)_4.Al_2O_3.Fe_2O_3$, C_4AF	0-18%	Ferric oxide, Fe_2O_3, *F*	0-6%
Gypsum $CaSO_4$	2-10%	Sulfate	

Setting and Hardening: When water is mixed with portland cement, the product sets in a few hours and hardens over a period of weeks. These processes can vary widely depending upon the mix used and the conditions of curing of the product, but a typical concrete sets (i.e. becomes rigid) in about 6 hours and develops a compressive strength of 8 MPa in 24 hours. The strength rises to 15 MPa at 3 days, 23 MPa at one week, 35 MPa at 4 weeks and 41 MPa at three months. In principle, the strength continues to rise slowly as long as water is available for continued hydration, but concrete is usually allowed to dry out after a few weeks and this causes strength growth to stop.

Setting and hardening of portland cement are caused by the formation of water-containing compounds, forming as a result of reactions between cement components and water. Usually, cement reacts in a plastic mixture only at water/cement ratios between 0.25 and 0.75. The reaction and the reaction products are referred to as hydration and hydrates or hydrate phases respectively. As a result of the reactions (which start immediately), a stiffening can be observed which is very small in the beginning, but which increases with time. The point in time at which it reaches a certain level is called the start of setting. The consecutive further consolidation is called setting, after which the phase of hardening begins.

$$2Ca_3OSiO_4 + 6H_2O \rightarrow 3CaO.2SiO_2.3H_2O + 3Ca(OH)_2$$

This is a relatively fast reaction, causing setting and strength development in the first few weeks. The reaction of belite is:

$$2Ca_2SiO_4 + 4H_2O \rightarrow 3CaO.2SiO_2.3H_2O + Ca(OH)_2$$

This reaction is relatively slow and is mainly responsible for strength growth after one week. Tricalcium aluminate hydration is controlled by the added calcium sulfate, which immediately goes into solution when water is added. First of all, ettringite is rapidly formed, causing a slowing of the hydration :

$$Ca_3(AlO_3)_2 + 3CaSO_4 + 32H_2O \rightarrow Ca_6(AlO_3)_2(SO_4)_3.32H_2O$$

The ettringite subsequently reacts slowly with further tricalcium aluminate to form "monosulfate" - an "AFm phase":

$$Ca_6(AlO_3)_2(SO_4)_3.32H_2O + Ca_3(AlO_3)_2 + 4H_2O \rightarrow 3Ca_4(AlO_3)_2(SO_4).12H_2O$$

This reaction is complete after 1-2 days. The calcium aluminoferrite reacts slowly due to precipitation of hydrated iron oxide:

$$2Ca_2AlFeO_5 + CaSO_4 + 16H_2O \rightarrow Ca_4(AlO_3)_2(SO_4).12H_2O + Ca(OH)_2 + 2Fe(OH)_3$$

pH-value of the pore solution reaches comparably high values and is of importance for most of the hydration reactions.

Plaster of Paris: Plaster of Paris, or simply plaster, is a type of building material based on calcium sulfate hemihydrate (gypsum), nominally $CaSO_4 \cdot 0.5H_2O$. It is created by heating gypsum to about 150 °C.

$$2CaSO_4 \cdot 4H_2O \rightarrow 2CaSO_4 \cdot H_2O + 3H_2O \text{ (released as steam)}$$

A large gypsum deposit at Montmartre in Paris is the source of the name. When the dry plaster powder is mixed with water, it re-forms into gypsum. Plaster is used as a building material similar to mortar or cement. Like those materials, plaster starts as a dry powder that is mixed with water to form a paste, which then hardens. Unlike mortar and cement, plaster remains quite soft after drying and can be easily manipulated with metal tools or even sandpaper. These characteristics make plaster suitable for a finishing, rather than a load-bearing material.

Applications of Plaster of Paris:

Use in Room Interiors: Plaster was a common building material for wall surfaces in a process known as lath and plaster, whereby a series of wooden strips are covered with a semi-dry plaster and then hardened into surface. The plaster used in most lath-and-plaster construction was mainly lime plaster. Lime plaster cure time is about a month. To stabilize the lime plaster during curing, small amounts of Plaster of Paris were mixed into the putty. Interior may be geometric (simulating wood or stone) or naturalistic (simulating leaves, vines and flowers).

Use in Theatres and Movie Sets : One of the skills used in movie and theatrical sets is that of "plasterer" and the material is often used to simulate the appearance of surfaces of wood, stone, or metal. Now a days, plasterers are just like expanded polystyrene, although the job title remains unchanged.

Use in Medicine: Plaster is widely used as a support for broken bones; a bandage impregnated with plaster is moistened and then wrapped around the damaged limb, setting into a close-fitting yet easily removed tube, known as a cast. Plaster is also used within radiotherapy while making immobilisation casts for patients. Plaster bandages are used when constructing an impression of the patients head and neck and liquid plaster is used to fill the impression and produce a plaster bust.

Cement Plaster:
Cement Plaster is a mixture of suitable plaster sand, portland cement and water which is normally applied to masonry interiors and exteriors to achieve a smooth surface. Interior surfaces sometimes receive a final layer of gypsum plaster. Walls constructed with stock bricks are normally plastered while face brick walls are not plastered. Various cement-based plasters are also used as proprietary spray fireproofing products the world over. These usually use vermiculite as lightweight aggregate. Heavy versions of such plasters are also in use for exterior fireproofing, to protect LPG vessels, pipe bridges and vessel skirts.

Passive fire protection: Plasters have been in use in passive fire protection, as fireproofing products, for many decades. They are subject to stringent bounding. The plaster provides a layer of insulation to retard heat flow into structural steel elements, that would otherwise lose their strength and collapse in fire.

5.15 REFRACTORY

The term refractory refers to the quality of a material to retain its strength at high temperatures. Refractory materials are used to make crucibles and linings for furnaces, kilns and incinerators. There is no clearly established boundary between refractory and non-refractory materials, though a practical requirement often cited is the ability of the material to withstand temperatures above 1100 °C without softening.

Refractory materials: Refractory materials are defined as inorganic materials which can withstand high temperatures without softening or suffering deformation or melting in shape. They must be strong at high temperatures, resistant to thermal shock, chemically inert, have low thermal conductivities and coefficients of expansion. The oxides of magnesium (magnesia) and calcium (lime) are the most important refractory materials, though fireclay is widely used as well. Zirconia is used when the material must withstand extremely high temperatures. Silicon carbide is another refractory material. It is very strong at high temperatures, but will burn in the presence of oxygen, if the protective silica coating comes off. Refractories must be chosen according to the conditions they will face. For example, carbon cannot be used when it will be in contact with oxygen, as it will burn.

Classification of Refractories: These are classified into three main types on the basis of chemical properties of their constituent substances:

1. **Acid refractories**: They consist of acidic material like alumina (Al_2O_3) and silica (SiO_2). They are not attacked by acid but easily attacked by basic materials. e.g. Alumina, Silica, Fire clay refractories.
2. **Basic refractories**: They consist of basic materials like CaO, MgO etc. They are not attacked by basic material but attacked by acidic materials e.g. magnesite, dolomite, chrome magnesite etc.
3. **Neutral refractories**: These are not attacked by slightly acidic or basic media. They consist of

weakly/ acid/ basic material like carbon, chromite, graphite, silicon, carbide, zirconia and carborundum (SiC).

Acidic refractories cannot be used in a basic environment and basic refractories cannot be used in acidic environment because they will be corroded. Zircon, fireclay and silica are acidic, dolomite and magnesite are basic and alumina, chromite, silicon carbide, carbon and mullite are neutral. Refractory metals are also frequently used.

Refractory metals: There are a class of metals extraordinarily resistant to heat, wear and corrosion. These properties make them useful in many applications. Household incandescent bulbs contain refractory metals in their tungsten filaments. The five refractory metals are:

Tungsten (W), Molybdenum (Mo) ,Niobium (Nb), Tantalum (Ta) and Rhenium (Re).

Refractory metals are used in lighting, tools, lubricants, nuclear reaction control rods as catalysts and for their chemical or electrical properties. Because of their high melting point, refractory metal components are never fabricated by casting. The process of powder metallurgy is used. Powders of the pure metal are compacted, heated using electric current and further fabricated by cold working with annealing steps. Refractory metals can be worked into wire, ingots, bars, sheets or foil.

Properties of Refractories:

a) Refractoriness: It is the ability of a refractory material to withstand the heat without appreciable softening or deformation under given service conditions. It is generally measured as the softening temperature.It should have the higher softening temperature than the operating temperature of the furnace in which it is to be used.

Measurement of Refractoriness: The softening temperatures of the refractories are determined by Segar cones (also called pyrometric cones) test.In this test behaviour of heat on cone of refractory (to be tested) and series of Segar cones of standard dimensions are compared.These cones are small pyramid shaped with triangular base, 38 mm high with 19 mm long sides. The test refractory in the form of a cone is kept along the side of similar sized standard cones and all are heated uniformly at 20^0 C/ hr,100^0C/ hr or 150^0C / hr or occasionally at 600 ^{0} C/ hr. As Segar cones are made of a particular refractory of a definite softening temperature, so they are assigned ascending Segar cone numbers with increasing softening temperature. When the test cone softens and loses its shape, one of the standard Segar cone also softens and loses its shape provided its refractoriness is close to that of the test cone. The serial number of this standard Segar cone is noted and number is the Pyrometric cone equivalent (PCE) of the refractory under that test. When the test cone softens earlier than one standard cone, but later than the previous one, the PCE value of the test sample is approximated as average of the two. The temperature at which the softening or fusion of the test- cone occurs is indicated by touching its base.

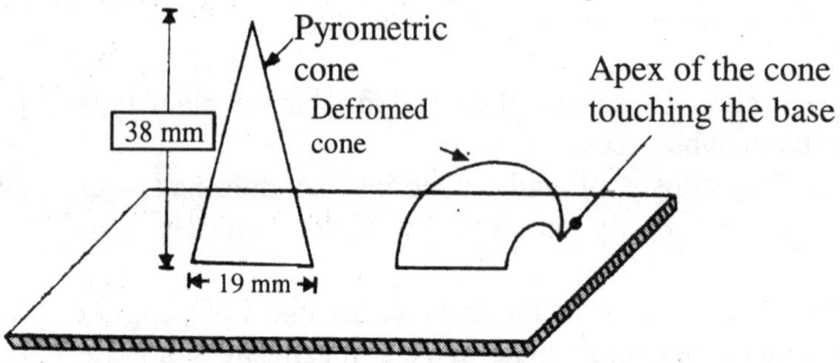

Fig. 5.34: Pyrometric cone equivalent test

b) Refractoriness-underload (or strength): Temperature resistance and load bearing capacity are the two essential qualities of a refractory. This is due to the fact that commercial refractories which are used for lining high temperature furnace are expected to withstand varying loads of the charge. Hence they should possess high strength and excellent temperature resistance.

Measurement: Refractoriness under load test is performed by applying a load of (3.5 or 1.75 kg/ cm^2) to the refractory specimen (of size 5 cm, 2 cm and 75 cm high).The sample is then kept in carbon – resistance furnace and heating is started at the rate of 10^0C/ minute. The height of the specimen is plotted vs. temperature and RUL is expresed as the temperature at which 10 % deformation takes place. Based on R.U.L test, refractory material is classified into following three categories:

i) A high heat – duty brick (which does not deform more than 10 % at 1350 ^{0} C)

ii) An intermediate heat – duty brick (which does not deform more than 10 % at 1300 ^{0}C).

iii) A moderate heat- duty brick (which does not deform more than 10% at 1100 ^{0}C).

c) Dimensional stability: Dimensional stability is the resistance of a material to any change in volume when it is exposed to high temperature over a prolonged time.

Types of Dimensional Changes:

i) **Permanent Contraction:** When a refractory is subjected to high temperatures for long duration, either low fusible constituent melts away forming liquid which fills the pores of the refractory body causing shrinkage and vitrification. Fire clay brick shows such type of behaviour or transformation of one crystalline form of material into another more dense form can also take place. For example, consider magnesite brick:

$$\underset{(sp.gr = 3.05)}{\text{Amorphous MgO}} \longrightarrow \underset{(sp.gr. = 3.54)}{\text{Crystalline, Periclase}}$$

With the increase in density, there is shrinkage in magnesite brick.

ii) **Permanent expansion:** Transformation of one crystalline form of refractory into another of low density leads to expansion when a refractory is subjected to high temperature for longer duration. Silica brick is one example, which undergoes permanent expansion in service. For instance, crystalline transformation in silica brick is given below:

$$\underset{(sp.gr = 2.65)}{\text{Quartz}} \longrightarrow \underset{(sp.gr = 2.26)}{\text{tridymite}} \longrightarrow \underset{(sp.gr = 2.32)}{\text{cristobalite}}$$

d) Chemical inertness: The refractory material which is used as lining for furnace walls should be chemically inert to the chemicals charged into a furnace. It should not react with the reactants, slags, furnace gases, fuels, ashes and the products involved inside the furnace. Such reaction can contaminate the product and gradually corrode the furnace. Hence, it is not advisable to employ an acid refractory in contact with an alkaline product or vice-versa.

e) Thermal expansion and contraction: A good refractory material should have least possible coefficient of thermal expansion. Since like other materials, refractory also expands when heated and contracts when cooled. Repeated expansion and contraction contribute much towards rapid wear and tear of the refractory structure and its rapid breakdown. Sustained strong binding between the refractory lining, base structure and within the refractory matter is possible only when the thermal effect or volume (coefficient of expansion) is negligible. Due to thermal shock, a sub standard refractory develops cracks and then detaches itself from the furnace wall. It is essential therefore that allowance should be made for thermal expansion.

f) Thermal spalling: Rapid changes in temperature cause uneven expansion and contraction of refractory material, thereby leading to development of internal stresses and strains. This in turn is responsible for cracking, breaking or fracturing of a refractory brick of block under high temperature, collectively known as thermal spalling. Thermal spalling can also be caused by the variation in the coefficient of expansion due to slag penetration in the refractory brick. A good refractory must show a good resistance to thermal spalling. Thermal spalling can be decreased by minimising the development of internal stressed by:

1. Using a refractory with high porosity, good thermal conductivity and low coefficient of expansion,
2. Avoiding sudden temperature changes,
3. Proper furnace design.

g) Permeability: It is a measure of rate of diffusion of molten solids, liquids and gases through the connected pores of refractory. The higher is the porosity of a refractory brick, the more easily it is penetrated by gases and molten fluxes. Permeability depends on the size and number of connected pores. A good refractory material should show low permeability.

h) Texture: Texture can be coarse or fine. Porosity of coarse or light textured bricks is higher than fine or dense- textured bricks. That is why coarse textured refractory bricks have
i) Good resistance to thermal spalling.
ii) Low crushing strength.
iii) Low abrasion and corrosion resistance.

i) Porosity: Porosity of a refractory material is ratio of its pore's volume to the bulk volume. Pores are present in all refractory materials and these can be open or closed. Porosity affects many characteristics of a refractory material. For instance, flue gases, slag and / or molten charge can penetrate to greater depth and may react and reduce the life of refractory material of porous refractory. Porosity can also increase thermal shock resistance.

5.16 REFRACTORY BRICKS

Dolomite: It is the name of a sedimentary carbonate rock and a mineral, both composed of calcium magnesium carbonate Ca, Mg $(CO_3)_2$ found in crystals. Dolomite rock (also dolostone) is composed predominantly of the mineral dolomite. Limestone that is partially replaced by dolomite is referred to as dolomitic limestone or in old U.S. geologic literature as magnesian limestone. Dolomite was first described in 1791 as the rock by the French naturalist and geologist, Déodat Gratet de Dolomieu (1750-1801) for exposures in the Dolomite Alps of northern Italy.

The mineral dolomite crystallizes in the trigonal - rhombohedral system. It forms white, grey to pink, commonly curved crystals although it is usually massive. It has physical properties similar to those of the mineral calcite, but does not rapidly dissolve or effervesce (fizz) in dilute hydrochloric acid. The Mg hardness is 3.5 to 4 and the specific gravity is 2.85. Crystal twinning is common. A solid solution series exists between dolomite and iron rich ankerite. Small amounts of iron in the structure give the crystals a yellow to brown tint. High manganese content gives the crystals a rosy pink colour. A series with the manganese rich kutnohorite may exist. Lead and zinc also substitute in the structure for magnesium.

Alumina: Aluminium oxide is an amphoteric oxide of aluminium with the chemical formula Al_2O_3. It is also commonly referred to as alumina in the mining, ceramic and materials science communities. Aluminium oxide is a good thermal insulator and electrical insulator. In its most commonly occurring crystalline form, called corundum or α-aluminum oxide, its hardness makes it suitable for use as an abrasive and as a component in cutting tools.Aluminium oxide is responsible for metallic aluminium's resistance to weathering. Metallic aluminium is very reactive with atmospheric oxygen and a thin passive layer of alumina quickly forms on any exposed aluminium surface. This layer protects the metal from further oxidation. The thickness and properties of this oxide layer can be enhanced using a process called anodising. A number of alloys, such as aluminium bronzes, exploit this property by including a proportion of aluminium in the alloy to enhance corrosion resistance. The alumina generated by anodising is typically amorphous, but discharge assisted oxidation processes such as plasma electrolytic oxidation results in a significant proportion of crystalline alumina in the coating, enhancing its hardness. Aluminium oxide was taken off the EPA's chemicals lists in 1988. Aluminium oxide is on EPA's TRI list if it is a fibrous form.

Silica: Silicon carbide (SiC) is a ceramic compound of silicon and carbon that is manufactured on a large scale for use mainly as an abrasive but also occurs in nature as the extremely rare mineral. Silicon carbide exists in at least 70 crystalline forms. Alpha silicon carbide (α-SiC) is the most commonly encountered polymorph, it is formed at temperatures greater than 2000°C and has a hexagonal crystal structure (similar to Wurtzite). The beta modification (β-SiC), with a face-centered cubic crystal structure (similar to diamond and zincblende or sphalerite), is formed at temperatures below 2000°C. Until recently, the beta form has had relatively few commercial uses, although there is now increasing interest in its use as a support for heterogeneous catalysts, owing to its higher surface area compared to the alpha form.

Silicon carbide has a specific gravity of 3.2 and its high sublimation temperature (approximately 2700 °C) makes it useful for bearings and furnace parts. Silicon carbide does not melt at any known pressure. It is also highly inert chemically. There is currently much interest in its use as a semiconductor material in electronics, where its high thermal conductivity, high electric field breakdown strength and high maximum current density make it more promising than silicon for high-powered devices. In addition, it has strong coupling to microwave radiation, which together with its high melting point, permits practical use in heating and casting metals. SiC also has a very low coefficient of thermal expansion and experiences no phase transitions that would cause discontinuities in thermal expansion.Pure SiC is clear. The brown to black colour of industrial product results from iron impurities. The rainbow-like lustre of the crystals is caused by a passivation layer of silicon dioxide that forms on the surface.Pure α-SiC is an intrinsic semiconductor with band gaps of 3.28 eV (4H) and 3.03 eV (6H) respectively.

OBJECTIVE QUESTIONS

1. Beer- Lambert's law states that:
   (a) A = ϵCl (b) A = ϵ/Cl
   (c) A = Cl/ ϵ (d) A = ϵC / l
2. Porosity in a refractory brick generally increases:
   (a) Resistance to spalling (b) Strength
   (c) Density (d) Melting point
3. Silica bricks are the example of:
   (a) Acid refractories (b) Basic refectories
   (c) Neutral refectories (d) All of the above
4. In rotary cement kiln quick-lime is obtained in:
   (a) Drying zone (b) Calcination zone
   (c) Clinkering zone (d) (a) and (c) both
5. According to ISI specification of cement, the Lime saturation factor should be:
   (a) between 1.02 to 0.66 (b) between 10 to 12
   (c) between 102 to 166 (d) between 6 to 12
6. A mixture of volatile compounds can be easily separated by:
   (a) Column chromatography (b) Ion-exchange chromatography
   (c) Gas chromatography (d) Thin-layer chromatography
7. Clay mainly contains:
   (a) Alumina (b) Silica
   (c) Alumina and Silica (d) Lime
8. Iron oxide is present in:
   (a) Porcelain (b) Bricks
   c) China clay (d) All
9. Clay is formed by the weathering of:
   (a) Igneous rocks (b) Felspar rocks
   (c) Both (d) None
10. Which of the following possesses good strength, translucency and very low porosity?
   (a) Earthen ware (b) White ware
   (c) Stone ware (d) Bricks and tile
11. Porosity of Refractory brick increases its?
   (a) Strength (b) Corrosion resistance
   (c) Abrasion resistance (d) Resistance to thermal spalling
12. Alumina refractory is:
   (a) Acidic (b) Basic
   (c) Alumina (d) Fire clay
13. Which refractory is obtained from bauxite?
   (a) Chromate brick (b) Dolomite brick
   (c) Alumina brick (d) Fire clay brick
14. It is used in nuclear engineering as moderator:
   (a) Beryllia brick (b) Fire clay brick
   (c) Carborundum (d) Chromite brick
15. Breaking or cracking of Refractory material under high temperature is called:
   (a) Fusion (b) Spalling
   (c) Chemical cracking (d) Thermal expansion

16. High resistance to spalling is shown by:
(a) Magnesite refractory (b) Dolomite
(c) Alumina (d) Lime refractory
17. In acidic environment, which of the refractory is not suitable?
(a) Acidic (b) Basic
(c) Neutral (d) None
18. Fusion temperature of alumina refractory is above:
(a) 200 ^{0} C (b) 2000 ^{0} C
(c) 20,000 ^{0} C (d) None
19. Good thermal conductivity of a refractory is desirable for:
(a) Blast furnace (b) Reverberatory furnace
(c) Muffle furnace (d) All
20. Which one is neutral refractory?
(a) Dolomite brick (b) Fire clay
(c) Silica brick (d) Chromite brick
21. Hydrogen discharge lamp provides which of the following radiation:
(a) Infra Red (b) Microwave
(c) Ultraviolet (d) Visible
22. Which method is employed for coloured substances?
(a) Coloured substances (b) Calorimetric analysis
(c) NMR Spectroscopy (d) IR Spectroscopy
23. Which complexing agent is used for estimation of cuprous ions?
(a) Ammonium Hydroxide (b) Ammonium Sulphate
(c) Sodium Hydroxide (d) Calcium Nitrate
24. The current generated in photo cell is directly proportional to which of the following
(a) Wave length of light transmitted (b) Amount of light transmitted
(c) Colour of light transmitted (d) Frequency of light transmitted
25. In UV spectrum which group absorbs radiation?
(a) Unsaturated (b) Conjugated
(c) Both (d) None
26. Chromosphores are:
(a) –OH (b) $-NH_2$
(c) >C=O (d) $-NH_3$
27. Unit of molar absorptivity is:
(a) mol m^{-1} (b) mol^{-1} m^{-1}
(c) dm^3 mol^{-1} m^{-1} (d) m^3 mol^{-1} m^{-1}
28. Absorbance is equal to
(a) ln (I_0/I) (b) log (I_0/I)
(c) ϵCl (d) Both a and b
29. The number of photons that pass through in unit area in unit time is:
(a) Amplitude of light (b) Frequency of light
(c) Intensity of light (d) Wave length of light
30. A photochemical reaction takes place by absorption of:
(a) Visible and UV radiation (b) Heat energy
(c) Both a and b (d) None
31. Lambert's Beer Law is applicable only to:
(a) Concentrated solutions (b) Dilute solution
(c) Acidic solution (d) Buffer solution

32. Which radiation possesses lowest energy?
    (a) X-ray (b) Visible
    (c) Infra red (d) Ultra violet
33. The ratio of energy per Einstein and that of a photon is:
    (a) Equivalent number (b) Einstein number
    (c) Lambert's number (d) Avogadro's number
34. Identification of functional groups in a compound can be done by:
    (a) IR Spectroscopy (b) Gas chromatography
    (c) UV Spectroscopy (d) NMR
35. Separation of constituents of gases can be carried out by using:
    (a) IR Spectroscopy (b) Gas chromatography
    (c) UV-Visible Spectroscopy (d) None of these.
36. The energy associated with a photon is given by the equation:
    (a) $E=h\lambda$ (b) $E=hv$
    (c) $E= hc$ (d) $E =h c^2$
37. Photochemistry deals with the study of:
    (a) Photon (b) Photos
    (c) Reaction which proceeds with absorption of UV light
    d) Reaction which proceeds with absorption of IR light
38. The instrument used to measure the amount of electromagnetic radiation absorbed by organic molecules is called:
    (a) Spectrum analyzer (b) Spectrophotometer
    (c) Colourimeter (d) Monochromator
39. The wave length of UV and Visible regions of EMR is:
    (a) Less than 2000 ^{0}A (b) More than 8000^0 A
    (c) 200 to 8000^0 A (d) None of these
40. Which one is an auxochrome?
    (a) >C=C < (b) >C= N
    (c) –OH (d) N=N
41. Which of the wavelength falls in IR Spectrum?
    (a) 110 nm (b) 800 nm
    (c) 2,000 nm (d) 10 cm
42. Gas Chromatography can be used to:
    (a) Separate benzene and cyclohexane mixture.
    (b) Determine the ethyl alcohol content in blood with high accuracy.
    (c) Analysis of synthetic rubber and plastic intermediates.
    (d) All of these.
43. A glass of certain thickness is found to have transmission of 70% of light. If the thickness of glass is reduced to half, the transmission of light would:
    (a) Decrease (b) Increase
    (c) Remains the same (d) Reduce to zero
44. In GSC and GLC, stationary phases are respectively.
    (a) Liquid and solid (b) Liquid and gas
    (c) Solid and liquid (d) Solid and gas.
45. A substance in a cell length (l) absorbs 20% of incident light. If the cell length is changed to 5.l the fraction of incident light that will be absorbed is:
    (a) Also increased (b) Decreased
    (c) Unchanged (d) None of these.

Answer Key

(1)a (2)b (3)a (4)b (5)a (6)c (7)c (8)b (9)c (10)b (11)a (12)a (13)c (14)a
(15)b (16)a (17)b (18)b (19)c (20)d (21)c (22)a (23)a (24)b (25)c (26)c (27)c (28)b
(29)c (30)a (31)b (32)c (33)d (34)a (35)b (36)b (37)a (38)b (39)a (40)c (41)d (42)b
(43)b (44)c (45)b

THEORETICAL QUESTIONS

1. Derive Lambert's –Beer's law? Wirte applications of colorimetry? **[RGPV 01, 09]**
2. Define the term chromatography. Write the principle of gas chromatography. **[RGPV 01.09]**
3. Write any two application of I.R spectroscopy. **[RGPV 01, 07]**
4. Differentiate between I.R and U.V spectrum. **[RGPV 01, 07]**
5. In colourimeter estimation of each metal ion in a solution, a particular filter is selected why? **[RGPV 01, 07]**
6. Explain Lambert's –Beer law. **[RGPV01, 07]**
7. Write explanatory note on Gas Chromatography **[RGPV 01, 08,10]**
8. Write short note on Plaster of Paris and their setting. **[RGPV 08]**
9. Why is gypsum added to cement? **[RGPV 01, 08]**
10. Explain briefly of the following: **[RGPV 01, 03,08]**
    a) Beer – Lamberts law b) NMR Spectroscopy
11. Write short note on :
    a) Silica Refractory b) Thermal Spalling
    c) Pyrometric cone equivalent d) Portland cement **[RGPV 01, 03, 09]**
12. Write short note on refractoriness and thermal spalling. **[RGPV 03, 09]**
13. Write role of gypsum in cement. **[RGPV 03]**
14. Write the chemical reaction involved in manufacture of Portland cement. **[RGPV 01, 09]**
15. Describe in brief manufacture of cement, give percentage composition of the constitutional compounds of cement and the reactions involved during setting and hardening of cement. **[RGPV 02]**
16. Write short notes on any two: **[RGPV 02]**
    a) Colourimetry b) Chromatography
    c) IR- Spectroscopy d) UV-Spectroscopy
17. Explain briefly any four of the following: **[RGPV 03, 08]**
    a) Beer- Lambert's law b) NMR Spectroscopy
    c) Various techniques of chromatography d) IR Spectroscopy
    e) Applications of UV Spectroscopy
18. Write short note on: **[RGPV 03]**
    a) Silica refractory b) Thermal spalling
    c) Pyrometric come equivalent d) Portland cement
19. Write short note on refractoriness and thermal spalling. **[RGPV 07]**
20. Write role of gypsum in cement.
21. Draw labeled diagram of rotary kiln used for the manufacture of Portland cement by wet process and give chemical reactions taking place in the furnace. **[RGPV 03, 08]**
22. Write short note on any two: **[RGPV 03, 09]**
    a) Chromatography and its application b) Beer-Lambert's law
    c) IR- Spectroscopy and its application d) UV-Spectroscopy and its application
23. Give % composition of Portland cement constituents; Explain setting and hardening reactions of

Cement. **[RGPV 04]**

24. Define and classify refractories giving at least two examples of each class. Describe any two important characteristics of refractories. **[RGPV04, 08, 09, 10]**
25. Explain briefly the following: **[RGPV 05]**
    a) Beer- Lambert's law b) Application of IR- Spectroscopy
    c) Application of UV- Spectroscopy d) Industrial uses of refractories
26. What is the I.S.I. Specification of Portland cement? **[RGPV 06]**
27. Write the significance of following properties of refractory bricks: **[RGPV 06, 08, 09]**
    i) PCE test ii) RUL test
28. What are merits and demerits of instrumental analysis? **[RGPV 06]**
29. Discuss in brief the following: **[RGPV 06]**
    i) Classification and uses of Chromatographic methods.
    ii) Classification of electronic transitions.
    iii) Types of Molecular Vibration.
30. Write informative notes on any two of the following: **[RGPV 06]**
    a) Chromatography b) IR- Spectroscopy c) UV-Spectroscopy d) Colourimetry
31. Discuss the Classification of Refractory. **[RGPV 06]**
32. How can you manufacture Portland cement by rotary kiln Draw labeled diagram and write chemical reaction involved in it. **[RGPV 06, 07]**
33. What are the refractory materials? What is their importance in industry? **[RGPV07]**
34. Write a short note on Portland Cement.
35. Write a short note on Gas chromatography. **[RGPV 07]**
36. Write about ISI specification of cements. **[RGPV 07]**
37. Give preparation, properties and uses of Dolomite bricks. **[RGPV 07]**
38. Discuss in brief introduction of electronic spectroscopy. **[RGPV 07]**
39. How refractoriness of a refractory material can be determined by pyrometric cone equivalent (PCE) method? **[RGPV 07]**
40. Discuss Setting and Hardening of Portland Cement with chemical reaction involved in it. **[RGPV 07]**
41. Write a short note on Chromatography. **[RGPV 07]**
42. Write informative notes on any two of the following:
    (a) Lambert's and Beer's law (b) UV- visible spectroscopy (c) IR- spectroscopy **[RGPV 07]**
43. Draw a block diagram of colourimeter and explain its working giving experimental technique. **[RGPV 07]**
44. Give Preparation, Properties and Uses of Fire clay Refractories. **[RGPV 07]**
45. Draw a block diagram of a gas chromatograph. Write the names of different detectors used. **[RGPV 07]**
46. Define the following: 1.Chemical shift 2.R_f value 3.Chromophore **[RGPV 08]**
47. What is chromatography? Write important types of chromatographic techniques. Draw a well lablled block diagram of a gas chromatograph. **[RGPV 08]**
48. Explain refractoriness and R.U.L. **[RGPV 08]**
49. What is Plaster of Paris? Give its manufacture and important applications. **[RGPV 08]**
50. (a) Define and classify refractories. Discuss the following properties of refractories:
    (i) R.U. L. (ii) Thermal spalling **[RGPV 10]**
51. (a) Describe with the help of a neat diagram, the various steps involved in the manufacture of Portland cement.
    (b) Discuss principle, instrumentation and applications of colorimetry. **[RGPV 10]**

………*………

Table of Symbols, Atomic Number and Relative Atomic Masses

Element	Symbol	Atomic Number	Relative Atomic Mass
Actinium	Ac	89	227
Aluminium	Al	13	27
Americium	Am	95	243
Antimony	Sb	51	122
Argon	Ar	19	40
Arsenic	As	38	75
Astatine	At	95	210
Barium	Ba	56	137
Berkelium	Bk	97	247
Beryllium	Be	4	9
Bismuth	Bi	83	209
Boron	B	5	11
Bromine	Br	35	80
Cadmium	Cd	49	112
Caesium	Cs	55	133
Calcium	Ca	20	40
Californium	Cf	98	251
Carbon	C	6	12
Cerium	Ce	58	140
Chlorine	Cl	17	35.5
Chromium	Cr	24	52
Cobalt	Co	27	59
Copper	Cu	29	63.5
Curium	Cm	96	247
Dysprosium	Dy	66	162.5
Einsteinium	Es	99	254
Erbium	Er	68	167
Europium	Eu	63	152
Fermium	Fm	100	253
Fluorine	F	9	19
Francium	Fr	87	223
Gadolinium	Gd	64	157
Gallium	Ga	31	70
Germanium	Ge	32	72.5
Gold	Au	79	197
Hafnium	Hf	72	178
Helium	He	2	4
Holmium	Ho	67	164
Hydrogen	H	1	1
Indium	In	49	115
Iodine	I	53	127
Iridium	Ir	77	192
Iron	Fe	26	56
Krypton	Kr	36	84

Lanthanum	La	57	139
Lawrencium	Lr	103	257
Lead	Pb	82	207
Lithium	Li	3	7
Lutecium	Lu	71	175
Magnesium	Mg	12	24
Manganese	Mn	25	55
Mendelevium	Md	101	256
Mercury	Hg	80	201
Molybdenum	Mo	42	96
Neodymium	Nd	60	144
Neon	Ne	10	20
Neptunium	Np	93	237
Nickel	Ni	26	59
Niobium	Nb	41	93
Nitrogen	N	7	14
Nobelium	No	102	254
Osmium	Os	76	190
Oxygen	O	8	16
Palladium	Pb	46	106
Phosphorus	P	15	31
Platinum	Pt	76	195
Plutonium	Pu	94	242
Polonium	Po	64	210
Potassium	K	19	39
Praesodymium	Pr	59	141
Promethium	Pm	61	147
Protactinium	Pa	91	231
Radium	Ra	66	226
Radon	Rn	66	222
Rhenium	Re	75	166
Rhodium	Rh	45	103
Rubidium	Rb	37	85
Ruthenium	Ru	44	101
Samarium	Sm	62	150
Scandium	Sc	21	45
Selenium	Se	34	79
Silicon	Si	14	26
Silver	Ag	47	108
Sodium	Na	11	23
Strontium	Sr	38	87
Sulphur	S	16	32
Tantalum	Ta	73	181
Technetium	Tc	43	99
Tellurium	Te	52	127
Terbium	Tb	65	159
Thallium	TI	81	204

Thorium	Th	90	232
Thulium	Tm	69	169
Tin	Sn	50	119
Titanium	Ti	22	48
Tungsten	W	74	184
Uranium	U	92	238
Vanadium	V	23	51
Xenon	Xe	54	131
Ytterbium	Yb	70	173
Yttrium	V	39	89
Zinc	Zn	30	65
Zirconium	Zr	40	91

Temperature Conversion table

From	To Fahrenheit	To Celsius	To Kelvin
Fahrenheit (F)	F	(F - 32) * 5/9	(F - 32) * 5/9 + 273.15
Celsius (C or o)	(C * 9/5) + 32	C	C + 273.15
Kelvin (K)	(K - 273.15) * 9/5 + 32	K - 273.15	K

Units and Conversion Factors

Volume

Unit	Multiplied by	Approximate Conversion Factor	Equals	Unit
barrels of oil (bbl)	X	42	=	US gallons (gal)
barrels of oil (bbl)	X	34.97	=	Imperial gallons (UK gal)
barrels of oil (bbl)	X	0.136	=	tonnes of oil equivalent (toe)
barrels of oil (bbl)	X	0.1589873	=	cubic metres
barrels of oil equivalent (boe)	X	5,658.53	=	cubic feet (f3) of natural gas
tonnes of oil equivalent (toe)	X	7.33 [1]	=	barrels of oil equivalent (boe)
cubic yards (y3)	X	0.764555	=	cubic meters
cubic feet (f3)	X	0.02831685	=	cubic meters
cubic feet (f3) of natural gas	X	0.0001767	=	barrels of oil equivalent (boe)
US gallons (gal)	X	0.0238095	=	barrels (bbl)
US gallons (gal)	X	3.785412	=	liters (l)
US gallons (gal)	X	0.8326394	=	Imperial gallons (UK gal)
Imperial gallons (UK gal)	X	1.201	=	US gallon (gal)
Imperial gallons (UK gal)	X	4.545	=	liters (l)
[1] This conversion can range from 6.5 to 7.9 depending on the type of crude oil. This factor is intended to provide an approximation that can be used when the exact factor is unknown.				

Mass / Weight

Unit	Multiplied by	Approximate Conversion Factor	Equals	Unit
short tons	X	2,000	=	pounds (lb)
short tons	X	0.9071847	=	metric tonnes (t)
long tons	X	1.016047	=	metric tonnes (t)
long tons	X	2,240	=	pounds (lb)
metric tonnes (t)	X	1,000	=	kilograms (kg)
metric tonnes (t)	X	0.9842	=	long tons
metric tonnes (t)	X	1.102	=	short tons
pounds (lb)	X	0.45359237	=	kilograms (kg)
kilograms (kg)	X	2.2046	=	pounds (lb)

Length

Unit	Multiplied by	Approximate Conversion Factor	Equals	Unit
miles (mi)	X	1.609344	=	kilometers (km)
yards (yd)	X	0.9144	=	meters (m)
feet (ft)	X	0.3048	=	meters (m)
inches (in)	X	2.54	=	centimeters (cm)
kilometer (km)	X	0.62137	=	miles (mi)

Area

Unit	multiplied by	Approximate Conversion Factor	Equals	Unit
acres	X	0.40469	=	hectares (ha)
square miles (mi2)	X	2.589988	=	square kilometers (km2)
square yards (yd2)	X	0.8361274	=	square meters (m2)
square feet (ft2)	X	0.09290304	=	square meters (m2)
square inches (in2)	X	6.4516	=	square centimeters (cm2)

Energy

Unit	Multiplied by	Approximate Conversion Factor	equals	Unit
British Thermal Units (Btus)	X	1,055.05585262	=	joules (J)
calories (cal)	X	4.1868	=	joules (J)
kilowatt hours (kWh)	X	3.6	=	mega joules (MJ)
therms	X	100,000	=	British thermal units (Btus)
tonnes of oil equivalent	X	10,000,000	=	kilocalories (kcal)
tonnes of oil equivalent	X	396.83	=	therms
tonnes of oil equivalent	X	41.868	=	Giga joules (GJ)
tonnes of oil equivalent	X	11,630	=	kilowatt hours (kWh)
cubic feet of natural gas	X	1,025	=	British Thermal Units (Btus)

Approximate Heat Content of Petroleum Products
Million Btu (MMBtu) per Barrel

Energy Source	MMBtu/bbl	Energy Source	MMBtu/bbl
Crude Oil	5.800	Natural Gasoline	4.620
Natural Gas Plant Liquids	3.735	Pentanes Plus	4.620
Asphalt	6.636	Petrochemical Feedstocks	
Aviation Gasoline	5.048	Naphtha < 401° F	5.248
Butane	4.326	Other oils >= 401° F	5.825
Butane-Propane (60/40) Mixture	4.130	Still Gas	6.000
Distillate Fuel Oil	5.825	Petroleum Coke	6.024
Ethane	3.082	Plant Condensate	5.418
Ethane-Propane (70/30) Mixture	3.308	Propane	3.836
Isobutane	3.974	Residual Fuel Oil	6.287
Jet Fuel, Kerosene-type	5.670	Road Oil	6.636
Jet Fuel, Naphtha-type	5.355	Special Naphtha's	5.248
Kerosene	5.670	Still Gas	6.000
Lubricants	6.065	Unfinished Oils	5.825
Motor Gasoline - Conventional	5.253	Unfractionated Stream	5.418
Motor Gasoline - Oxygenated or Reformulated	5.150	Waxes	5.537
Motor Gasoline - Fuel Ethanol	3.539	Miscellaneous	5.796
Source: U.S. Department of Energy, Energy Information Administration (2001)			

The following constants and conversion factors are useful in calculations about molecular manufacturing systems and various applications of such systems. In general, SI units are preferred in nanotechnology SI prefixes:

Y: 10^{24} yotta
Z: 10^{21} zetta
E: 10^{18} exa
P: 10^{15} peta
T: 10^{12} tera
G: 10^{9} giga
M: 10^{6} mega
K: 10^{3} kilo
H: 10^{2} hector
da: 10^{1} deka
d: 10^{-1} deci
c: 10^{-2} centi
m: 10^{-3} milli
mu: 10^{-6} micro
n: 10^{-9} nano
p: 10^{-12} pico
f: 10^{-15} femto
a: 10^{-18} atto
z: 10^{-21} zepto

y: $10^{\wedge -24}$ yocto
Fundamental units:
m: meters (length)
kg: kilogram (mass)
s: seconds (time)
A: ampere (electric current)
K: kelvin (thermodynamic temperature)
mol: mole (amount of substance)
cd: candela (luminous intensity)
Derived units:
J: joules (work, energy, heat) N*m, Kg*m$^{\wedge 2}$/s$^{\wedge 2}$
N: newton, (force) kg*m/(s$^{\wedge 2}$)
Pa: pascal, (pressure, stress) N/m$^{\wedge 2}$
W: watt, (power) J/s
C: coulomb, (electric charge) A*s
V: volt (electric potential, emf) J/C, W/A
Greek omega: ohm (resistance) V/A
S: siemens (conductance) A/V
Wb: weber (magnetic flux) V*s
H: henry (inductance) Wb/A
F: farad (capacitance) C/V
T: Tesla (magnetic flux density) Wb/m$^{\wedge 2}$, N/(A*m)
Bq: becquerel (radioactivity) 1/s

Constants:

c: 299,792,458 m/s; speed of light in vacuum
mu_0: 12.566 370 614... x $10^{\wedge -7}$ N/A$^{\wedge 2}$; Permeability of vacuum
e_0: 8.854 187 817 x $10^{\wedge -12}$ F/m, or 1/(mu0 * c$^{\wedge 2}$); permittivity of vacuum
G: 6.672 59 x $10^{\wedge -11}$ m$^{\wedge 3}$/(kg*s$^{\wedge 2}$); Newtonian constant of gravitation
h: 6.626 075 5 x $10^{\wedge -34}$ J*s; Planck's constant
e: 1.602 177 33 x $10^{\wedge -19}$ C; elementary charge on proton, electron
a_0: 0.529 177 249 x $10^{\wedge -10}$ m; Bohr radius
E_h: 4.359 748 2 x $10^{\wedge -18}$ J; Hartree (energy)
m_e: 9.109 389 7 x $10^{\wedge -31}$ kg; mass of the electron
m_p: 1.672 623 1 x $10^{\wedge -27}$ kg; mass of the proton
m_n: 1.674 928 6 x $10^{\wedge -27}$ kg; mass of the neutron
N_A: 6.022 136 7 x $10^{\wedge 23}$ mol$^{\wedge -1}$; Avogadro's number
mu: 1.660 540 2 x $10^{\wedge -27}$ kg; atomic mass constant, amu
R: 8.314 510 J/(mol*K); molar gas constant
k: 1.380 658 x $10^{\wedge -23}$ J/K; Boltzmann's constant R/N_A
V_m: 0.022 414 10 m$^{\wedge 3}$/mol; molar volume of ideal gas, R*T/p at 273.15 K, 101,325 Pa
Volume occupied by one gas molecule at STP: ~37.22 nm$^{\wedge 3}$ (V_m / N_A)
Lattice spacing of diamond (300 K): 0.356 683 nm
Lattice spacing of silicon (300 K): 0.543 095 nm
Lattice spacing of germanium (300 K): 0.564 613 nm
Lattice spacing of grey tin (300 K): 0.648 920 nm
C-C bond length in diamond: 0.154 448 nm it's the lattice spacing * sqrt
C-C bond length in graphite: 0.142 nm

1-3 distance in graphite: 0.246 nm; C-C bond length * sqrt
Density of carbon atoms in a monoatomic sheet of graphite: 38.2 atoms/nm^2; (C-C bond length)^2*3*sqrt
Distance between adjacent sheets in graphite: 0.335 nm
Basal surface energy of graphite: 0.234 J/m^2
Band gap of diamond: 5.47 ev
Band gap of silicon: 1.12 ev
Mobility of electron in diamond: 1800 cm$^{\wedge 2}$/(V*s)
Mobility of electron in silicon: 1500 cm$^{\wedge 2}$/(V*s)
g_n: 9.806 65 m/s$^{\wedge 2}$; acceleration of gravity
Solar constant: 1,367.5 W/m$^{\wedge 2}$; number of watts in sunlight near Earth's orbit, variable with Earth's distance from the sun and solar activity
Solar output: 3.87 x 10$^{\wedge 26}$ W (computed from solar constant)
Typical power consumption of a human being: ~100 W
Energy used by the United States in 1990: 8.6 x 10$^{\wedge 19}$ J
Energy used per person per year in the US in 1990: 3.5 x 10$^{\wedge 11}$ J
Power used per person in the US in 1990: 11,000 W
Energy used by the world in 1990: 1.4 x 10$^{\wedge 20}$ J

Power consumption of the world in 1990: 4.4 x 10$^{\wedge 12}$ W
Energy used per person per year in the world in 1990: 2.7 x 10$^{\wedge 10}$ J
Power used per person in the world in 1990: 850 W
Total world population in 1990: 5.3 x 10$^{\wedge 9}$
Earth's equatorial radius: 6,378,160 m
Earth's surface area (4 pi r$^{\wedge 2}$, r from above): 5.1 x 10$^{\wedge 14}$ m$^{\wedge 2}$
Solar power intercepted by the Earth: 1.74 x 10$^{\wedge 17}$ W (derived from above)
Earth's mass: 5.975 x 10$^{\wedge 24}$ kg
Earth's distance from sun (average): 1.5 x 10$^{\wedge 11}$ m
Fraction of nitrogen in Earth's atmosphere (by volume): 0.780 84
Fraction of oxygen in Earth's atmosphere (by volume): 0.209 46
Fraction of water in Earth's atmosphere: variable. Arctic air might have 0.01% water by weight while tropical air might have 3%.
Fraction of argon in Earth's atmosphere (by volume): 0.00934
Fraction of CO2 in Earth's atmosphere (by volume): 0.00031
Stiffness of carbon-carbon single bond: 440 N/m
Energy required in breaking carbon-carbon single bond: 0.556 aJ
Young's modulus of diamond: 1.05 x 10$^{\wedge 12}$ Pa
Strength of diamond: 5 x 10$^{\wedge 10}$ Pa (an underestimate)
Density of diamond: 3500 kg/m$^{\wedge 3}$

Periodic Table of Elements

Key: Atomic # / Symbol / Name / Atomic Mass

C Solid | Hg Liquid | H Gas | Rf Unknown

Metals: Alkali metals; Alkaline earth metals; Lanthanoids; Actinoids; Transition metals; Poor metals

Nonmetals: Other nonmetals; Noble gases

	1	2	3	4	5	6	7	8	9	10	11	12	13	14	15	16	17	18
1	1 H Hydrogen 1.00794																	2 He Helium 4.002602
2	3 Li Lithium 6.941	4 Be Beryllium 9.012182											5 B Boron 10.811	6 C Carbon 12.0107	7 N Nitrogen 14.0067	8 O Oxygen 15.9994	9 F Fluorine 18.9984032	10 Ne Neon 20.1797
3	11 Na Sodium 22.98976928	12 Mg Magnesium 24.3050											13 Al Aluminium 26.9815386	14 Si Silicon 28.0855	15 P Phosphorus 30.973762	16 S Sulfur 32.065	17 Cl Chlorine 35.453	18 Ar Argon 39.948
4	19 K Potassium 39.0983	20 Ca Calcium 40.078	21 Sc Scandium 44.955912	22 Ti Titanium 47.867	23 V Vanadium 50.9415	24 Cr Chromium 51.9961	25 Mn Manganese 54.938045	26 Fe Iron 55.845	27 Co Cobalt 58.933195	28 Ni Nickel 58.6934	29 Cu Copper 63.546	30 Zn Zinc 65.38	31 Ga Gallium 69.723	32 Ge Germanium 72.64	33 As Arsenic 74.92160	34 Se Selenium 78.96	35 Br Bromine 79.904	36 Kr Krypton 83.798
5	37 Rb Rubidium 85.4678	38 Sr Strontium 87.62	39 Y Yttrium 88.90585	40 Zr Zirconium 91.224	41 Nb Niobium 92.90638	42 Mo Molybdenum 95.96	43 Tc Technetium (97.9072)	44 Ru Ruthenium 101.07	45 Rh Rhodium 102.90550	46 Pd Palladium 106.42	47 Ag Silver 107.8682	48 Cd Cadmium 112.411	49 In Indium 114.818	50 Sn Tin 118.710	51 Sb Antimony 121.760	52 Te Tellurium 127.60	53 I Iodine 126.90447	54 Xe Xenon 131.293
6	55 Cs Caesium 132.9054519	56 Ba Barium 137.327	57–71	72 Hf Hafnium 178.49	73 Ta Tantalum 180.94788	74 W Tungsten 183.84	75 Re Rhenium 186.207	76 Os Osmium 190.23	77 Ir Iridium 192.217	78 Pt Platinum 195.084	79 Au Gold 196.966569	80 Hg Mercury 200.59	81 Tl Thallium 204.3833	82 Pb Lead 207.2	83 Bi Bismuth 208.98040	84 Po Polonium (208.9824)	85 At Astatine (209.9871)	86 Rn Radon (222.0176)
7	87 Fr Francium (223)	88 Ra Radium (226)	89–103	104 Rf Rutherfordium (261)	105 Db Dubnium (262)	106 Sg Seaborgium (266)	107 Bh Bohrium (264)	108 Hs Hassium (277)	109 Mt Meitnerium (268)	110 Ds Darmstadtium (271)	111 Rg Roentgenium (272)	112 Uub Ununbium (285)	113 Uut Ununtrium (284)	114 Uuq Ununquadium (289)	115 Uup Ununpentium (288)	116 Uuh Ununhexium (292)	117 Uus Ununseptium	118 Uuo Ununoctium (294)

For elements with no stable isotopes, the mass number of the isotope with the longest half-life is in parentheses.

57 La Lanthanum 138.90547	58 Ce Cerium 140.116	59 Pr Praseodymium 140.90765	60 Nd Neodymium 144.242	61 Pm Promethium (145)	62 Sm Samarium 150.36	63 Eu Europium 151.964	64 Gd Gadolinium 157.25	65 Tb Terbium 158.92535	66 Dy Dysprosium 162.500	67 Ho Holmium 164.93032	68 Er Erbium 167.259	69 Tm Thulium 168.93421	70 Yb Ytterbium 173.054	71 Lu Lutetium 174.9668
89 Ac Actinium (227)	90 Th Thorium 232.03806	91 Pa Protactinium 231.03588	92 U Uranium 238.02891	93 Np Neptunium (237)	94 Pu Plutonium (244)	95 Am Americium (243)	96 Cm Curium (247)	97 Bk Berkelium (247)	98 Cf Californium (251)	99 Es Einsteinium (252)	100 Fm Fermium (257)	101 Md Mendelevium (258)	102 No Nobelium (259)	103 Lr Lawrencium (262)